Digest of United Kingdom Energy Statistics 2006

Production team: Mike Janes (Managing editor)
Sally Mercer (Production editor)
Richard Notley
Angeli Enriquez
Clive Sarjantson
and chapter authors

A National Statistics publication   **London: The Stationery Office**

Digest of United Kingdom Energy Statistics

Enquiries about statistics in this publication should be made to the contact named at the end of the relevant chapter. Brief extracts from this publication may be reproduced provided that the source is fully acknowledged. General enquiries about the publication, and proposals for reproduction of larger extracts, should be addressed to the Production Editor, Sally Mercer, at the address given in paragraph XXIX of the Introduction.

Department of Trade and Industry reserves the right to revise or discontinue the text or any table contained in this Digest without prior notice.

About TSO's Standing Order Service

The Standing Order Service, open to all TSO account holders, allows customers to automatically receive the publications they require in a specified subject area, thereby saving them the time, trouble and expense of placing individual orders, also without handling charges normally incurred when placing ad-hoc orders.

Customers may choose from over 4,000 classifications arranged in 250 sub groups under 30 major subject areas. These classifications enable customers to choose from a wide variety of subjects, those publications that are of special interest to them. This is a particularly valuable service for the specialist library or research body. All publications will be dispatched immediately after publication date. A Standing Orders Handbook describing the service in detail and a complete list of classifications may be obtained on request. Write to TSO, Standing Order Department, PO Box 29, St Crispins, Duke Street, Norwich, NR3 1GN, quoting reference 12.01.013. Alternatively telephone 0870 600 5522 and select the Standing Order Department (option 2); fax us on 0870 600 5533; or finally e-mail us at book.standing.orders@tso.co.uk.

National Statistics

National Statistics are produced to high professional standards set out in the National Statistics Code of Practice. They undergo regular quality assurance reviews to ensure that they meet customer needs. They are produced free from any political interference.

You can find a range of National Statistics on the Internet – www.statistics.gov.uk

---

Contents

Monthly and quarterly data are also available for Energy, Solid fuels and derived gases, Petroleum, Gas and Electricity at:

www.dti.gov.uk/energy/statistics/source/index.html

Information on Energy Prices is available at:

www.dti.gov.uk/energy/statistics/publications/prices/index.html

A list of tables

Chapter 7 Renewable sources of energy

Annex A Energy, commodity balances, calorific values and conversion factors

Introduction

I   This issue of the Digest of United Kingdom Energy Statistics continues a series which commenced with the Ministry of Fuel and Power Statistical Digest for the years 1948 and 1949, published in 1950. The Ministry of Fuel and Power Statistical Digest was previously published as a Command Paper, the first being that for the years 1938 to 1943, published in July 1944 (Cmd. 6538).

II   The current issue updates the figures given in the Department of Trade and Industry's (DTI) *Digest of United Kingdom Energy Statistics 2005*, published in July 2005.

III   This printed and bound issue consists of seven chapters and four annexes. The first chapter deals with overall energy. The other chapters cover the specific fuels, combined heat and power and renewable sources of energy. The annexes cover calorific values and conversion factors, a glossary of terms, further sources of information and major events in the energy industries.

IV   This Digest is also available on the Internet. Some additional information appears on the Internet only. The tables on the Internet are provided in Microsoft Excel format. Most Internet versions of the tables include data for earlier years, which are not provided in the printed copy publication. For example commodity and energy balances (see VII and VIII, below) for 1998 to 2002, are included on the Internet, and tables that show five years in this printed version show 8 years in their Internet form because page sizes are not a limiting factor. In addition, the following appear on the Internet version only:

> Long term trends text and tables
> Major events from 1990 to 2006 - Annex D
> (only Major events for 2004 to 2006 appear in the printed and bound version)
> Energy and the environment – Annex E
> UK oil and gas resources - Annex F
> Foreign Trade – Annex G

V   Annual information on prices is included in the publication *Quarterly Energy Prices*. This is available together with *Energy Trends* on subscription from the DTI. Further information on these publications can be found in Annex C.

VI   Where necessary, data have been converted or adjusted to provide consistent series. However, in some cases changes in methods of data collection have affected the continuity of the series. The presence of remaining discontinuities is indicated in the chapter text or in footnotes to the tables.

VII   Chapters 2, 3, 4, 5 and 7 contain production and consumption of individual fuels and are presented using *commodity balances*. A commodity balance illustrates the flows of an individual fuel through from production to final consumption, showing its use in transformation (including heat generation) and energy industry own use. Further details of commodity balances and their use are given in Annex A, paragraphs A.7 to A.42.

VIII   The individual commodity balances are combined in an *energy balance,* presented in Chapter 1, *Energy*. The energy balance differs from a commodity balance in that it shows the interactions between different fuels in addition to illustrating their consumption. The energy balance thus gives a fuller picture of the production, transformation and use of energy showing all the flows. Expenditure on energy is also presented in energy balance format in Chapter 1. Further details of the energy balance and its use, including the methodology introduced in the 2002 Digest for heat, are given in Annex A, paragraphs A.43 to A.58.

IX   Chapter 1 also covers general energy statistics and includes tables showing energy consumption by final users and an analysis of energy consumption by main industrial groups. Fuel production and consumption statistics are derived mainly from the records of fuel producers and suppliers.

X   Chapters 6 and 7 summarise the results of surveys conducted by Future Energy Solutions (part of AEA Technology) on behalf of the DTI. These chapters estimate the contribution made by combined heat and power (CHP) and renewable energy sources to energy production and consumption in the United Kingdom.

XI   Some of the data shown in this Digest may contain unpublished revisions and estimates of trade from additional sources.

Definitions

XII   The text at the beginning of each chapter explains the main features of the tables. Technical notes and definitions, given at the end of this text, provide detailed explanations of the figures in the tables and how they are derived. Explanations of the logic behind an energy balance and for commodity balances are given in Annex A.

XIII   Most chapters contain some information on 'oil' or 'petroleum'; these terms are used in a general sense and vary according to usage in the field examined. In their widest sense they are used to include all mineral oil and related hydrocarbons (except methane) and any derived products.

XIV   An explanation of the terms used to describe electricity generating companies is given in Chapter 5, paragraphs 5.48 to 5.50.

XV   Data in this issue have been prepared on the basis of the Standard Industrial Classification (SIC 2003) as far as is practicable. For further details of classification of consumers see Chapter 1, paragraphs 1.52 to 1.56.

XVI   Where appropriate, further explanations and qualifications are given in footnotes to the tables.

Proposed change to use net calorific values when producing energy statistics

XVII   A consultation was launched in the 2005 edition of DUKES seeking views of users as to whether net calorific values (NCVs) should be used in place of Gross Calorific Values (GCVs). As a result of this consultation, DTI recognised that there are good arguments both for and against moving from GCV to NCV. However at present it has been concluded that there would be no demonstrable advantage to changing the method of presenting UK Energy statistics, and so GCVs continue to be used in this edition and will be used in future editions of the Digest. The fuel specific NCVs will continue to be published, and are shown in Annex A. Further information on this decision is shown in Chapter 1 on page 11.

Geographical coverage

XVIII The geographical coverage of the statistics is the United Kingdom. Shipments to the Channel Islands and the Isle of Man from the United Kingdom are not classed as exports. Supplies of solid fuel and petroleum to these islands are therefore included as part of United Kingdom inland consumption or deliveries.

Periods

XIX   Data in this Digest are for calendar years or periods of 52 weeks, depending on the reporting procedures within the fuel industry concerned. Actual periods covered are given in the notes to the individual fuel chapters

Revisions

XX   The tables contain revisions to some of the previously published figures, and where practicable the revised data have been indicated by an 'r'. The 'r' marker is used whenever the figure has been revised from that published in the printed copy of the 2005 Digest, even though some figures may have been amended on the Internet version of the tables. Statistics on energy in this Digest are classified as National Statistics. This means that they are produced to the professional standards set out in the National Statistics Code of Practice and relevant protocols. The National Statistics protocol on revisions requires that "Each organisation responsible for producing National Statistics will publish and maintain a general statement describing its practice on revisions". The following statement outlines the policy on revisions for energy statistics.

Revisions to data published in the *Digest of UK Energy Statistics*.
It is intended that any revisions should be made to previous years' data only at the time of the publication of the Digest (ie in July 2006 when this Digest is published, revisions can be made to 2004 and earlier years). In exceptional circumstances previous years' data can be amended between Digest publication dates, but this will only take place when quarterly *Energy Trends* is published. The reasons for substantial revisions will be explained in the 'Highlights' sheet of the Internet version of the table concerned. Valid reasons for revisions of Digest data include:
> revised and validated data received from a data supplier;
> the figure in the Digest was wrong because of a typographical or similar error.

In addition, when provisional annual data for a new calendar year (eg 2006) are published in *Energy Trends* in March of the following year (eg March 2007), percentage growth rates are liable to be distorted if the prior year (ie 2005) data are constrained to the Digest total, when revisions are known to have been made. In these circumstances the prior year (ie 2005) data will be amended for all affected tables in *Energy Trends* and Internet versions of all affected Digest tables will be clearly annotated to show that the data has been up-dated in *Energy Trends*.

Revisions to current years data published in *Energy Trends* but not in the *Digest of UK Energy Statistics*.
> All validated amendments from data suppliers will be updated when received and published in the next statistical release.
> All errors will be amended as soon as identified and published in the next statistical release.
> Data in energy and commodity balances format will be revised on a quarterly basis, to coincide with the publication of *Energy Trends*.

Further details on National Statistics Code of Practice and related protocols can be found at: www.statistics.gov.uk/about_ns/cop/default.asp.

Energy data on the Internet
XXI   Energy data are held on the energy area of the DTI web site, under "statistics". The Digest is available at www.dti.gov.uk/energy/statistics/publications/dukes/page29812.html. Information on further DTI energy publications available both in printed copy format and on the Internet is given in Annex C.

XXII   A new DTI web site was launched in May 2006, as a result the DTI web addresses used in this edition of the Digest publication are different from previous years. The change has meant that the version of the Digest accessible from the Internet contains all sections within the printed copy and those sections that are only published on the Internet. Links to other sections of the Digest are in the form of 'go-to' links on the Internet version.

XXIII   Short term statistics are published:
> monthly, by the DTI on the Internet at www.dti.gov.uk/energy/statistics/source/index.
> quarterly, by the DTI in paper and on the Internet in *Energy Trends,* and *Quarterly Energy Prices*: www.dti.gov.uk/energy/statistics/publications.

> quarterly, by the DTI in Statistical Press Release which provides a summary of information published in *Energy Trends* and *Quarterly Energy Prices* publications: www.gnn.gov.uk/

> monthly, by the Office for National Statistics in the Monthly Digest of Statistics (Palgrave Macmillan).

To subscribe to *Energy Trends* and *Quarterly Energy Prices,* please contact Clive Sarjantson at the address given at paragraph XXIX. Single copies are available from the DTI Publications Orderline, as given in Annex C, priced £6 for Energy Trends and £8 for Quarterly Energy Prices.

Table numbering
XXIV   Page 10 contains a list showing the tables in the order in which they appear in this issue, and their corresponding numbers in previous issues.

Symbols used
XXV   The following symbols are used in this Digest:

..   not available
-    nil or negligible (less than half the final digit shown)
r   Revised since the previous edition

Rounding convention
XXVI   Individual entries in the tables are rounded independently and this can result in totals, which are different from the sum of their constituent items.

Acknowledgements
XXVII   Acknowledgement is made to the main coal producing companies, the electricity companies, the oil companies, the gas pipeline operators, the gas suppliers, National Grid, the Institute of Petroleum, the Coal Authority, the United Kingdom Iron and Steel Statistics Bureau, the National Environmental Technology Centre, Future Energy Solutions, the Department for Environment, Food and Rural Affairs, the Department for Transport, OFGEM, Building Research Establishment, HM Revenue and Customs, the Office for National Statistics, and other contributors to the enquiries used in producing this publication.

Cover photograph
XXVIII The cover illustration used for this Digest and other 2005-2006 DTI energy statistics publications is from a photograph by Peter Askew. It was a winning entry in the DTI News Photographic Competition in 2002.

Contacts
XXIX   For general enquiries on energy statistics contact:

Clive Sarjantson on 020 7215 2698   Sally Mercer on 020 7215 2717
(E-mail:clive.sarjantson@dti.gsi.gov.uk)   **or**   (E-mail:sally.mercer@dti.gsi.gov.uk)

Department of Trade and Industry
Bay 209
1 Victoria Street
London SW1H 0ET
Fax: 020 7215 2723

Enquirers with hearing difficulties can contact the Department on the DTI Textphone: 020 7215 6740.

XXX   For enquiries concerning particular data series or chapters contact those named on page 9 or at the end of the relevant chapter.

Sally Mercer, Production Editor
July 2006

Contact List

The following people in the Department of Trade and Industry may be contacted for further information about the topics listed:

Chapter	Contact	Telephone 020 7215	E-mail
Total energy statistics	Julian Prime	6178	Julian.Prime@dti.gsi.gov.uk
Solid fuels and derived gases	Sally Mercer Charanjit Ransi	2717 2718	Sally.Mercer@dti.gsi.gov.uk Charanjit.Ransi@dti.gsi.gov.uk
Oil and upstream gas resources	Clive Evans Martin Young	5189 5184	Clive.Evans@dti.gsi.gov.uk Martin.Young@dti.gsi.gov.uk
North Sea profits, operating costs and investments	Suhail Siddiqui	5262	Suhail.Siddiqui@dti.gsi.gov.uk
Petroleum (downstream)	Kelly Adams Martin Young	2712 5184	Kelly.Adams@dti.gsi.gov.uk Martin.Young@dti.gsi.gov.uk
Gas supply (downstream)	Sally Mercer Joe Ewins	2717 5190	Sally.Mercer@dti.gsi.gov.uk Joe.Ewins@dti.gsi.gov.uk
Electricity	Mike Janes Joe Ewins	5186 5190	Mike.Janes@dti.gsi.gov.uk Joe.Ewins@dti.gsi.gov.uk
Combined heat and power	Mike Janes	5186	Mike.Janes@dti.gsi.gov.uk
Prices and values Industrial, international and oil prices	Peter Matejic Jo Marvin	2720 6935	Peter.Matejic@dti.gsi.gov.uk Jo.Marvin@dti.gsi.gov.uk
Renewable sources of energy	Mike Janes	5186	Mike.Janes@dti.gsi.gov.uk
Calorific values and conversion factors	Julian Prime Martin Young	6178 5184	Julian.Prime@dti.gsi.gov.uk Martin.Young@dti.gsi.gov.uk
General enquiries (energy helpdesk)	Clive Sarjantson	2698	Clive.Sarjantson@dti.gsi.gov.uk

All the above can be contacted by fax on 020 7215 2723

Tables as they appear in this issue and their corresponding numbers in the previous three issues

Chapter	2003	2004	2005	2006
ENERGY	-	-	-	1.1
	-	-	1.1	1.2
	-	1.1	1.2	1.3
	1.1	1.2	1.3	-
	1.2	1.3	-	-
	1.3	-	-	-
	-	-	-	1.4
	-	-	1.4	1.5
	-	1.4	1.5	1.6
	1.4	1.5	1.6	-
	1.5	1.6	-	-
	1.6	-	-	-
	1.7	1.7	1.7	1.7
	1.8	1.8	1.8	1.8
	1.9	1.9	1.9	1.9
SOLID FUELS & DERIVED GASES	-	-	-	2.1
	-	-	2.1	2.2
	-	2.1	2.2	2.3
	2.1	2.2	2.3	-
	2.2	2.3	-	-
	2.3	-	-	-
	-	-	-	2.4
	-	-	2.4	2.5
	-	2.4	2.5	2.6
	2.4	2.5	2.6	-
	2.5	2.6	-	-
	2.6	-	-	-
	2.7	2.7	2.7	2.7
	2.8	2.8	2.8	2.8
	2.9	2.9	2.9	2.9
	2.10	2.10	2.10	2.10
	2.11	2.11	2.11	2.11
PETROLEUM	-	-	-	3.1
	-	-	3.1	3.2
	-	3.1	3.2	3.3
	3.1	3.2	3.3	-
	3.2	3.3	-	-
	3.3	-	-	-
	-	-	-	3.4
	-	-	3.4	3.5
	-	3.4	3.5	3.6
	3.4	3.5	3.6	-
	3.5	3.6	-	-
	3.6	-	-	-
	3.7	3.7	3.7	3.7
	3.8	3.8	3.8	3.8
	3.9	3.9	3.9	3.9
	3.10	3.10	3.10	3.10

Chapter	2003	2004	2005	2006
NATURAL GAS	4.1	4.1	4.1	4.1
	4.2	4.2	4.2	4.2
	4.3	4.3	4.3	4.3
ELECTRICITY	5.1	5.1	5.1	5.1
	5.2	5.2	5.2	5.2
	5.3	5.3	5.3	5.3
	5.4	5.4	5.4	5.4
	5.5	5.5	5.5	5.5
	5.6	5.6	5.6	5.6
	5.7	5.7	5.7	5.7
	-	5.8	5.8	5.8
	5.8	5.9	5.9	5.9
	5.9	5.10	5.10	5.10
	5.10	5.11	5.11	5.11
	-	-	5.12	5.12
COMBINED HEAT AND POWER	6.1	6.1	6.1	6.1
	6.2	6.2	6.2	6.2
	6.3	6.3	6.3	6.3
	6.4	6.4	6.4	6.4
	6.5	6.5	6.5	6.5
	6.6	6.6	6.6	6.6
	6.7	6.7	6.7	6.7
	6.8	6.8	6.8	6.8
	6.9	6.9	6.9	6.9
RENEWABLE SOURCES	-	-	-	7.1
	-	-	7.1	7.2
	-	7.1	7.2	7.3
	7.1	7.2	7.3	-
	7.2	7.3	-	-
	7.3	-	-	-
	7.4	7.4	7.4	7.4
	-	-	7.5	7.5
	7.5	7.5	7.6	7.6
	7.6	7.6	7.7	7.7
ANNEX A CALORIFIC VALUES	A.1	A.1	A.1	A.1
	A.2	A.2	A.2	A.2
	-	-	A.3	A.3

Chapter 1
Energy

Introduction

1.1   This chapter presents figures on overall energy production and consumption. Figures showing the flow of energy from production, transformation and energy industry use through to final consumption are presented in the format of an energy balance based on the individual commodity balances presented in Chapters 2 to 5 and 7.

1.2   The chapter begins with aggregate energy balances covering the last three years (Tables 1.1 to 1.3) starting with the latest year, 2005. Energy value balances then follow this for the same years (Tables 1.4 to 1.6) and Table 1.7 shows sales of electricity and gas by sector in value terms. Table 1.8 covers final energy consumption by the main industrial sectors over the last five years followed by Table 1.9, which shows the fuels used for electricity generation by these industrial sectors. The explanation of the principles behind the energy balance and commodity balance presentations is set out in Annex A. Long term trends commentary and Tables (1.1.1 to 1.1.8) for energy production, consumption and expenditure on energy, temperatures as well as analyses such as the relationship between energy consumption and the economy of the UK appear on DTI's energy statistics web site only at:

http://www.dti.gov.uk/energy/statistics/publications/dukes/page29812.html

Proposed change to use net calorific values when producing energy statistics

1.3   A consultation was launched in the 2005 edition of the Digest seeking views of users as to whether net calorific values (NCVs) should be used in place of Gross Calorific Values (GCVs). Five written responses were received to the consultation: three were from energy related businesses, one from a major user of energy data, and one personal response from a mechanical engineer. During the consultation period a meeting was held with the major data user. Two of the respondents welcomed the proposed change from GCV to NCV, however three respondents had concerns with the proposed changes to NCV reporting, particularly for gaseous fuels. The concerns related to use of NCVs for gaseous fuels. In addition, fuel specific NCVs as well as GCVs were published for the first time in an annex in the 2005 edition of the Digest. Reaction to this additional information was favourable. Two users (who did not formally respond to the consultation) felt that the provision of this information was useful because it enabled them to make their own conversions; these users did not feel that publishing energy balances using NCVs would serve a useful purpose.   In conclusion DTI recognise that there are good arguments both for and against moving from GCV to NCV.   However, at present it has been concluded that there would be no demonstrable advantage to changing the method of presenting UK Energy statistics, and so GCVs are still being used in this edition, and will be used in future editions of the Digest. The fuel specific NCVs will continue to be published, and are shown at Annex A.

The energy industries

1.4   The energy industries in the UK play a central role in the economy by producing, transforming and supplying energy in its various forms to all sectors. They are also major contributors to the UK's Balance of Payments through the exports of crude oil and oil products. The box below summarises the energy industries' contribution to the economy:

- 3.2 per cent of GDP;

- 5.8 per cent of total investment;

- 32.6 per cent of industrial investment;

- 135,000 people directly employed (4 per cent of industrial employment);

- Many others indirectly employed (eg an estimated 260,000 in support of UK Continental Shelf activities);

Aggregate energy balance (Tables 1.1, 1.2 and 1.3)

1.5   These tables show the flows of energy in the United Kingdom from production to final consumption through conversion into secondary fuels such as coke, petroleum products, secondary electricity and heat sold. The principles behind the presentation used in the Digest and how this links with the figures presented in other chapters are explained in Annex A. The figures are presented on an energy supplied basis, in tonnes of oil equivalent.

1.6   In 2005, the primary supply of fuels was 246.8 million tonnes of oil equivalent, a ½ per cent increase compared to 2004. Indigenous production in 2005 was 9½ per cent lower than in 2004. Chart 1.1 illustrates the figures for the production and consumption of individual primary fuels in 2005. In 2005, overall primary fuel consumption was not met by indigenous production; this continues the trend from 2004 when the UK became a net importer of fuel. The UK imported more coal, manufactured fuels, crude oil, electricity and gas than it exported; however we were a net exporter of petroleum products.

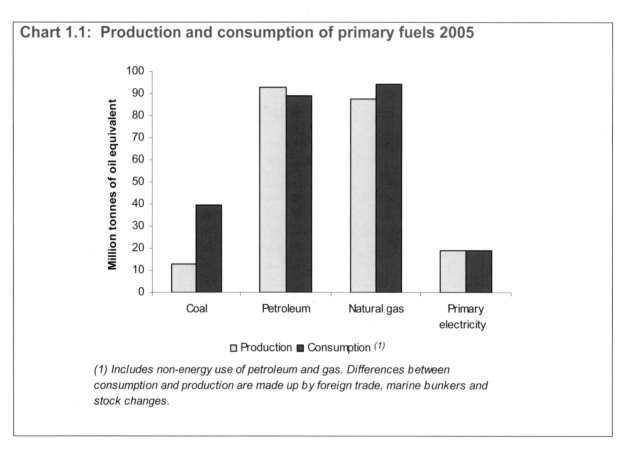

Chart 1.1: Production and consumption of primary fuels 2005

□ Production ■ Consumption *(1)*

(1) Includes non-energy use of petroleum and gas. Differences between consumption and production are made up by foreign trade, marine bunkers and stock changes.

1.7   Total primary energy demand was ½ per cent higher in 2005 than in 2004 at 246.9 million tonnes of oil equivalent. Chart 1.2 shows the composition of primary demand in 2005.

1.8   The transfers row in Tables 1.1 to 1.3 should ideally sum to zero with transfers from primary oils to petroleum products amounting to a net figure of zero. Similarly the manufactured gases and natural gas transfers should sum to zero. However differences in calorific values between the transferred fuels can result in non-zero values.

1.9   The transformation section of the energy balance shows, for each fuel, the net inputs for transformation uses. For example, on Table 1.1, 4,047 thousand tonnes of oil equivalent of coal feeds into the production of 4,009 thousand tonnes of oil equivalent of coke, representing a loss of 38 thousand tonnes of oil equivalent in the manufacture of coke in 2005. In 2005, energy losses during the production of electricity and other secondary fuels amounted to 54,371 thousand tonnes of oil equivalent, shown in the transformation row in Table 1.1.

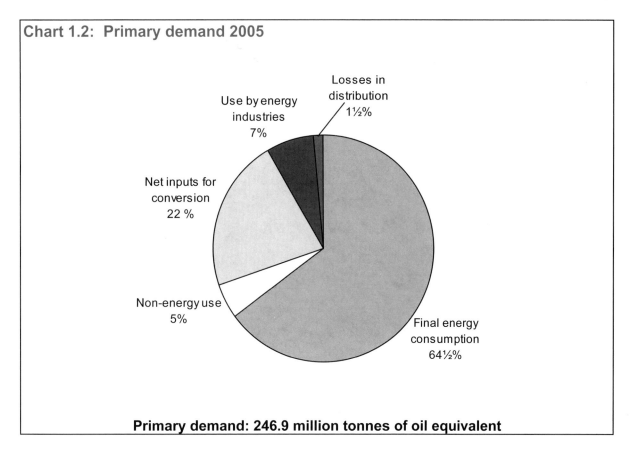

Chart 1.2: Primary demand 2005

Losses in distribution 1½%

Use by energy industries 7%

Net inputs for conversion 22 %

Non-energy use 5%

Final energy consumption 64½%

Primary demand: 246.9 million tonnes of oil equivalent

1.10   The next section of the table represents use of fuels by the energy industries themselves. This section also includes consumption by those parts of the iron and steel industry which behave like an energy industry ie they are involved in the transformation processes (see paragraph A.29 of Annex A). In 2005, energy industry use amounted to 16,523 thousand tonnes of oil equivalent of energy, virtually unchanged from the use in 2004.

1.11   Losses presented in the energy balance include distribution and transmission losses in the supply of manufactured gases, natural gas, and electricity. Recorded losses increased by 6 per cent between 2004 and 2005, and are now at their highest level since 2000. Losses in North Sea gas production are no longer separately identified in a simplified Petroleum Product Reporting System, which was introduced in January 2001. This has improved the quality of production data and reduced reported losses. Further details can be found in paragraph 4.30 in Chapter 4.

1.12   Total final consumption, which includes non-energy use of fuels, in 2005 was 172,111 thousand tonnes of oil equivalent; this is a 224 thousand tones of oil equivalent reduction on the comsumption in 2004. Final energy consumption in 2005 was mainly accounted for by the transport sector (34½ per cent), the domestic sector (27½ per cent), the industrial sector (19 per cent), the commercial sector (5½ per cent) and non-energy use (7½ per cent). These figures are illustrated in Chart 1.3. Recent trends in industrial consumption are shown in Table 1.8 and discussed in paragraphs 1.20 to 1.22.

1.13   The main fuels used by final consumers in 2005 were petroleum products (47½ per cent), natural gas (32½ per cent) and electricity (17 per cent). Of the petroleum products consumed by final users 14½ per cent was for non-energy purposes; for natural gas 1½ per cent was consumed for non-energy purposes. The amount of heat that was bought for final consumption accounted for 1 per cent of the total.

1.14   Non-energy use of fuels includes use as chemical feedstocks and other uses such as lubricants. Non-energy use of fuels for 2005 are shown in Table 1A. Further details of non-energy use are given in Chapter 3, paragraphs 3.55 to 3.61 and Chapter 4, paragraphs 4.17.

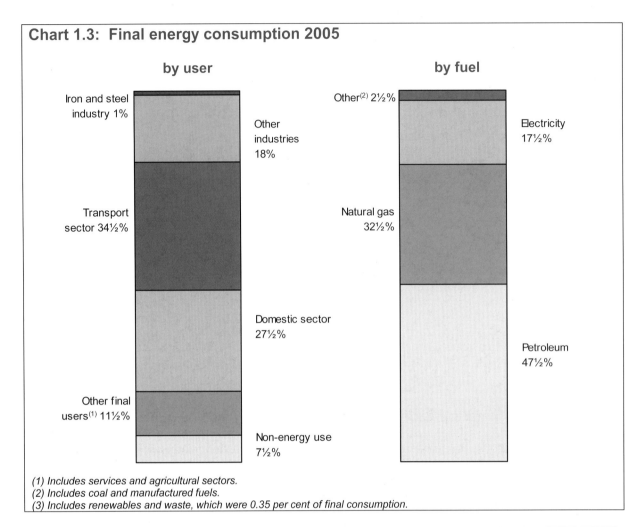

Chart 1.3: Final energy consumption 2005

by user

Iron and steel industry 1%

Other industries 18%

Transport sector 34½%

Domestic sector 27½%

Other final users[(1)] 11½%

Non-energy use 7½%

by fuel

Other[(2)] 2½%

Electricity 17½%

Natural gas 32½%

Petroleum 47½%

(1) Includes services and agricultural sectors.
(2) Includes coal and manufactured fuels.
(3) Includes renewables and waste, which were 0.35 per cent of final consumption.

Table 1A: Non-energy use of fuels 2005

	Thousand tonnes of oil equivalent	
	Petroleum	Natural gas
Petrochemical feedstocks	7,179	836
Other	4,569	-
Total	**11,748**	**836**

Value balance of traded energy (Tables 1.4, 1.5 and 1.6)

1.15   Tables 1.4 to 1.6 present the value of traded energy in a similar format to the energy balances. The balance shows how the value of inland energy supply is made up from the value of indigenous production, trade, tax and margins (profit and distribution costs). The lower half of the table then shows how this value is generated from the final expenditure on energy through transformation processes and other energy sector users as well as from the industrial and domestic sectors. The balances only contain values of energy which is traded ie where a transparent market price is applicable. Further technical notes are given in paragraphs 1.24 to 1.57. In keeping with the energy balances, the value balances have since 2000 included data on heat generation and heat sold. Additionally, an estimate of the amount of Climate Change Levy paid is included in Tables 1.4, 1.5 and 1.6. This levy was introduced in April 2001 and is payable by non-domestic final consumers of gas, electricity, coal, coke and LPG.

1.16   Total expenditure by final consumers in 2005 is estimated at £85,715 million, (£85,310 million shown as actual final consumption and £405 million of coal consumed by the iron and steel sector in producing coke for their own consumption).

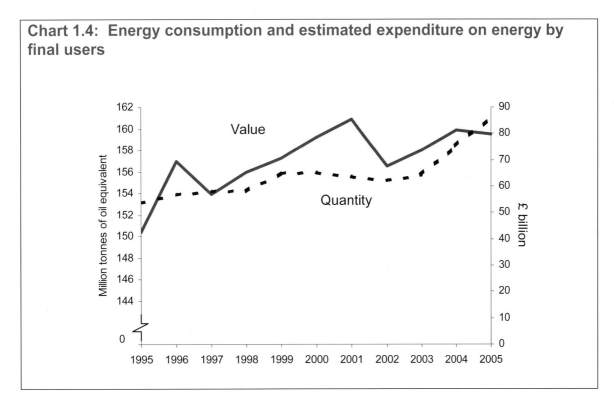

Chart 1.4: Energy consumption and estimated expenditure on energy by final users

1.17   This balance provides a guide on how the value chain works in the production and consumption of energy. For example in 2005, £19,220 million of crude oil were indigenously produced, of which £11,415 million were exported, and £11,565 million of crude oil were imported. Allowing for stock changes this provides a total value of inland crude oil supply of £19,310 million. This fuel was then completely consumed within the petroleum industry in the process of producing £22,790 million of petroleum products. Again some external trade and stock changes took place before arriving at a basic value of petroleum products of £21,560 million. In supplying the fuel to final consumers distribution costs were incurred and some profit was made amounting to £3,275 million, whilst duty and tax meant a further £28,970 million was added to the basic price to arrive at the final market value of £53,810 million. This was the value of petroleum products purchased of which industry purchased £2,005 million, domestic consumers for heating purposes purchased £1,050 million, with the vast majority purchased within the transportation sectors, £47,540 million.

1.18   Of the total final expenditure on energy in 2005 (£85,715 million) the biggest share, 56 per cent, fell to the transport sector. Of the remaining 44 per cent, industry purchased around a quarter or £9,975 million, with the domestic sector purchasing over a half or £20,510 million.

Sales of electricity and gas by sector (Table 1.7)
1.19   Table 1.7 shows broad estimates for the total value of electricity and gas to final consumption. Net selling values provide some indication of typical prices paid in broad sectors and can be of use to supplement more detailed and accurate information contained in the rest of this chapter.

Energy consumption by main industrial groups (Table 1.8)
1.20   This table presents final energy consumption for the main industrial sub-sectors over the last 5 years.

1.21   So far as is practicable, the user categories have been grouped on the basis of the 2003 Standard Industrial Classification (see paragraphs 1.52 to 1.56). However, some data suppliers have difficulty in classifying consumers to this level of detail and the breakdown presented in these tables must therefore be treated with caution. The groupings used are consistent with those used in Table 1.9 which show industrial sectors' use of fuels for generation of electricity (autogeneration).

1.22   In 2005, 33.1 million tonnes of oil equivalent were consumed by the main industrial groups. The largest consuming groups were chemicals (19 per cent), metal products, machinery and equipment (12½ per cent), food, beverages and tobacco (11½ per cent), iron and steel and non-ferrous metals (8½ per cent), mineral products (8½ per cent), and paper, printing and publishing (7½ per cent). The figures are illustrated in Chart 1.5.

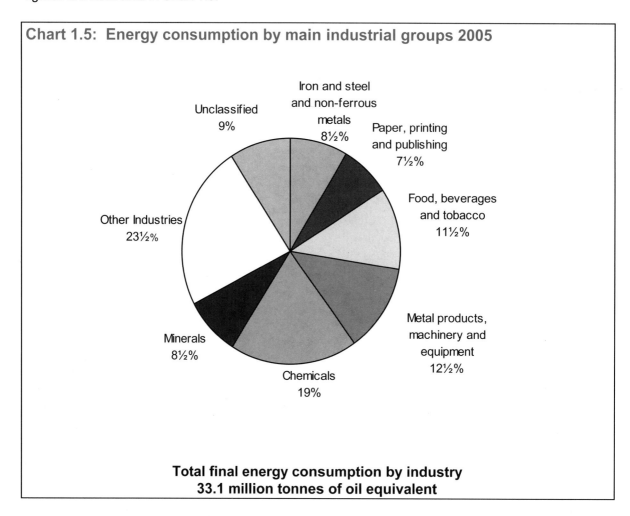

Chart 1.5: Energy consumption by main industrial groups 2005

Total final energy consumption by industry
33.1 million tonnes of oil equivalent

Fuels consumed for electricity generation by main industrial groups (autogeneration) (Table 1.9)

1.23   This table gives details of the amount of each fuel consumed by industries in order to generate electricity for their own use.   Fuel consumption is consistent with the figures given for "other generators" in Table 5.4 of Chapter 5. The term autogeneration is explained further in paragraphs 1.29 and 1.30. Electricity produced via autogeneration is included within the figures for electricity consumed by industrial sectors in Table 1.8. Table 1.9 has been produced using the information currently available and shows the same sector detail as Table 1.8, data cannot be given in as much detail as in the individual commodity balances and the energy balance because it could disclose information about individual companies.   Table 1.9 allows users to allocate the fuel used for autogeneration to individual industry groups in place of the electricity consumed. Further information on the way Table 1.9 links with the other tables is given in paragraph 1.30.

Technical notes and definitions

I Units and measurement of energy

Units of measurement
1.24 The original units of measurement appropriate to each fuel are used in the individual fuel chapters. A common unit of measurement, the tonne of oil equivalent (toe), which enables different fuels to be compared and aggregated, is used in Chapter 1. In common with the International Energy Agency and with the Statistical Office of the European Communities, the tonne of oil equivalent is defined as follows:

1 tonne of oil equivalent

$= 10^7$ kilocalories
$= 396.83$ therms
$= 41.868$ Gigajoules (GJ)
$= 11,630$ kWh

1.25 This unit should be regarded as a measure of energy content rather than a physical quantity. There is no intention to represent an actual physical tonne of oil, and indeed actual tonnes of oil will normally have measurements in tonnes of oil equivalent which differ from units.

Thermal content - energy supplied basis of measurement
1.26 Tables 1.1 to 1.3, 1.8 and 1.1.1 to 1.1.5 (available on DTI's energy statistics site at http://www.dti.gov.uk/energy/statistics/source/total/page18424.html) are compiled on an energy-supplied basis. Detailed data for individual fuels are converted from original units to tonnes of oil equivalent using gross calorific values and conversion factors appropriate to each category of fuel. The results are then aggregated according to the categories used in the tables. Gross calorific values represent the total energy content of the fuel, including the energy needed to evaporate the water present in the fuel (see also paragraph 1.50).

1.27 Estimated gross and net calorific values for 2005 are given on page 206. Calorific values are reviewed each year in collaboration with the fuel industries, and figures for earlier years can be found in Table A.2 and A.3 on pages 207 and 208. To construct energy balances on an energy supplied basis calorific values are required for production, trade, and stocks, as follows:

Coal The weighted average gross calorific value of all indigenous coal consumed is used to derive the thermal content of coal production and undistributed stocks. Thermal contents of imports and exports allow for the quality of coal. Thermal contents of changes in coal stocks at secondary fuel producers are the average calorific values of indigenous coal consumed.

Petroleum Work carried out in 1997 to revise calorific values for petroleum products did not find any recent work on the subject.   In the absence of such work, the gross calorific values, included in Annex A, and used in the construction of these energy balances from 1990 onwards have been calculated using a formula derived by the US Bureau of Standards. This formula estimates the gross calorific value of products according to their density as follows:

$Gj = 51.83 - 8.78 \times d^2$, where d is the density of the product in terms of kilograms per litre.

For crude petroleum and refinery losses, the weighted average calorific value for all petroleum products from UK refineries is used. A notional figure of 42.9 GJ per tonne is used for non-energy petroleum products (industrial and white spirits, lubricants, bitumen, petroleum coke, waxes and miscellaneous products).

Gases Although the original unit for gases is the cubic metre, figures for gases are generally presented in the fuel sections of this Digest in gigawatt hours (GWh), having been converted from cubic metres using gross calorific values provided by the industries concerned. Conversion factors between units of energy are given on the flap inside the back cover.

Electricity and heat Unlike other fuels, the original unit used to measure electricity and heat is a measure of energy. The figures for electricity and heat can therefore be converted directly to toe using the conversion factors on the flap inside the back cover.

Primary electricity Hydro electricity and net imports of electricity are presented in terms of the energy content of the electricity produced (the energy supplied basis). This is consistent with international practice. Primary inputs for nuclear electricity assume the thermal efficiencies at nuclear stations given in Chapter 5, Table 5.10 (38.2 per cent in 2005). (See Chapter 5, paragraphs 5.26 and 5.57.)

Non-energy uses of fuel

1.28 Energy use of fuel mainly comprises use for lighting, heating, motive power and power for appliances. Non-energy use includes use as chemical feedstocks, solvents, lubricants and road making material. It should be noted that the amounts of non-energy use of natural gas included in the Digest are approximate. Further discussion of non-energy uses of lubricating oils and petroleum coke appears in Chapter 3, paragraphs 3.55 to 3.61.

Autogeneration of electricity

1.29 Autogeneration is defined as the generation of electricity by companies whose main business is not electricity generation, the electricity being produced mainly for that company's own use. Estimated amounts of fuel used for thermal generation of electricity by such companies, the output of electricity and the thermal losses incurred in generation are included within the Transformation sector in the energy balances shown in Tables 1.1 to 1.3. Electricity used in the power generation process by autogenerators is shown within the Energy Industry Use section. Electricity consumed by industry and commerce from its own generation is included as part of Final consumption. This treatment is in line with the practice in international energy statistics.

1.30 Figures on total amount of fuel used and electricity generated by autogenerators, and the amount of electricity for own consumption is shown in Tables 1.9, 5.1, 5.3 to 5.6. Table 1.9 summarises the figures by broad industrial groups. Much of the power generated is from combined heat and power (CHP) plants and data from Chapter 6 are included within Table 1.9. Differences will occur where CHP plants are classified to major power producers, and this mainly affects the chemicals sector. The method of allocating fuel used in CHP plants between electricity production and heat production is described in Chapter 6 paragraphs 6.34 to 6.36. This method can give rise to high implied conversion efficiencies in some sectors, most notably in the iron and steel sector.

Final consumption, deliveries, stock changes

1.31 Figures for final consumption relate to deliveries, if fuels can be stored by users and data on actual consumption are not available. Final consumption of petroleum and solid fuels is on deliveries basis throughout, except for the use of solid fuels by the iron and steel industry. Figures for domestic use of coal are based on deliveries to merchants. Figures for stock changes in Tables 1.1 to 1.3 cover stocks held by primary and secondary fuel producers, major distributors of petroleum products, and stocks of coke and breeze held by the iron and steel industry; for coal they also include an estimate of volumes in transit. Figures for stock changes in natural gas represent the net amount put into storage by gas companies operating pipelines.

1.32 Figures for final consumption of electricity include sales by the public distribution system and consumption of electricity produced by generators other than the major electricity producing companies. Thus electricity consumption includes that produced by industry and figures for deliveries of other fuels to industry exclude amounts used to generate electricity (except for years prior to 1987).

Heat sold

1.33 Heat sold is defined as heat that is produced and sold under the provision of a contract. The heat sold figures have been derived from two sources covering CHP plants and community heating schemes without CHP plants. Data for heat sold were supplied by CHP plants to the Combined Heat and Power Quality Assurance Programme and were processed by Future Energy Solutions (part of AEA Technology Environment). Data for heat consumption from community heating schemes were derived from the Building Research Establishment's (BRE) 'Nationwide Survey of Community Heating' that was carried out in 1997, a database of community heating schemes in social housing in 2000, and Community Heating Sales Surveys undertaken since between 2003 and 2005. The estimates from these sources have been used to derive heat sold figures since 1999. When information about where the heat was generated was not available from the BRE sources, it was assumed that domestic sector heat consumption was provided by the commercial sector, public sector heat consumption was provided by the public administration and industrial sectors (using proportions derived from CHP statistics) and that industrial sector heat consumption was provided by the industrial sector. The introduction of heat sold into the energy balances has not affected the individual fuel totals, since the energy used to generate the heat has been deducted from the final consumption section of the energy balance and transferred to the transformation section. The figures that are included in the balances should be treated as indicative of the amount of heat sold.

II Energy balances (Tables 1.1, 1.2 and 1.3)

1.34   Tables 1.1, 1.2 and 1.3 show the energy flows as the primary fuels are processed (or used) and as the consequent secondary fuels are used. The net inputs to transformation are shown in the transformation rows and hence outputs from transformation processes into which primary fuels are input (such as electricity generation, heat generation or petroleum refining) appear as positive figures under the secondary product's heading in the tables. Similarly the net inputs are shown as negative figures under the primary fuel headings.

III Value balances (Tables 1.4, 1.5, 1.6, 1.1.6)

Valuation of energy purchases

1.35   In common with the rest of the chapter, these tables covering energy expenditure follow a balance format. While a user may derive data on a similar basis as that previously published, the balance table allows for more varied use and interpretation of traded energy value data. That said, the table continues to only show values for energy that has to be purchased and therefore does not include estimated values of a sector's internal consumption, such as coal used in the process of coal extraction.

The value balance

1.36   The table balances around **market value of inland consumption** with the lower half of the table showing the total value of consumption by end users, sub divided into energy sector users and final users both for energy and non-energy use. The top half of the table shows the supply components that go to make up the final market value of inland consumption, namely upstream cost of production, imports, taxes and the margins and costs of delivering and packaging the fuel for the final consumer. The total final consumers value of energy consumption is represented by the lines 'total non energy sector use' and iron and steel sectors purchases of coal for use in solid fuel manufacture.

1.37   All figures are estimates and have been rounded to the nearest £5 million.

Fuel definitions in value balances

1.38   **Crude oil** includes NGLs and refinery feedstocks. **Natural gas** does not include colliery methane. **Electricity** only includes electricity delivered via the public distribution system and therefore does not value electricity produced and consumed by autogenerators, however the fuels used by autogenerators are included under Transformation. **Manufactured solid fuels** includes coke, breeze and other solid manufactured fuels, mainly products from patent fuel and carbonisation plants. **Other fuels** includes all other fuels not separately listed, where they can be clearly considered as traded and some reasonable valuation can be made. Fuels mainly contributing to this year's values are wood, coke oven and colliery methane gases sold on to other industrial users and some use of waste products such as poultry litter.

Energy end use

1.39   Values represent the cost to the final user including transportation of the fuel. They are derived, except where actual values are available, from the traded element of the volumes presented in aggregate energy balance and end user prices collected from information supplied by users or energy suppliers. The **energy sector** consists of those industries engaged in the production and sale of energy products, but values are not given for consumption of self-generated fuels eg coke oven gas used by coke producers. Many of the processes in the **iron and steel** industry are considered to be part of the energy sector in the energy balances, but for the purposes of this economic balance their genuine purchases are treated as those of final consumers, except for purchases of coal directly used in coke manufacture, which is shown separately as part of manufacture of solid fuel. Coal used directly in or to heat blast furnaces is shown as iron and steel final use. **Transformation** includes those fuels used directly in producing other fuels eg crude oil in petroleum products. **Electricity generators** keep and use significant stocks of coal and the stocks used in consumption each year are shown separately. The value and margins for these being assumed to be the same as other coal purchased in the year. **Road transport** includes all motor spirit and DERV use. **Commercial and other users** includes public administration and miscellaneous uses not classified to the industrial sector.

Supply

1.40 The supply side money chain is derived using various methods. **Indigenous production** represents the estimated basic value of in-year sales by the upstream producers. This value is gross of any taxes or cost they must meet. The valuation problems in attributing network losses in gas and electricity between upstream and downstream within this value chain, means any costs borne are included in the production value. **Imports and exports** are valued in accordance with data published by HM Revenue and Customs, contained in Annex G (which can be found on the Internet at http://www.dti.gov.uk/energy/statistics/publications/dukes/page29812.html). However crude oil is treated differently where the value is formed from price data taken from a census survey of refiners and volume data taken from Tables 3.1 to 3.3. These values are considered to reflect the complete money chain more accurately than Tables G.1 to G.4. **Stock changes** are those for undistributed stocks except for coal where coke oven and generators stocks are included. A stock increase takes money out of the money chain and is therefore represented as a negative. **Distribution costs** are arrived at by removing an estimate of producers value along with any taxes from the end user values shown. For most fuel the estimate of producer value is derived from the consumption used for end use and the producer price taken from survey of producers. No sector breakdown is given for gas and electricity margins because it is not possible to accurately measure delivery costs for each sector. **Taxes** include VAT where not refundable and duties paid on downstream sales. Excluded are the gas and fossil fuel levies, petroleum revenue tax and production royalties and licence fees. The proceeds from the fossil fuel levy are redistributed across the electricity industry, whilst the rest are treated as part of the production costs.

Sales of electricity and gas by sector (Table 1.7)

1.41 This table provides data on the total value of gas and electricity sold to final consumers. The data are collected from the energy supply companies. The data are useful in indicating relative total expenditure between sectors, but the quality of data provided in terms of industrial classification has been worsening in recent years. Net selling values provide an indication of typical prices paid in broad sectors.

IV Measurement of energy consumption

Primary fuel input basis

1.42 Energy consumption is usually measured in one of three different ways. The first, known as the primary fuel input basis, assesses the total input of primary fuels and their equivalents. This measure includes energy used or lost in the conversion of primary fuels to secondary fuels (for example in power stations and oil refineries), energy lost in the distribution of fuels (for example in transmission lines) and energy conversion losses by final users. Primary demands as in Table 1.1, 1.2 and 1.3 are on this basis.

Final consumption - energy supplied basis

1.43 The second method, known as the energy supplied basis, measures the energy content of the fuels, both primary and secondary, supplied to final users. Thus it is net of fuel industry own use and conversion, transmission and distribution losses, but it includes conversion losses by final users. Table 1B presents shares of final consumption on this basis. The final consumption figures are presented on this basis throughout Chapter 1.

1.44 Although this is the usual and most direct way to measure final energy consumption, it is also possible to present final consumption on a primary fuel input basis. This can be done by allocating the conversion losses, distribution losses and energy industry use to final users. This approach can be used to compare the total primary fuel use which each sector of the economy accounts for. Table 1C presents shares of final consumption on this basis.

Final consumption - useful energy basis

1.45   Thirdly, final consumption may be expressed in the form of useful energy available after deduction of the losses incurred when final users convert energy supplied into space or process heat, motive power or light. Such losses depend on the type and quality of fuel and the equipment used and on the purpose, conditions, duration and intensity of use.   Statistics on useful energy are not sufficiently reliable to be given in this Digest; there is a lack of data on utilisation efficiencies and on the purposes for which fuels are used.

Shares of each fuel in energy supply and demand

1.46   The relative importance of the energy consumption of each sector of the economy depends on the method used to measure consumption. Shares of final consumption on an energy supplied basis (that is in terms of the primary and secondary fuels directly consumed) in 2005 are presented in Table 1B. For comparison, Table 1C presents shares of final consumption on a primary fuel input basis.

Table 1B: Primary and secondary fuels consumed by final users in 2005 – energy supplied basis

| | Percentage of each fuel | | | | | | Percentage of each sector | | | | |
	Industry	Transport	Domestic	Others	Total		Solid fuels	Petrol-eum	Gas	Secondary electricity	Total
Solid fuels	74	-	25	1	100	Industry	6	22	40	32	100
Petroleum	10	83	4	2	100	Transport	-	99	-	1	100
Gas	23	-	60	17	100	Domestic	1	7	70	22	100
Electricity	34	2	34	29	100	Others	-	9	47	44	100
All fuels	**20**	**38**	**30**	**12**	**100**	**All users**	**2**	**45**	**35**	**19**	**100**

Table 1C: Total primary fuel consumption by final users in 2005 - primary input basis

| | Percentage of each fuel | | | | | | Percentage of each sector | | | | |
	Industry	Transport	Domestic	Others	Total		Coal	Petrol-eum	Gas	Primary electricity	Total
Coal	37	2	33	27	100	Industry	27	15	46	13	100
Petroleum	10	82	5	3	100	Transport	1	97	1	1	100
Gas	27	1	51	21	100	Domestic	18	5	67	10	100
Primary electricity	34	2	34	29	100	Others	28	6	51	16	100
All fuels	**24**	**29**	**31**	**17**	**100**	**All users**	**17**	**34**	**40**	**9**	**100**

1.47   In 2005, every 1 toe of secondary electricity consumed by final users required, on average, 1.0 toe of coal, 0.9 toe of natural gas, 0.5 toe of primary electricity (nuclear, natural flow hydro and imports) and 0.1 toe of oil and renewables combined. The extent of this primary consumption is hidden in Table 1B, which presents final consumption only in terms of the fuels directly consumed. When all such primary consumption is allocated to final users, as in Table 1C, the relative importance of fuels and sectors changes; the transport sector, which uses very little electricity, declines in importance, whilst the true cost of final consumption in terms of coal use can now be seen.

1.48   Another view comes from shares of users' expenditure on each fuel (Table 1D based on Table 1.4). In this case the importance of fuels which require most handling by the user (solids and liquid fuels) is slightly understated, and the importance of uses taxed at higher rates (transport) is overstated in the "All users" line.

Table 1D: Value of fuels purchased by final users in 2005

	Solid fuels	Petroleum	Gas	Secondary electricity	Heat	Percentage of each sector Total
Industry	3	21	22	53	1	100
Transport	-	99	-	1	-	100
Domestic	1	5	45	49	-	100
Others	-	8	22	69	1	100
All users	**1**	**60**	**15**	**24**	**0**	**100**

Systems of measurement - international statistics

1.49   The systems of energy measurement used in various international statistics differ from the methods of the Digest as follows:

Net calorific values

1.50   Calorific values (thermal contents) used internationally are net rather than gross.   The difference between the net and gross thermal content is the amount of energy necessary to evaporate the water present in the fuel or formed during the combustion process.   The differences between gross and net values are taken to be 5 per cent for liquid and solid fuels (except for coke and coke breeze where there is no difference), 10 per cent for gases (except for blast furnace gas, 1 per cent), 15 per cent for straw, and 16 per cent for poultry litter.   The calorific value of wood is highly dependent on its moisture content.   In Annex A, the gross calorific value is given as 10 GJ per tonne at 50 per cent moisture content and this rises to 14.5 GJ at 25 per cent moisture content and 19 GJ for dry wood (equivalent to a net calorific value). Both gross and net calorific values are shown in Annex A.

V Definitions of fuels

1.51   The following paragraphs explain what is covered under the terms "primary" and "secondary" fuels.

Primary fuels

Coal - Production comprises all grades of coal, including slurry.

Primary oils - This includes crude oil, natural gas liquids (NGLs) and feedstock.

Natural gas liquids - Natural gas liquids (NGLs) consist of condensates (C_5 or heavier) and petroleum gases other than methane C_1, that is ethane C_2, propane C_3 and butane C_4, obtained from the onshore processing of associated and non-associated gas.   These are treated as primary fuels when looking at primary supply but in the consumption data presented in this chapter these fuels are treated as secondary fuels, being transferred from the primary oils column in Tables 1.1, 1.2 and 1.3.

Natural gas - Production relates to associated or non-associated methane C_1 from land and the United Kingdom sector of the Continental Shelf.   It includes that used for drilling production and pumping operations, but excludes gas flared or re-injected.   It also includes colliery methane piped to the surface and consumed by collieries or others.

Nuclear electricity - Electricity generated by nuclear power stations belonging to the major power producers.   See Chapter 5, paragraphs 5.49 and 5.51.

Natural flow hydro-electricity - Electricity generated by natural flow hydroelectric power stations, whether they belong to major power producers or other generators.   Pumped storage stations are not included (see under secondary electricity below).

Renewable energy sources - In this chapter figures are presented for renewables and waste in total. Further details, including a detailed breakdown of the commodities and technologies covered are in Chapter 7.

Secondary fuels

Manufactured fuel - This heading includes manufactured solid fuels such as coke and breeze, other manufactured solid fuels, liquids such as benzole and tars and gases such as coke oven gas and blast furnace gas.   Further details are given in Chapter 2, Tables 2.4, 2.5 and 2.6.

Coke and breeze - Coke oven coke and hard coke breeze. Further details are given in Chapter 2, Tables 2.4, 2.5 and 2.6.

Other manufactured solid fuels – Manufactured solid fuels produced at low temperature carbonisation plants and other manufactured fuel and briquetting plants. Further details are given in Chapter 2, Tables 2.4, 2.5 and 2.6.

Coke oven gas - Gas produced at coke ovens, excluding low temperature carbonisation plants. Gas bled or burnt to waste is included in production and losses. Further details are given in Chapter 2, Tables 2.4, 2.5 and 2.6.

Blast furnace gas - Blast furnace gas is mainly produced and consumed within the iron and steel industry. Further details are given in Chapter 2, Tables 2.4, 2.5 and 2.6.

Petroleum products - Petroleum products produced mainly at refineries, together with inland deliveries of natural gas liquids.

Secondary electricity - Secondary electricity is that generated by the combustion of another fuel, usually coal, natural gas, biofuels or oil. The figure for outputs from transformation in the electricity column of Tables 1.1, 1.2 and 1.3 is the total of primary and secondary electricity, and the subsequent analysis of consumption is based on this total.

Heat sold – Heat sold is heat that is produced and sold under the provision of a contract.

VI Classification of consumers

1.52   The Digest has been prepared, as far as is practicable, on the basis of the *Standard Industrial Classification (SIC)2003* (http://www.statistics.gov.uk/about/data/classifications/default.asp). SIC(2003) replaced SIC(1992) on 1 January 2003. SIC(1992) had been the basis of the industrial classification of energy statistics since 1995. Between 1986 and 1994 data in the Digest were prepared on the basis of the previous classification, SIC(1980). The changes in classification between SIC(1992) and SIC(2003) are mainly in the very detailed classifications at the four or five digit level. As such the classifications used for energy statistics are unaffected by these changes. However, not all consumption/disposals data are on this new basis, and where they are, there are sometimes constraints on the detail available. In particular the sectoral breakdown in the petroleum chapter is based on data that continue to be classified according to SIC (1968) by the oil industry. The main differences between the 1968 SIC (which was used as the basis for most data published for years prior to 1984) and the 1980 SIC were described in the 1986 and 1987 issues of the Digest. The differences between SIC 1980 and SIC 1992 are relatively minor. At the time of the change from the 1980 SIC to the 1992 SIC the main difference was that under the former showrooms belonging to the fuel supply industries were classified to the energy sector, whilst in the latter they are in the commercial sector. Since privatisation few gas, coal and electricity companies have retained showrooms and the difference is therefore minimal.

1.53   Table 1E shows the categories of consumers together with their codes in SIC 2003. The coverage varies between tables (eg in some instances the 'other' category is split into major constituents, whereas elsewhere it may include transport). This is because the coverage is dictated by what data suppliers can provide. The table also shows the disaggregation available within industry. This disaggregation forms the basis of virtually all the tables that show a disaggregated industrial breakdown.

Table 1E: SIC 2003 classifications

Fuel producers	10-12, 23, 40

Final consumers:

Industrial

Unclassified	See paragraph 1.54 below
Iron and steel	27, *excluding 27.4*, 27.53, 27.54
Non-ferrous metals	27.4, 27.53, 27.54
Mineral products	14, 26
Chemicals	24
Mechanical engineering and metal products	28, 29
Electrical and instrument engineering	30-33
Vehicles	34, 35
Food, beverages & tobacco	15, 16
Textiles, clothing, leather, & footwear	17-19
Paper, printing & publishing	21, 22
Other industries	13, 20, 25, 36, 37, 41
Construction	45

Transport, storage and communications 60-63

Other final users

Domestic	Not covered by SIC 2003.
Public administration	75, 80, 85
Commercial	50-52, 55, 64-67, 70-74
Agriculture	01, 02, 05
Miscellaneous	90-93, 99

1.54   There is also an 'unclassified' category in the industry sector (see Table 1E). Wherever the data supplier is unable to allocate an amount between categories, but the Department of Trade and Industry has additional information, from other data sources, with which to allocate between categories, then this has been done. Where such additional information is not available the data are included in the 'unclassified' category, enabling the reader to decide whether to accept a residual, pro-rate, or otherwise adjust the figures. The 'miscellaneous' category also contains some unallocated figures for the services sector.

1.55   In Tables 6.8 and 6.9 of Chapter 6 the following abbreviated grouping of industries, based on SIC 2003, is used in order to prevent disclosure of information about individual companies.

Table 1F: Abbreviated grouping of Industry

Iron and steel and non-ferrous metal	27
Chemicals	24
Oil refineries	23.2
Paper, printing and publishing	21, 22
Food, beverages and tobacco	15, 16
Metal products, machinery and equipment	28, 29, 30, 31, 32, 34, 35
Mineral products, extraction, mining and agglomeration of solid fuels	10, 11, 14, 26
Sewage Treatment	(parts of 41 and 90)
Electricity supply	40.1
Other industrial branches	12, 13, 17, 18, 19, 20, 23.1, 23.3, 25, 33, 36, 37, 40.2, 41 (remainder) 45
Transport, commerce, and administration	1, 2, 5, 50 to 99 (except 90 and 92)
Other	40.3, 90 (remainder), 92

1.56 In Tables 1.8 and 1.9 the list above is further condensed and includes only manufacturing industry and construction as follows.

Table 1G: Abbreviated grouping of Industry for Tables 1.8 and 1.9

Iron and steel and non-ferrous metals	27
Chemicals	24
Paper, printing and publishing	21, 22
Food, beverages and tobacco	15, 16
Metal products, machinery and equipment	28, 29, 30, 31, 32, 34, 35
Other (including construction)	12, 13, 14, 17, 18, 19, 20, 23.1, 23.3, 25, 26, 33, 36, 37, 45

VI Monthly and quarterly data

1.57 Monthly and quarterly data on energy production and consumption (including on a seasonally adjusted and temperature corrected basis) split by fuel type are provided on the DTI website at http://www.dti.gov.uk/energy/statistics/source/total/page18424.html. Quarterly figures are also published in the DTI's quarterly statistical bulletin *Energy Trends* and *Quarterly Energy Prices*. See Annex C for more information about these bulletins.

Contact: *Julian Prime (Statistician)*
             Energy demand
             julian.prime@dti.gsi.gov.uk
             020-7215 6178

             Chris Michaels
             chris.michaels@dti.gsi.gov.uk
             020-7215 2710

Peter Matejic (Statistician)
Energy prices
peter.matejic@dti.gsi.gov.uk
020-7215 2720

1.1 Aggregate energy balance 2005

Thousand tonnes of oil equivalent

	Coal	Manufactured fuel(1)	Primary oils	Petroleum products	Natural gas(2)	Renewable & waste(3)	Primary electricity	Electricity	Heat	Total
Supply										
Indigenous production	12,738	-	92,883	-	87,586	3,192	19,048	-	-	215,447
Imports	28,624	628	64,255	24,577	14,904	755	-	960	-	134,702
Exports	-418	-89	-59,177	-32,321	-8,270	-	-	-244	-	-100,519
Marine bunkers	-	-	-	-2,180	-	-	-	-	-	-2,180
Stock change(4)	-1,396	-97	-416	+1,157	+114	-	-	-	-	-637
Primary supply	**39,548**	**442**	**97,546**	**-8,766**	**94,333**	**3,947**	**19,048**	**715**	**-**	**246,813**
Statistical difference(5)	+44	-6	-121	-179	+55	-	-	+136	-	-71
Primary demand	**39,504**	**448**	**97,667**	**-8,587**	**94,278**	**3,947**	**19,048**	**580**	**-**	**246,884**
Transfers	-	-112	-3,643	+3,646	-4	-	-677	+677	-	-114
Transformation	**-37,815**	**1,751**	**-94,023**	**93,060**	**-30,483**	**-3,346**	**-18,370**	**33,510**	**1,347**	**-54,371**
Electricity generation	-32,503	-987	-	-704	-28,705	-3,346	-18,370	33,510	-	-51,107
Major power producers	-31,608	-	-	-263	-25,421	-810	-18,370	30,564	-	-45,909
Autogenerators	-895	-987	-	-441	-3,284	-2,537	-	2,946	-	-5,198
Heat generation	-320	-51	-	-64	-1,777	-	-	-	1,347	-867
Petroleum refineries	-	-	-94,023	94,108	-	-	-	-	-	84
Coke manufacture	-4,047	4,009	-	-	-	-	-	-	-	-38
Blast furnaces	-755	-1,420	-	-280	-	-	-	-	-	-2,455
Patent fuel manufacture	-189	200	-	-	-	-	-	-	-	11
Other	-	-	-	-	-	-	-	-	-	-
Energy industry use	**4**	**820**	**-**	**5,974**	**7,240**	**-**	**-**	**2,448**	**37**	**16,523**
Electricity generation	-	-	-	-	-	-	-	1,535	26	1,561
Oil and gas extraction	-	-	-	-	6,333	-	-	43	-	6,376
Petroleum refineries	-	-	-	5,974	171	-	-	484	11	6,640
Coal extraction	4	-	-	-	13	-	-	92	-	109
Coke manufacture	-	396	-	-	-	-	-	8	-	404
Blast furnaces	-	424	-	-	81	-	-	44	-	549
Patent fuel manufacture	-	-	-	-	-	-	-	-	-	-
Pumped storage	-	-	-	-	-	-	-	67	-	67
Other	-	-	-	-	642	-	-	175	-	817
Losses	**-**	**211**	**-**	**-**	**919**	**-**	**-**	**2,634**	**-**	**3,765**
Final consumption	**1,684**	**1,056**	**-**	**82,145**	**55,632**	**600**		**29,684**	**1,309**	**172,111**
Industry	**1,188**	**832**	**-**	**7,065**	**12,790**	**151**	**-**	**10,217**	**852**	**33,095**
Unclassified	-	239	-	2,665	6	151	-	-	-	3,060
Iron and steel	-	593	-	15	723	-	-	432	-	1,762
Non-ferrous metals	24	-	-	53	270	-	-	661	-	1,008
Mineral products	746	-	-	216	1,107	-	-	685	-	2,754
Chemicals	89	-	-	194	3,562	-	-	1,992	387	6,223
Mechanical engineering etc	10	-	-	118	729	-	-	748	1	1,604
Electrical engineering etc	3	-	-	35	372	-	-	639	-	1,049
Vehicles	38	-	-	139	851	-	-	504	-	1,531
Food, beverages etc	17	-	-	323	2,381	-	-	1,083	1	3,805
Textiles, leather etc	50	-	-	110	580	-	-	299	-	1,039
Paper, printing etc	98	-	-	86	1,124	-	-	1,122	57	2,488
Other industries	113	-	-	2,921	862	-	-	1,888	407	6,191
Construction	-	-	-	190	224	-	-	166	-	579
Transport (6)	**-**	**-**	**-**	**58,485**	**-**	**-**	**-**	**740**	**-**	**59,225**
Air	-	-	-	13,856	-	-	-	-	-	13,856
Rail	-	-	-	869	-	-	-	-	-	869
Road	-	-	-	42,390	-	-	-	-	-	42,390
National navigation	-	-	-	1,370	-	-	-	-	-	1,370
Pipelines	-	-	-	-	-	-	-	-	-	-
Other	**496**	**224**	**-**	**4,847**	**42,006**	**450**	**-**	**18,727**	**457**	**67,207**
Domestic	474	224	-	3,093	32,836	256	-	10,044	52	46,979
Public administration	11	-	-	549	4,246	100	-	1,852	405	7,162
Commercial	4	-	-	381	3,006	-	-	6,474	-	9,866
Agriculture	6	-	-	364	189	74	-	357	-	990
Miscellaneous	1	-	-	461	1,729	20	-	-	-	2,211
Non energy use	**-**	**-**	**-**	**11,748**	**836**	**-**	**-**	**-**	**-**	**12,583**

(1) Includes all manufactured solid fuels, benzole, tars, coke oven gas and blast furnace gas.
(2) Includes colliery methane.
(3) Includes geothermal and solar heat.
(4) Stock fall (+), stock rise (-).
(5) Primary supply minus primary demand.
(6) See paragraph 5.14 regarding electricity use in transport

1.2 Aggregate energy balance 2004

Thousand tonnes of oil equivalent

	Coal	Manufactured fuel(1)	Primary oils	Petroleum products	Natural gas(2)	Renewable & waste(3)	Primary electricity	Electricity	Heat	Total
Supply										
Indigenous production	15,647r	-	104,547	-	96,006	3,080r	18,754r	-	-	238,034r
Imports	23,619r	724r	68,214	20,181r	11,439	402r	-	841	-	125,420r
Exports	-448r	-124	-70,513	-32,860	-9,812	-	-	-197	-	-113,954r
Marine bunkers	-	-	-	-2,220	-	-	-	-	-	-2,220
Stock change (4)	-56r	-83r	-149	-327	-536	-	-	-	-	-1,151r
Primary supply	**38,763r**	**517r**	**102,099**	**-15,226r**	**97,097**	**3,482r**	**18,754r**	**644**	**-**	**246,129r**
Statistical difference (5)	+68r	+60r	-176r	-43r	+69r	-	-	+289r	-	+267r
Primary demand	**38,696r**	**456**	**102,275r**	**-15,183r**	**97,028r**	**3,482r**	**18,754r**	**355r**	**-**	**245,863r**
Transfers	-	-118	-4,196r	+4,176	-3	-	-591r	+591r	-	-140
Transformation	**-36,713r**	**1,706r**	**-98,080**	**97,279r**	**-31,040r**	**-2,767r**	**-18,163r**	**33,172r**	**1,261r**	**-53,346r**
Electricity generation	-31,532r	-921r	-	-645r	-29,330r	-2,767r	-18,163r	33,172r	-	-50,187r
Major power producers	-30,635	-	-	-153	-26,182	-539	-18,163r	30,246r	-	-45,426r
Autogenerators	-897r	-921r	-	-492r	-3,148r	-2,228r	-	2,926r	-	-4,760r
Heat generation	-299r	-51r	-	-64r	-1,710r	-	-	-	1,261r	-864r
Petroleum refineries	-	-	-98,080	98,297	-	-	-	-	-	217
Coke manufacture	-3,997	3,978r	-	-	-	-	-	-	-	-18
Blast furnaces	-652	-1,541	-	-309	-	-	-	-	-	-2,502
Patent fuel manufacture	-233	241	-	-	-	-	-	-	-	8
Other	-	-	-	-	-	-	-	-	-	-
Energy industry use	**6**	**849r**	**-**	**5,810**	**7,485r**	**-**	**-**	**2,332r**	**13**	**16,496r**
Electricity generation	-	-	-	-	-	-	-	1,475r	2	1,477r
Oil and gas extraction	-	-	-	-	6,612	-	-	48	-	6,660
Petroleum refineries	-	-	-	5,809	154r	-	-	425r	11	6,400r
Coal extraction	6	-	-	-	13	-	-	88	-	107
Coke manufacture	-	397r	-	1	-	-	-	8	-	407
Blast furnaces	-	449	-	-	63	-	-	40	-	552
Patent fuel manufacture	-	3	-	-	-	-	-	-	-	3
Pumped storage	-	-	-	-	-	-	-	73	-	73
Other	-	-	-	-	643	-	-	174r	-	817r
Losses	**-**	**201**	**-**	**-**	**703**	**-**	**-**	**2,642**	**-**	**3,546**
Final consumption	**1,977r**	**994r**	**-**	**80,462r**	**57,796r**	**715r**		**29,144r**	**1,247r**	**172,335r**
Industry	**1,228r**	**727r**	**-**	**6,751r**	**13,214r**	**265r**	**-**	**9,961r**	**832r**	**32,979r**
Unclassified	-	145r	-	2,632	6	265r	-	-	-	3,048r
Iron and steel	-	582r	-	35	835r	-	-	465	-	1,918r
Non-ferrous metals	7r	-	-	53r	275r	-	-	627	-	962r
Mineral products	751r	-	-	201	1,152r	-	-	673r	-	2,778r
Chemicals	94r	-	-	203r	3,606r	-	-	1,899r	394r	6,196r
Mechanical engineering etc.	10r	-	-	117	740r	-	-	732	2r	1,601r
Electrical engineering etc.	3r	-	-	38r	353r	-	-	586	-	981r
Vehicles	55r	-	-	109r	879r	-	-	489	-	1,532r
Food, beverages, etc.	26r	-	-	345	2,428r	-	-	1,063r	2	3,864r
Textiles, leather, etc.	58r	-	-	74	612r	-	-	293r	-	1,036r
Paper, printing etc.	97r	-	-	59	1,193r	-	-	1,111r	27r	2,487r
Other industries	127r	-	-	2,730r	881r	-	-	1,867r	407r	6,013r
Construction	-	-	-	156	252r	-	-	155	-	563r
Transport (6)	**-**	**-**	**-**	**57,440r**	**-**	**-**	**-**	**726r**	**-**	**58,166r**
Air	-	-	-	13,157	-	-	-	-	-	13,157
Rail	-	-	-	867r	-	-	-	-	-	867r
Road	-	-	-	42,221	-	-	-	-	-	42,221
National navigation	-	-	-	1,195	-	-	-	-	-	1,195
Pipelines	-	-	-	-	-	-	-	-	-	-
Other	**749r**	**267r**	**-**	**4,703**	**43,721r**	**449**	**-**	**18,457r**	**415r**	**68,761r**
Domestic	733r	267r	-	3,265r	34,085	252r	-	9,933	52	48,587r
Public administration	6r	-	-	504r	4,380r	104	-	1,781r	363r	7,138r
Commercial	4r	-	-	417	3,231r	-	-	6,381	-	10,033r
Agriculture	5r	-	-	277	202	74	-	361	-	918r
Miscellaneous	1r	-	-	240r	1,823r	20r	-	-	-	2,084r
Non energy use	**-**	**-**	**-**	**11,568**	**862**	**-**	**-**	**-**	**-**	**12,429**

(1) Includes all manufactured solid fuels, benzole, tars, coke oven gas and blast furnace gas.
(2) Includes colliery methane.
(3) Includes geothermal and solar heat.
(4) Stock fall (+), stock rise (-).
(5) Primary supply minus primary demand.
(6) See paragraph 5.14 regarding electricity use in transport

1.3 Aggregate energy balance 2003

Thousand tonnes of oil equivalent

	Coal	Manufactured fuel(1)	Primary oils	Petroleum products	Natural gas(2)	Renewable & waste(3)	Primary electricity	Electricity	Heat	Total
Supply										
Indigenous production	17,636r	-	116,242	-	102,926	3,008r	20,428	-	-	260,240r
Imports	20,703r	694r	59,114	17,948r	7,420	110	-	440	-	106,430r
Exports	-396	-133	-81,927	-25,274	-15,223	-	-	-254	-	-123,208r
Marine bunkers	-	-	-	-1,879	-	-	-	-	-	-1,879
Stock change (4)	+2,070r	-91r	+511	-294	+304	-	-	-	-	+2,499r
Primary supply	**40,013r**	**469r**	**93,940**	**-9,500r**	**95,427**	**3,118r**	**20,428**	**186**	**-**	**244,082r**
Statistical difference (5)	-97r	+66	+210	-660r	+64r	-	-	+190r	-	-226r
Primary demand	**40,109r**	**403r**	**93,730**	**-8,840r**	**95,363r**	**3,118r**	**20,428**	**-4r**	**-**	**244,308r**
Transfers	-	-124	-1,367	+1,294	-7	-	-388	+388	-	-204
Transformation	**-38,027r**	**1,853r**	**-92,363r**	**91,547r**	**-29,614**	**-2,408r**	**-20,040**	**33,616r**	**1,789**	**-53,648r**
Electricity generation	-32,548r	-934r	-	-590r	-27,909	-2,408r	-20,040	33,616r	-	-50,813r
Major power producers	-31,592	-	-	-105	-24,476r	-381	-20,040	30,722	-	-45,872
Autogenerators	-956r	-934r	-	-486r	-3,432	-2,027r	-	2,894r	-	-4,941
Heat generation	-386r	-116	-	-158	-1,705	-	-	-	1,789	-576r
Petroleum refineries	-	-	-92,363	92,533	-	-	-	-	-	170
Coke manufacture	-4,170r	4,212	-	-r	-	-	-	-	-	42r
Blast furnaces	-642	-1,601	-	-238	-	-	-	-	-	-2,481
Patent fuel manufacture	-282	292r	-	-	-	-	-	-	-	10
Other	-	-	-	-	-	-	-	-	-	-
Energy industry use	**4**	**898r**	**-**	**5,806r**	**7,645**	**-**	**-**	**2,523r**	**2**	**16,878r**
Electricity generation	-	-	-	-	-	-	-	1,559r	2	1,562r
Oil and gas extraction	-	-	-	-	6,607	-	-	47	-	6,654
Petroleum refineries	-	-	-	5,804r	238	-	-	496r	-	6,539r
Coal extraction	4	-	-	-	16	-	-	94	-	114
Coke manufacture	-	421	-	2r	-	-	-	9	-	431r
Blast furnaces	-	473	-	-	46	-	-	42	-	562
Patent fuel manufacture	-	3	-	-	-	-	-	-	-	3
Pumped storage	-	-	-	-	-	-	-	70	-	70
Other	-	-	-	-	737	-	-	206r	-	943r
Losses	-	160	-	-	535r	-	-	2,568	-	3,262
Final consumption	**2,078r**	**1,075**	**-**	**78,194r**	**57,563r**	**710r**		**28,910r**	**1,787**	**170,316r**
Industry	**1,248r**	**729**	**-**	**6,249r**	**14,292**	**267r**	**-**	**9,747r**	**1,128**	**33,660r**
Unclassified	-	140	-	2,014	6	267r	-	-	-	2,426r
Iron and steel	-	572	-	19	888	-	-	467	-	1,947
Non-ferrous metals	8r	17	-	48r	411r	-	-	626r	-	1,110r
Mineral products	799r	-	-	243r	1,213r	-	-	658	-	2,913r
Chemicals	46r	-	-	197r	3,873r	-	-	1,801r	1,097	7,014
Mechanical engineering etc.	10r	-	-	151r	785	-	-	760	12	1,718r
Electrical engineering etc.	1	-	-	28r	378	-	-	518	-	925r
Vehicles	49r	-	-	100r	999r	-	-	487	14	1,648r
Food, beverages, etc.	36r	-	-	222r	2,476r	-	-	1,027	5	3,767r
Textiles, leather, etc.	61r	-	-	110r	679r	-	-	296	-	1,146r
Paper, printing etc.	88r	-	-	56r	1,367r	-	-	1,096	-	2,607r
Other industries	148r	-	-	2,741r	957r	-	-	1,865r	-	5,710r
Construction	-	-	-	322	259r	-	-	146	-	727r
Transport (6)	**-**	**-**	**-**	**55,817r**	**-**	**-**	**-**	**706r**	**-**	**56,523r**
Air	-	-	-	11,936	-	-	-	-	-	11,936
Rail	-	-	-	826r	-	-	-	-	-	826r
Road	-	-	-	41,823	-	-	-	-	-	41,823
National navigation	-	-	-	1,233	-	-	-	-	-	1,233
Pipelines	-	-	-	-	-	-	-	-	-	-
Other	**830r**	**346**	**-**	**4,704r**	**42,409r**	**443r**	**-**	**18,456r**	**659**	**67,847r**
Domestic	813r	346	-	3,559	33,232	247	-	9,954	11	48,161r
Public administration	8r	-	-	399r	3,814	104	-	1,773r	627	6,726r
Commercial	4r	-	-	326r	3,400	-	-	6,383	-	10,112r
Agriculture	4r	-	-	328	200	72	-	346	-	951r
Miscellaneous	2r	-	-	91	1,764r	20	-	-	21	1,897r
Non energy use	**-**	**-**	**-**	**11,424**	**862**	**-**	**-**	**-**	**-**	**12,286**

(1) Includes all manufactured solid fuels, benzole, tars, coke oven gas and blast furnace gas.
(2) Includes colliery methane.
(3) Includes geothermal and solar heat.
(4) Stock fall (+), stock rise (-).
(5) Primary supply minus primary demand.
(6) See paragraph 5.14 regarding electricity use in transport

1.4 Value balance of traded energy in 2005[1]

£million

	Coal	Manufactured solid fuels	Crude oil	Petroleum products	Natural gas	Electricity	Heat sold	Other fuels	Total
Supply									
Indigenous production	585	120	19,220	22,790	8,215	5,520	260	85	56,790
Imports	1,875	85	11,565	7,475	1,730	440	-	-	23,170
Exports	-40	-15	-11,415	-8,545	-745	-100	-	-	-20,860
Marine bunkers	-	-	-	-420	-	-	-	-	-420
Stock change	-80	-5	-60	+260	-	-	-	-	+115
Basic value of inland consumption	**2,340**	**180**	**19,310**	**21,560**	**9,205**	**5,860**	**260**	**85**	**58,795**
Tax and margins									
Distribution costs and margins	**260**	**65**	**-**	**3,275**	**6,650**	**13,885**	**-**	**-**	**24,135**
Electricity generation	30	-	-	25	-	-	-	-	55
Solid fuel manufacture	105	-	-	-	-	-	-	-	105
of which iron & steel sector	90	-	-	-	-	-	-	-	90
Iron & steel final use	20	45	-	15	-	-	-	-	80
Other industry	15	15	-	335	-	-	-	-	360
Air transport	-	-	-	25	-	-	-	-	25
Rail and national navigation	-	-	-	20	-	-	-	-	20
Road transport	-	-	-	2,265	-	-	-	-	2,265
Domestic	95	10	-	195	-	-	-	-	300
Agriculture	-	-	-	15	-	-	-	-	15
Commercial and other services	-	-	-	55	-	-	-	-	55
Non energy use	-	-	-	330	135	-	-	-	460
VAT and duties	**5**	**5**	**-**	**28,970**	**435**	**480**	**-**	**-**	**29,900**
Electricity generation	-	-	-	25	-	-	-	-	25
Iron & steel final use	-	-	-	-	-	-	-	-	-
Other industry	-	-	-	240	-	-	-	-	240
Air transport	-	-	-	20	-	-	-	-	20
Rail and national navigation	-	-	-	125	-	-	-	-	125
Road transport	-	-	-	28,415	-	-	-	-	28,415
Domestic	5	5	-	60	435	480	-	-	985
Agriculture	-	-	-	10	-	-	-	-	10
Commercial and other services	-	-	-	75	-	-	-	-	75
Climate Change Levy	**5**	**-**	**-**	**-**	**195**	**535**	**-**	**-**	**735**
Total tax and margins	**270**	**70**	**-**	**32,250**	**7,275**	**14,900**	**-**	**-**	**54,765**
Market value of inland consumption	**2,610**	**255**	**19,310**	**53,810**	**16,480**	**20,755**	**165**	**85**	**113,470**
Energy end use									
Total energy sector	**2,300**	**-**	**19,310**	**185**	**3,490**	**230**	**5**	**35**	**25,560**
Transformation	2,300	-	19,310	185	3,395	-	5	35	25,235
Electricity generation	1,830	-	-	170	3,370	-	5	35	5,415
of which from stocks	60	-	-	-	-	-	-	-	60
Heat Generation	15	-	-	15	20	-	-	-	50
Petroleum refineries	-	-	19,310	-	-	-	-	-	19,310
Solid fuel manufacture	455	-	-	-	-	-	-	-	455
of which iron & steel sector	405	-	-	-	-	-	-	-	405
Other energy sector use	-	-	-	-	95	230	-	-	330
Oil & gas extraction	-	-	-	-	-	25	-	-	25
Petroleum refineries	-	-	-	-	20	155	-	-	175
Coal extraction	-	-	-	-	-	50	-	-	50
Other energy sector	-	-	-	-	75	-	-	-	75
Total non energy sector use	**305**	**255**	**-**	**51,155**	**12,860**	**20,525**	**160**	**50**	**85,310**
Industry	**160**	**175**	**-**	**2,005**	**2,070**	**5,060**	**75**	**20**	**9,570**
Iron & steel final use	80	150	-	55	125	130	-	-	540
Other industry	80	25	-	1,955	1,950	4,930	75	20	9,030
Transport	**-**	**-**	**-**	**47,540**	**-**	**345**	**-**	**-**	**47,890**
Air	-	-	-	3,810	-	-	-	-	3,810
Rail and national navigation	-	-	-	625	-	345	-	-	975
Road	-	-	-	43,105	-	-	-	-	43,105
Other final users	**145**	**80**	**-**	**1,605**	**10,785**	**15,120**	**90**	**30**	**27,850**
Domestic	145	80	-	1,050	9,140	10,055	10	30	20,510
Agriculture	-	-	-	115	35	275	-	-	425
Commercial and other services	-	-	-	445	1,610	4,785	80	-	6,920
Total value of energy end use	**2,610**	**255**	**19,310**	**51,340**	**16,345**	**20,755**	**165**	**85**	**110,870**
Value of non energy end use	**-**	**-**	**-**	**2,465**	**135**	**-**	**-**	**-**	**2,600**
Market value of inland consumption	**2,610**	**255**	**19,310**	**53,810**	**16,480**	**20,755**	**165**	**85**	**113,470**

(1) For further information see paragraphs 1.35 to 1.40.

1.5 Value balance of traded energy in 2004[1]

£million

	Coal	Manufactured solid fuels	Crude oil	Petroleum products	Natural gas	Electricity	Heat sold	Other fuels	Total
Supply									
Indigenous production	585r	90	15,280r	19,780r	7,060r	5,800r	240r	65	48,905r
Imports	1,330	75	8,625r	4,805	670	345	-	-	15,850r
Exports	-35	-15	-9,905	-6,490r	-645r	-150r	-	-	-17,240r
Marine bunkers	-	-	-	-340	-	-	-	-	-340
Stock change	-	-5	-20	-75	-5	-	-	-	-110r
Basic value of inland consumption	1,875r	150	13,980r	17,685r	7,080	5,995	240r	65	47,070r
Tax and margins									
Distribution costs and margins	385r	50	-	2,385r	4,860r	8,935	-	-	16,615r
Electricity generation	155r	-	-	15r	-	-	-	-	170r
Solid fuel manufacture	70	-	-	-	-	-	-	-	70
of which iron & steel sector	65	-	-	-	-	-	-	-	65
Iron & steel final use	10	35	-	15	-	-	-	-	60
Other industry	10r	10	-	285r	-	-	-	-	305r
Air transport	-	-	-	80	-	-	-	-	80
Rail and national navigation	-	-	-	20r	-	-	-	-	20r
Road transport	-	-	-	1,380	-	-	-	-	1,380
Domestic	140r	5	-	110	-	-	-	-	255r
Agriculture	-	-	-	10	-	-	-	-	10
Commercial and other services	-	-	-	30r	-	-	-	-	30r
Non energy use	-	-	-	440	95	-	-	-	535
VAT and duties	10r	5	-	31,030r	330	385	-	-	31,760r
Electricity generation	-	-	-	15r	-	-	-	-	15r
Iron & steel final use	-	-	-	-	-	-	-	-	-
Other industry	-	-	-	180r	-	-	-	-	180r
Air transport	-	-	-	20	-	-	-	-	20
Rail and national navigation	-	-	-	90r	-	-	-	-	90r
Road transport	-	-	-	30,620r	-	-	-	-	30,620r
Domestic	10r	5	-	45r	330	385	-	-	775r
Agriculture	-	-	-	5	-	-	-	-	5
Commercial and other services	-	-	-	50r	-	-	-	-	50r
Climate Change Levy	5	-	-	-	200r	570r	-	-	775
Total tax and margins	400r	55	-	33,415r	5,390r	9,890r	-	-	49,150r
Market value of inland consumption	2,270r	205	13,980r	51,100r	12,470r	15,890r	155r	65	96,135r
Energy end use									
Total energy sector	1,945r	-	13,980r	125	2,675r	170	-	25	18,925r
Transformation	1,945r	-	13,980r	125	2,605r	-	-	25	18,685r
Electricity generation	1,615r	-	-	115	2,590r	-	-	25	4,345r
of which from stocks	40r	-	-	-	-	-	-	-	40r
Heat Generation	15r	-	-	10	15r	-	-	-	40r
Petroleum refineries	-	-	13,980r	-	-	-	-	-	13,980r
Solid fuel manufacture	320	-	-	-	-	-	-	-	320
of which iron & steel sector	285	-	-	-	-	-	-	-	285
Other energy sector use	-	-	-	-	70r	170r	-	-	240r
Oil & gas extraction	-	-	-	-	-	20	-	-	20
Petroleum refineries	-	-	-	-	15	115r	-	-	125r
Coal extraction	-	-	-	-	-	40	-	-	40
Other energy sector	-	-	-	-	55	-	-	-	55
Total non energy sector use	325r	205	-	48,850r	9,695r	15,715	155r	40	74,985r
Industry	120r	120	-	1,485r	1,480r	3,255	75r	15	6,550r
Iron & steel final use	50	100	-	50	95r	110	-	-	400r
Other industry	70r	20	-	1,435r	1,385r	3,150	75r	15	6,150r
Transport	-	-	-	46,215r	-	260	-	-	46,475r
Air	-	-	-	2,785	-	-	-	-	2,785
Rail and national navigation	-	-	-	455r	-	260	-	-	715r
Road	-	-	-	42,975r	-	-	-	-	42,975r
Other final users	205r	80	-	1,150r	8,215r	12,200	80r	30	21,960r
Domestic	205r	80	-	805r	6,895	8,105	10	30	16,130r
Agriculture	-	-	-	65	30	230	-	-	325
Commercial and other services	-r	-	-	280r	1,290r	3,865	70r	-	5,505r
Total value of energy end use	2,270r	205	13,980r	48,970r	12,375r	15,890r	155r	65	93,915r
Value of non energy end use	-	-	-	2,125	95	-	-	-	2,225
Market value of inland consumption	2,270r	205	13,980r	51,100r	12,470r	15,890r	155r	65	96,135r

(1) For further information see paragraphs 1.35 to 1.40.

1.6 Value balance of traded energy in 2003[1]

£million

	Coal	Manufactured solid fuels	Crude oil	Petroleum products	Natural gas	Electricity	Heat sold	Other fuels	Total
Supply									
Indigenous production	710r	120	14,310	15,280r	7,160r	7,240	345	55	45,400r
Imports	925	70	6,495	3,615r	135	170	-	-	11,405r
Exports	-35	-15	-9,815	-4,950	-945r	-180r	-	-	-15,940r
Marine bunkers	-	-	-	-255	-	-	-	-	-255
Stock change	85r	-5	65	-45	-	-	-	-	95r
Basic value of inland consumption	**1,685r**	**170**	**11,055**	**13,635r**	**6,350**	**7,410r**	**345**	**55**	**40,705r**
Tax and margins									
Distribution costs and margins	**295r**	**20**	**-**	**2,590r**	**4,260**	**6,160**	**-**	**-**	**13,330r**
Electricity generation	80	-	-	10r	-	-	-	-	90r
Solid fuel manufacture	55r	-	-	-	-	-	-	-	55r
of which iron & steel sector	45	-	-	-	-	-	-	-	45
Iron & steel final use	10	5	-	5	-	-	-	-	20
Other industry	10r	5	-	270r	-	-	-	-	285r
Air transport	-	-	-	110	-	-	-	-	110
Rail and national navigation	-	-	-	20r	-	-	-	-	20r
Road transport	-	-	-	1,660	-	-	-	-	1,660
Domestic	145r	5	-	90	-	-	-	-	245r
Agriculture	-	-	-	10	-	-	-	-	10
Commercial and other services	-	-	-	20	-	-	-	-	25
Non energy use	-	-	-	390	80	-	-	-	470
VAT and duties	**10**	**5**	**-**	**25,940r**	**300**	**365**	**-**	**-**	**26,620r**
Electricity generation	-	-	-	10r	-	-	-	-	10r
Iron & steel final use	-	-	-	-	-	-	-	-	-
Other industry	-	-	-	185r	-	-	-	-	185r
Air transport	-	-	-	20	-	-	-	-	20
Rail and national navigation	-	-	-	90r	-	-	-	-	90r
Road transport	-	-	-	25,545	-	-	-	-	25,545
Domestic	10	5	-	45	300	365	-	-	725
Agriculture	-	-	-	10	-	-	-	-	10
Commercial and other services	-	-	-	35r	-	-	-	-	35r
Climate Change Levy	**5**	**-**	**-**	**-**	**195**	**620**	**-**	**-**	**820**
Total tax and margins	**310r**	**25**	**-**	**28,530r**	**4,755r**	**7,145**	**-**	**-**	**40,765r**
Market value of inland consumption	**1,995r**	**190**	**11,055**	**42,165r**	**11,105r**	**14,560**	**335**	**55**	**81,465r**
Energy end use									
Total energy sector	**1,685**	**-**	**11,055**	**125r**	**2,300**	**145**	**-**	**20**	**15,325r**
Transformation	**1,685**	**-**	**11,055**	**125r**	**2,225**	**-**	**-**	**20**	**15,105r**
Electricity generation	1,445	-	-	105r	2,210	-	-	20	3,775r
of which from stocks	35	-	-	-	-	-	-	-	35
Heat Generation	15	-	-	25	15	-	-	-	55
Petroleum refineries	-	-	11,055	-	-	-	-	-	11,055
Solid fuel manufacture	220	-	-	-	-	-	-	-	220
of which iron & steel sector	195	-	-	-	-	-	-	-	195
Other energy sector use	**-**	**-**	**-**	**-**	**75**	**145**	**-**	**-**	**220**
Oil & gas extraction	-	-	-	-	-	15	-	-	15
Petroleum refineries	-	-	-	-	20	95r	-	-	115
Coal extraction	-	-	-	-	-	30	-	-	30
Other energy sector	-	-	-	-	60	-	-	-	60
Total non energy sector use	**310r**	**190**	**-**	**40,135r**	**8,725r**	**14,415**	**335**	**40**	**64,150r**
Industry	**95r**	**90**	**-**	**1,240r**	**1,345**	**2,925**	**210**	**10**	**5,920r**
Iron & steel final use	30	70	-	35	85	100	-	-	320
Other industry	65r	20	-	1,205r	1,265	2,830	210	10	5,600r
Transport	**-**	**-**	**-**	**37,915r**	**-**	**215**	**-**	**-**	**38,135r**
Air	-	-	-	2,445	-	-	-	-	2,445
Rail and national navigation	-	-	-	420r	-	215	-	-	635r
Road	-	-	-	35,055	-	-	-	-	35,055
Other final users	**215r**	**105**	**-**	**975r**	**7,380r**	**11,270**	**125**	**30**	**20,100r**
Domestic	215r	105	-	730	6,260	7,660	-	30	15,000r
Agriculture	-	-	-	70	30	195	-	-	295r
Commercial and other services	5	-	-	175r	1,090r	3,420	125	-	4,805r
Total value of energy end use	**1,995r**	**190**	**11,055**	**40,260r**	**11,025r**	**14,560**	**335**	**55**	**79,480r**
Value of non energy end use	**-**	**-**	**-**	**1,905**	**80**	**-**	**-**	**-**	**1,985**
Market value of inland consumption	**1,995r**	**190**	**11,055**	**42,165r**	**11,105r**	**14,560**	**335**	**55**	**81,465r**

(1) For further information see paragraphs 1.35 to 1.40.

1.7 Sales of electricity and gas by sector
United Kingdom

	2001	2002	2003	2004	2005
Total selling value (£ million)[(1)]					
Electricity generation - Gas	2,065	2,006	2,209	2,591r	3,377
Industrial - Gas	1,749	1,519	1,567	1,630r	2,422
- Electricity	3,319	3,146	3,071	3,429r	5,291
of which:					
Fuel industries	175	152	144	171	232
Industrial sector	3,144	2,994	2,927	3,257	5,059
Domestic sector - Gas	5,460	5,798	5,964	6,565	8,707
- Electricity	7,182	7,154	7,295	7,719	9,579
Other - Gas	1,413	1,283	1,325	1,534r	1,923
- Electricity	4,327	4,046	3,827	4,354	5,408
of which:					
Agricultural sector	227	213	193	228	276
Commercial sector	3,072	2,895	2,748	3,115	3,857
Transport sector	242	218	216	260	346
Public lighting	86	75	75	82	106
Public admin. and other services	706	645	595	669	823
Total, all consumers	**25,515**	**24,952**	**25,258**	**27,822r**	**36,707**
of which gas	**10,687**	**10,606**	**11,065**	**12,320r**	**16,429**
of which electricity	**14,828**	**14,346**	**14,193**	**15,502r**	**20,278**
Average net selling value per kWh sold (pence)[(1)]					
Electricity generation - Gas	0.667	0.609	0.682	0.761	1.015
Industrial - Gas	0.838	0.840	0.872	0.969	1.469
- Electricity	3.247	3.096	2.971	3.320	4.998
of which:					
Fuel industries	3.362	3.194	2.974	3.672	4.791
Industrial sector	3.241	3.092	2.971	3.304	5.008
Domestic sector - Gas	1.440	1.540	1.543	1.656	2.280
- Electricity	6.227	6.246	6.302	6.682	8.200
Other - Gas	1.114	1.147	1.133	1.277	1.672
- Electricity	4.180	3.903	3.637	4.149	5.084
of which:					
Agricultural sector	5.537	5.149	4.804	5.447	6.648
Commercial sector	4.266	3.967	3.701	4.197	5.122
Transport sector	3.247	3.085	2.872	3.546	4.641
Public lighting	4.207	3.913	3.651	4.140	5.052
Public admin. and other services	3.945	3.669	3.423	3.881	4.737
Average, all consumers	**1.896**	**1.893**	**1.897**	**2.063**	**2.773**
of which gas	**1.043**	**1.062**	**1.099**	**1.202**	**1.652**
of which electricity	**4.618**	**4.486**	**4.376**	**4.788r**	**6.162**

(1) Excludes VAT where payable - see paragraph 1.41 for a definition of average net selling value.

1.8 Final energy consumption by main industrial groups[1]

Thousand tonnes of oil equivalent

	2001	2002	2003	2004	2005
Iron and steel and non-ferrous metals					
Coal	8r	14r	8r	7r	24
Manufactured solid fuels (2)	717	477	504	482	489
Blast furnace gas	272	226	36	32r	28
Coke oven gas	123	75	49	67r	76
Natural gas	1,218	1,208	1,299r	1,110r	994
Petroleum	160r	162r	67r	87r	68
Electricity	1,086	985	1,094r	1,093r	1,092
Total iron and steel and non-ferrous metals	**3,585r**	**3,147r**	**3,057r**	**2,879r**	**2,770**
Chemicals					
Coal	23r	40r	46r	94r	89
Natural gas	4,305	3,807	3,873r	3,606r	3,562
Petroleum	253r	229r	197r	203r	194
Electricity	1,812	1,966	1,801r	1,899r	1,992
Heat sold	988	1,310r	1,097	394r	387
Total chemicals	**7,382r**	**7,352r**	**7,014r**	**6,196r**	**6,223**
Metal products, machinery and equipment					
Coal	57r	58r	61r	68r	51
Natural gas	2,297	2,185	2,162r	1,973r	1,951
Petroleum	521	476r	279r	264r	292
Electricity	1,727	1,745	1,764	1,807	1,890
Heat sold	..	..	26	2r	1
Total metal products, machinery and equipment	**4,602r**	**4,464r**	**4,292r**	**4,115r**	**4,185**
Food, beverages and tobacco					
Coal	29r	32r	36r	26r	17
Natural gas	2,553	2,484	2,476r	2,428r	2,381
Petroleum	297r	256r	222r	345	323
Electricity	995	1,046	1,027	1,063r	1,083
Heat sold	..	6r	5	2	1
Total food, beverages and tobacco	**3,875r**	**3,825r**	**3,767r**	**3,864r**	**3,805**

(1) Industrial categories used are described in Table 1G. Data excludes energy used to generate heat for all fuels except manufactured solid fuels and electricity.

(2) Includes tars, benzole, coke and breeze and other manufactured solid fuels.

1.8 Final energy consumption by main industrial groups[1] (continued)

	2001	2002	2003	2004	2005
				Thousand tonnes of oil equivalent	
Paper, printing and publishing					
Coal	73r	82r	88r	97r	98
Natural gas	1,425	1,329	1,367r	1,193r	1,124
Petroleum	111	79r	56r	59	86
Electricity	990	1,031	1,096	1,111r	1,122
Heat sold	..	..	..	27r	57
Total paper, printing and publishing	**2,599r**	**2,521r**	**2,607r**	**2,487r**	**2,488**
Other industries					
Coal	1,004r	959r	1,009r	936r	909
Natural gas	3,657	3,182	3,108r	2,897r	2,773
Petroleum	2,988r	2,705r	3,414r	3,162r	3,437
Electricity	2,963	2,913	2,965r	2,989r	3,038
Heat sold	13	4	-	407r	407
Total other industries	**10,625r**	**9,763r**	**10,496r**	**10,390r**	**10,564**
Unclassified					
Manufactured solid fuels (2)	212	303	135	145r	239
Coke oven gas	32	3	5	-	-
Natural gas	9	8	6	6	6
Petroleum	2,122	1,654	2,014	2,632	2,665
Renewables & waste	243r	250r	267r	265r	151
Total unclassified	**2,617r**	**2,219r**	**2,426r**	**3,048r**	**3,060**
Total					
Coal	1,195r	1,186r	1,248r	1,228r	1,188
Manufactured solid fuels (2)	929	780	639r	627r	728
Blast furnace gas	272	226	36	32r	28
Coke oven gas	154	78	53	67r	76
Natural gas	15,464	14,202	14,292	13,214r	12,790
Petroleum	6,453r	5,560r	6,249r	6,751r	7,065
Renewables & waste	243r	250r	267r	265r	151
Electricity	9,573	9,686	9,747r	9,961r	10,217
Heat sold	1,001	1,321r	1,128	832r	852
Total	**35,284r**	**33,289r**	**33,660r**	**32,979r**	**33,095**

1.9 Fuels consumed for electricity generation (autogeneration) by main industrial groups[1]

Thousand tonnes of oil equivalent
(except where shown otherwise)

	2001	2002	2003	2004	2005
Iron and steel and non-ferrous metals					
Coal	769	750	766	764	788
Blast furnace gas	481	466	774	790r	801
Coke oven gas	124	123	136r	107	162
Natural gas	63	58	57	61	44
Petroleum	20	18	14	32r	19
Other (including renewables) *(2)*	55	57	47	64r	57
Total fuel input *(3)*	**1,512**	**1,471**	**1,795r**	**1,817r**	**1,871**
Electricity generated by iron & steel and non-ferrous	**504**	**402**	**474**	**481**	**488**
metals *(4)* *(in GWh)*	5,863	4,669	5,511	5,592	5,670
Electricity consumed by iron and steel and non-ferrous	**412**	**316**	**381r**	**403**	**427**
metals from own generation *(5)* *(in GWh)*	4,795	3,671	4,435r	4,686	4,969
Chemicals					
Coal	155	145	160	119r	117
Natural gas	868	968	938	886r	895
Petroleum	53	30	7	14r	19
Other (including renewables) *(2)*	270	302	353	363r	362
Total fuel input *(3)*	**1,346**	**1,445**	**1,458**	**1,382r**	**1,393**
Electricity generated by chemicals *(4)*	**792**	**759**	**791r**	**822r**	**779**
(in GWh)	9,208	8,830	9,204r	9,554r	9,063
Electricity consumed by chemicals from own generation *(5)*	**532**	**656**	**470r**	**643r**	**686**
(in GWh)	6,188	7,630	5,460r	7,476r	7,972
Metal products, machinery and equipment					
Coal	-	-	-	-	-
Natural gas	48	83	94	72r	60
Petroleum	6	6	6	6	6
Other (including renewables) *(2)*	-	-	-	-	-
Total fuel input *(3)*	**54**	**89**	**100**	**78r**	**66**
Electricity generated by metal products, machinery	**24**	**38**	**43**	**32**	**26**
and equipment *(4)* *(in GWh)*	274	447	505	375r	304
Electricity consumed by metal products, machinery	**22**	**36**	**41**	**31**	**25**
and equipment from own generation *(5)* *(in GWh)*	259	422	476r	361r	293
Food, beverages and tobacco					
Coal	20	20	18	16	16
Natural gas	269	322	326	275r	329
Petroleum	5	4	5	47	8
Other (including renewables) *(2)*	-	-	-	-	-
Total fuel input *(3)*	**295**	**347**	**349**	**339r**	**354**
Electricity generated by food, beverages and tobacco *(4)*	**144**	**169**	**170**	**165r**	**167**
(in GWh)	1,679	1,965	1,978	1,919r	1,943
Electricity consumed by food, beverages and tobacco	**83**	**124**	**96**	**146r**	**147**
from own generation *(5)* *(in GWh)*	966	1,438	1,112	1,694r	1,706

(1) Industrial categories used are described in Table 1G.
(2) Includes hydro electricity, solid and gaseous renewables and waste.
(3) Total fuels used for generation of electricity. Consistent with figures for fuels used by other generators in Table 5.4.

1.9 Fuels consumed for electricity generation (autogeneration) by main industrial groups [1] (continued)

Thousand tonnes of oil equivalent
(except where shown otherwise)

	2001	2002	2003	2004	2005
Paper, printing and publishing					
Coal	45	40	32	25	25
Natural gas	578	624	842	887r	858
Petroleum	12	9	7	7	11
Other (including renewables) (2)	-	-	-	-	-
Total fuel input (3)	**636**	**673**	**881**	**920r**	**894**
Electricity generated by paper, printing and publishing (4)	**296**	**319**	**411**	**439r**	**415**
(in GWh)	3,446	3,708	4,774	5,100r	4,829
Electricity consumed by paper, printing and publishing	**225**	**210**	**272**	**250r**	**242**
from own generation (5) (in GWh)	2,619	2,437	3,159	2,902r	2,816
Other industries					
Coal	19	14	-	-	-
Coke oven gas	5	5	7	24	25
Natural gas	112	153	201	187r	117
Petroleum	5	5	4	5r	5
Other (including renewables) (2)	946	1,006	1,187	1,437r	1,538
Total fuel input (3)	**1,087**	**1,183**	**1,399**	**1,653r**	**1,685**
Electricity generated by other industries (4)	**96**	**128**	**147**	**143r**	**106**
(in GWh)	1,115	1,484	1,714	1,660r	1,235
Electricity consumed by other industries from own	**52**	**80**	**93r**	**83r**	**74**
generation (5) (in GWh)	609	925	1,083r	960r	860
Total					
Coal	1,008	969	977	924r	946
Blast furnace gas	481	466	774	790r	801
Coke oven gas	130	128	143r	131	187
Natural gas	1,938	2,209	2,458	2,369r	2,304
Petroleum	102	72	44	110r	68
Other (including renewables) (2)	1,271	1,365	1,587	1,864r	1,957
Total fuel input (3)	**4,929**	**5,209**	**5,982r**	**6,188r**	**6,263**
Electricity generated (4)	**1,856**	**1,815**	**2,037r**	**2,081r**	**1,982**
(in GWh)	21,586	21,104	23,685r	24,200r	23,045
Electricity consumed from own generation (5)	**1,327**	**1,421**	**1,352r**	**1,555r**	**1,601**
(in GWh)	15,436	16,524	15,725r	18,080r	18,615

(4) Combined heat and power (CHP) generation (ie electrical output from Table 6.8) plus non-chp generation, so that the total electricity generated is consistent with the "other generators" figures in Table 5.6.

(5) This is the electricity consumed by the industrial sector from its own generation and is consistent with the other generators final users figures used within the electricity balances (Tables 5.1 and 5.2). These figures are less than the total generated because some of the electricity is sold to the public distribution system and other users.

(6) The figures presented here are consistent with other figures presented elsewhere in this publication as detailed at (3), (4), and (5) above but are further dissaggregated. Overall totals covering all autogenerators can be derived by adding in figures for transport, services and the fuel industries. These can be summarised as follows:

	Thousand tonnes of oil equivalent				
Fuel input	**2001**	**2002**	**2003**	**2004**	**2005**
All industry	4,929	5,209	5,982r	6,188r	6,263
Fuel industries	1,352r	1,316r	1,449r	1,242r	1,974
Transport, Commerce and Administration	470	428	251	301r	319
Services	808	1,009	977r	930r	1,129
Total fuel input	**7,559r**	**7,962r**	**8,659r**	**8,661r**	**9,684**
Electricity generated	**2,728**	**2,859**	**3,062r**	**3,173r**	**3,280**
Electricity consumed	**1,848**	**2,091**	**1,918r**	**2,102r**	**2,240**
					GWh
Electricity generated	**31,720**	**33,253**	**35,609r**	**36,900r**	**38,145**
Electricity consumed	**21,495**	**24,319**	**23,303r**	**24,447r**	**26,046**

Chapter 2
Solid fuels and derived gases

Introduction

2.1   This chapter presents figures on the supply and demand for coal and solid fuels derived from coal, and on the production and consumption of gases derived from the processing of solid fuels.

2.2   Balances for coal and manufactured fuels, covering each of the last three years, form the first six tables of this chapter (Tables 2.1 to 2.6). These are followed by a 5 year table showing the supply and consumption of coal as a time series (Table 2.7). Comparable 5 year tables bring together data for coke oven coke, coke breeze and manufactured solid fuels (Table 2.8) and coke oven gas, blast furnace gas, benzole and tars (Table 2.9). As in previous years, tables showing deep mines in production (Table 2.10) and opencast sites in production (Table 2.11) complete the chapter. The long term trends commentary and tables on coal production and stocks, and on coal consumption are on the DTI energy statistics web site at:
http://www.dti.gov.uk/energy/statistics/publications/dukes/page29812.html

2.3   Detailed statistics of imports and exports of solid fuels are in Annex G, also available on the DTI energy statistics web site at:
http://www.dti.gov.uk/energy/statistics/publications/dukes/page29812.html

2.4   Figures for actual consumption of coal are available for all fuel and power producers and for final use by the iron and steel industry. The remaining final users consumption figures are based on information on disposals to consumers by producers and on imports. For further details see the technical notes and definitions section which begins at paragraph 2.32 of this chapter.

Structure of the coal industry

2.5   At 31 December 2005, there were 8 major deep mines in production – 7 operated by UK Coal plc (including Rossington and Harworth, both of which may go on to 'care and maintenance' status shortly) plus Tower Colliery in S Wales – and 4 small deep mines (Aberpergwm – which is in development, Eckington, Hay Royds and Nanthir). Since then, work has started to re-open Hatfield Colliery, which closed in January 2004. Surface mine output in England continues to decline owing to increasing difficulty in obtaining necessary planning permissions; H J Banks & Son and UK Coal remain the main operators in this sector. Scotland, where Scottish Coal Co Ltd and ATH Resources are the largest operators, recently adopted planning guidance similar to that already in place in England and the impact of this on the Scottish industry will be monitored. Wales, where Celtic Energy remains the largest operator at present, is also considering adopting planning guidance which could make it harder to obtain permission for new coal developments in future.

2.6   The deep mines that were in operation at the end of March 2005 are listed in Table 2.10. Opencast coal producers are similarly listed in Table 2.11, as well as those that are developing and are not yet in operation. Further coal and slurry are supplied from recovery operations and shown in the tables under "Other sources".

Commodity balances for coal (Tables 2.1, 2.2 and 2.3)

2.7   These balance tables separately identify the three main types of coal, namely steam coal, coking coal and anthracite. They show the variation both in the sources of supply and where the various types of coal are mainly used.

2.8   In 2005 86½ per cent of coal demand was for steam coal, 10½ per cent was for coking coal and 3 per cent was for anthracite. Electricity generation accounted for 95 per cent of demand for steam coal and 68 per cent of demand for anthracite. Coking coal was nearly all used in coke ovens (84½ per cent) but 15½ per cent was directly injected into blast furnaces.

2.9   Only 4 per cent of the total demand for coal was for final consumption, where it was used for steam raising, space or hot water heating or heat for processing. Steam coal accounted for 86 per cent of this final consumption. 84½ per cent of which was by industry, where mineral products (eg cement, glass and bricks) and paper and printing were the largest users. The domestic sector accounted for 25 per cent of the final demand for coal, with 51½ per cent of this demand being for anthracite and the remainder for steam coal.

2.10   Chart 2.1 below, compares the sources of coal supplies in the UK in 2005, along with a breakdown of consumption by user and serves to illustrate some of the features brought out below.

2.11   In 2005, 15½ per cent of supply was met from deep-mined production, 17 per cent from opencast operations, 70½ per cent from net imports and 1 per cent from other sources such as slurry. In 2005 total stock levels were 3½ higher as generation companies appeared to build up stocks from the very low levels of last year.

2.12   Recent trends in coal production and consumption are described in paragraphs 2.20 to 2.26.

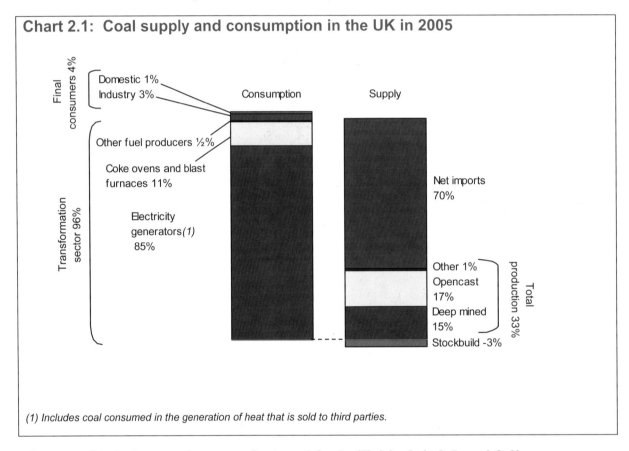

Chart 2.1: Coal supply and consumption in the UK in 2005

(1) Includes coal consumed in the generation of heat that is sold to third parties.

Commodity balances for manufactured fuels (Table 2.4, 2.5 and 2.6)

2.13   These tables cover fuels manufactured from coal and gases produced when coal is used in coke ovens and blast furnaces. Definitions of terms associated with coke, breeze, other manufactured solid fuels and manufactured gases are set out in paragraphs 2.44 to 2.48.

2.14   Around 87 per cent of coke oven coke and coke breeze is home produced but in 2005 the volume of imports was down 12 per cent from 2004. About 2½ per cent of home production was exported. The amount screened out by producers as breeze and fines amounted to about a fifth of production plus imports in 2005 and this appears as transfers in the coke breeze column of the balances. Transfers out of coke oven coke have not always been equal to transfers into coke oven breeze. This was due to differences arising from the timing, location of measurement and the practise adopted by the Iron and Steel works. But since 2000, the Iron and Steel Statistics Bureau have been able to reconcile these data. In 2005, 96½ per cent of the demand for coke oven coke was at blast furnaces (part of the transformation sector) with most of the remainder going into final consumption in the unclassified sector (eg foundry coke).

2.15   Most of the supply of **coke breeze** is from re-screened coke oven coke with direct production accounting for only 19 per cent of total supply. Some breeze is re-used in coke manufacture or in blast furnaces, but the majority is boiler fuel.

2.16   Patent fuels are manufactured smokeless fuels, produced mainly for the domestic market, as the balances show. A small amount of these fuels (only 2½ per cent of total supply in 2005) is imported, but exports generally exceed imports. Imports and exports of manufactured fuels can contain small quantities of non-smokeless fuels.

2.17   Chart 2.2 above shows the sources of coke, breeze and other manufactured solid fuels and a breakdown of their consumption.

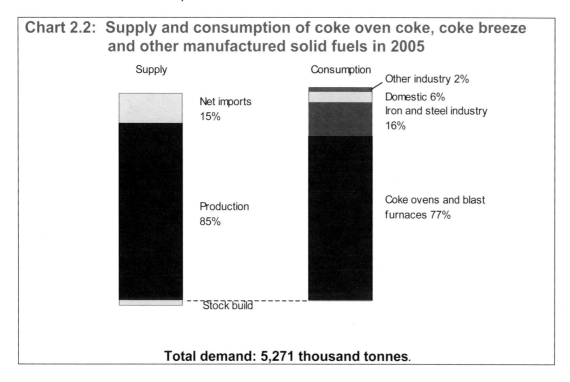

Chart 2.2: Supply and consumption of coke oven coke, coke breeze and other manufactured solid fuels in 2005

Supply

Consumption

Net imports 15%

Production 85%

Stock build

Other industry 2%

Domestic 6%
Iron and steel industry 16%

Coke ovens and blast furnaces 77%

Total demand: 5,271 thousand tonnes.

2.18   The carbonisation and gasification of solid fuels at coke ovens produces **coke oven gas** as a by-product. Some of this (46½ per cent in 2005) is used to fuel the coke ovens themselves while at steel works some is piped to blast furnaces and used in the production of steel (8 per cent in 2005). Elsewhere at steel works, the gas is used for electricity generation (23½ per cent) or for heat production and for other iron and steel making processes (17½ per cent). The remaining 5 per cent is lost.

2.19   **Blast furnace gas** is a by-product of iron smelting in a blast furnace. A similar product is obtained when steel is made in basic oxygen steel converters and "BOS" gas is included in this category. Most of this gas is used in other parts of integrated steel works. 57 per cent was used for electricity generation in 2005, 27½ per cent was used in coke ovens and blast furnaces themselves. 1 per cent was used for general heat production. The remaining 14½ per cent was lost or burned as waste.

Supply and consumption of coal (Table 2.7)

2.20   **Production** - Figures for 2005 show that coal production (including slurry) fell by 18½ per cent compared to production in 2004. Deep-mined production fell by 24 per cent while opencast production fell by 13 per cent. Geological and operational difficulties in deep mines meant that for the first time ever, more coal was mined by opencast methods in 2005. Overall demand for coal rose by 2½ per cent in 2005. Imports rose by 21½ per cent in 2005 to make up for declining indigenous production. Longer-term trends in production are illustrated in Chart 2.3 below.

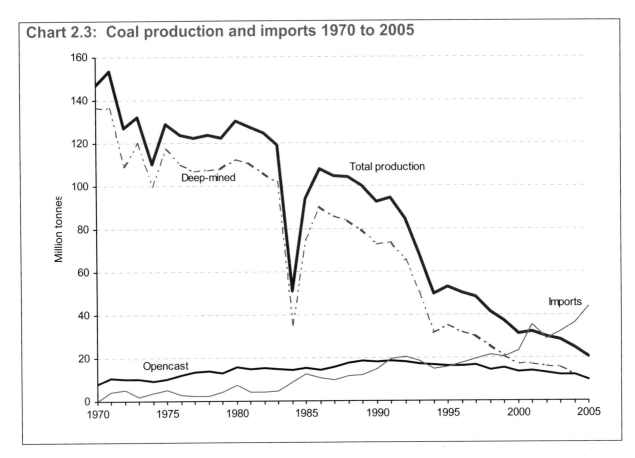

Chart 2.3: Coal production and imports 1970 to 2005

2.21   Table 2A shows how production of coal is divided between England, Wales and Scotland on a financial year basis. In 2005/06 53½ per cent of coal output was in England, 37½ per cent in Scotland and 9 per cent in Wales.

Table 2A: Output from UK coal mines and employment in UK coal mines [1][2]

| | **Million tonnes** | | | | **Number** | |
| | Output | | | | Employment | |
	April 2003 to March 2004	April 2004 to March 2005	April 2005 to March 2006	end March 2004	end March 2005	end March 2006
Deep-mined						
England	14.1	11.1	9.8	6,090	5,284	3,629
Wales	0.6	0.4	0.6	562	454	453
Total	14.7	11.5	10.3	6,652	5,738	4,082
Opencast						
England	3.7	2.7	1.2	1,062	676	206
Scotland	6.8	7.6	7.7	1,175	1,411	1,304
Wales	1.2	1.4	1.2	405	378	311
Total	11.6	11.8	10.2	2,642	2,465	1,821
Total						
England	17.8	13.8	11.0	7,152	5,960	3,835
Scotland	6.8	7.6	7.7	1,175	1,411	1,304
Wales	1.7	1.9	1.8	967	832	764
Total	26.3	23.3	20.5	9,294	8,203	5,903

Source: The Coal Authority
(1) Output is the tonnage declared by operators to the Coal Authority, including estimated tonnages. It excludes estimates of slurry recovered from dumps, ponds, rivers, etc.
(2) Employment includes contractors and is as declared by licensees to the Coal Authority at 31 March each year.

2.22   Table 2A also shows how numbers employed in the production of coal have changed over the last three years. During 2005/06 total employment, including contractors, was lower by 28 per cent. At 31 March 2005, 65 per cent of the 5,903 people employed in UK coal mining worked in England, while 22 per cent were employed in Scotland and 13 per cent in Wales. The closure of Longannet mine in 2002 brought employment in deep mining for coal in Scotland to an end.

2.23   **Foreign trade** - Imports of coal and other solid fuel in 2005 rose 20½ per cent to a new record of 44.9 million tonnes. Within the total, imports of steam coal rose by 25½ per cent – largely due to sharp increases in imports from Russia (71½ per cent) and South Africa (up 28½ per cent). As Table 2B shows, in 2005, 78½ per cent of the United Kingdom's imports of coal and other solid fuel came from just three countries: Australia, Russia and South Africa. A further 14½ per cent of coal imports came from three additional countries, Colombia (mainly steam coal), Indonesia (steam coal) and USA (mainly coking coal). Steam coal imports came mainly from Russia (45 per cent), South Africa (35 per cent) and Colombia (9 per cent). All but 11 per cent of UK coking coal imports came from just three countries, Australia (54 per cent), the USA (18½ per cent) and Canada (16½ per cent). For more details of imports and exports of solid fuels by country of origin see Annex G on the DTI energy statistics web site at:
http://www.dti.gov.uk/energy/statistics/publications/dukes/page29812.html

2.24   Major power producers have sourced an increasing proportion of their coal from imports over the last four years. In 1999 only 20 per cent of the coal they consumed was imported. This rose to a record level of 66 per cent in 2005.

Table 2B: Imports of coal and other solid fuel in 2005[1]

Thousand tonnes

	Steam coal	Coking coal	Anthracite	Other solid fuel	Total
European Union [2] [3]	1,001	28	37	208	1,274
Australia	932	3,532	-	-	4,464
Canada	-	1,084	-	-	1,084
Colombia	3,289	-	-	-	3,289
Indonesia	1,616	-	-	-	1,616
Malaysia	190	-	-	-	190
People's Republic of China	110	-	25	367	502
Republic of South Africa	12,980	-	49	-	13,029
Russia	16,748	697	76	125	17,646
Saudi Arabia	29	-	-	-	29
United States of America	299	1,210	-	-	1,509
Other countries	32	-	-	221	253
Total all countries	**37,225**	**6,551**	**187**	**921**	**44,885**

Source: H M Revenue and Customs, ISSB
(1) Country of origin basis.
(2) Includes extra-EU coal routed through the Netherlands.
(3) EU now includes Poland and Latvia

2.25   **Transformation** – The 2½ per cent rise in total coal consumption during 2005 compared to 2004 reflected an increase in electricity generation by major power producers. The increase of nearly 2 million tonnes was due to higher gas prices, which enabled coal fired generation to be more competitive. In addition, UK steel production especially in blast furnace use picked up in 2005 and this led to a rise of 3½ per cent in the use of coal for coke making and for injection at blast furnaces.

2.26   **Consumption** - Consumption by final consumers in 2005 fell by 13½ per cent from 2004. Industry sector consumption fell by 3 per cent. Domestic demand decreased by 35 per cent from last year, continuing the general decline in coal use in the sector.

2.27   Long term trends commentary and tables on the consumption of coal in the UK since 1970 onwards can be found on the DTI energy statistics web site:
http://www.dti.gov.uk/energy/statistics/publications/dukes/page29812.html

2.28   **Stocks** – Production and net imports together in 2005 were higher than the demand for coal. Consequently total stock levels were just over 2 million tonnes higher in 2005. Total stocks at the end of 2005 were equivalent to around a quarter of the year's coal consumption. Stocks held at collieries and opencast sites at the end of 2005 were 109 thousand tonnes lower than a year earlier but stocks at major power stations and coke areas rose by 2.2 million tonnes. The recent changes in coal stocks are illustrated in Chart 2.4 below.

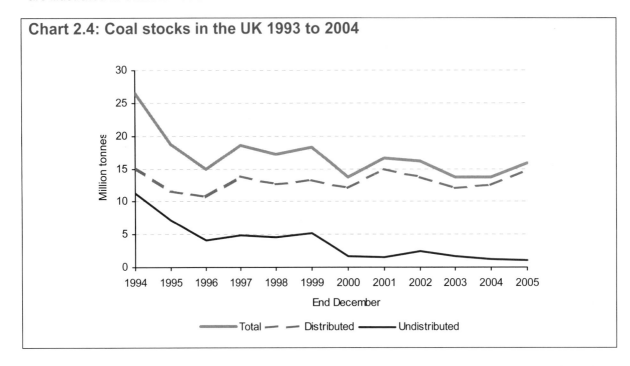

Chart 2.4: Coal stocks in the UK 1993 to 2004

Supply and consumption of coke oven coke, coke breeze and other manufactured fuels (Table 2.8)

2.29   This table presents figures for the most recent five years on the same basis as the balance tables. Figures for stocks are also included. Coal used to produce these manufactured fuels is shown in Table 2.7. For **coke oven coke,** demand fell by 2 per cent in 2005 while production rose by 1½ per cent. In 2005 imports fell by 19½ per cent from 2004 and exports fell by 20 per cent. As demand was lower, stock levels rose slightly in 2005.

2.30   In 2005, the demand for **coke breeze** fell by 4 per cent whilst production and re-screening fell by 13 and 3 per cent respectively. However, imports rose by 20½ per cent. The net effect was an increase in stock levels. There was a 20 per cent decline in the demand for **other manufactured solid fuels**, mainly because of a 100 per cent fall in industrial sector demand and a 15½ per cent fall in domestic sector demand.   UK production was down 19 per cent on 2004 levels.

Supply and consumption of coke oven gas, blast furnace gas, benzole and tars (Table 2.9)

2.31   This table presents figures for the most recent five years on the same basis as the other balance tables. In 2005, both production of and demand for **coke oven gas** rose by 2½ per cent. Use in coke ovens and blast furnaces fell but demand rose in electricity generation and in final consumption terms. Both production and demand for **blast furnace gas** rose by 27 per cent in 2005 compared to 2004.

Technical notes and definitions

2.32   These notes and definitions are in addition to the technical notes and definitions covering all fuels and energy as a whole in Chapter 1, paragraphs 1.24 to 1.57. For notes on the commodity balances and definitions of the terms used in the row headings see Annex A, paragraphs A.7 to A.42. While the data in the printed and bound copy of this Digest cover only the most recent 5 years, these notes also cover data for earlier years that are available on the DTI web site.

Steam coal, coking coal and anthracite

2.33   **Steam coal** is coal classified as such by UK coal producers and by importers of coal. It tends to have calorific values at the lower end of the range.

2.34   **Coking coal** is coal sold by producers for use in coke ovens and similar carbonising processes. The definition is not therefore determined by the calorific value or caking qualities of each batch of coal sold, although calorific values tend to be higher than for steam coal.

2.35   **Anthracite** is coal classified as such by UK coal producers and importers of coal. Typically it has a high heat content making it particularly suitable for certain industrial processes and for use as a domestic fuel. Some UK anthracite producers have found a market for their lower calorific value output at power stations.

Coal production

2.36   **Deep-mined** - The statistics cover saleable output from deep mines including coal obtained from working on both revenue and capital accounts. All licensed collieries (and British Coal collieries prior to 1995) are included, even where coal is only a subsidiary product.

2.37   **Opencast** - The figures cover saleable output and include the output of sites worked by operators under agency agreements and licences, as well as the output of sites licensed for the production of coal as a subsidiary to the production of other minerals.

2.38   **Other** - Estimates of slurry etc recovered and disposed of from dumps, ponds, rivers, etc.

Imports and exports of coal and other solid fuels

2.39   Figures are derived from returns made to HM Revenue and Customs and are broken down in greater detail in Annex G on the DTI energy statistics web site at:
http://www.dti.gov.uk/energy/statistics/publications/dukes/page29812.html

2.40   However, in Tables 2.4, 2.5, 2.6 and 2.8, the export figures used for hard coke, coke breeze and other manufactured solid fuels for the years before 1998 (as reported on the DTI web site) are quantities of fuel exported as reported to DTI by the companies concerned, rather than quantities recorded by HM Revenue and Customs in their Trade Statistics.

Allocation of imported coal

2.41   Although data are available on consumption of home produced coal, and also on consumption of imported coal by secondary fuel producers, there is only very limited direct information on consumption of imported coal by final users. The DTI carries out surveys of the destination of steam coal imports (excluding those used by electricity generators) from time to time. The most recent was in 1998 and concluded that it was appropriate to allocate 60 per cent of such imports each year to industry, 15 per cent to the public administration sector and 25 per cent to the domestic sector. This was revised for 2002 and 2003 to 70, 25 and 5 per cent to industry, domestic and public administration respectively. These proportions were revised again in 2004 to 75 per cent to industry, 20 per cent to domestic and 5 per cent to public administration. In addition, 10 per cent of anthracite imports, excluding cleaned smalls, are allocated to industry, with 90 per cent to the domestic sector in all years shown in the tables. From 2000, imports have been allocated within the overall industry sector using the results of the Office for National Statistics Purchases Inquiry. All imports of coking coal and cleaned anthracite smalls are allocated to coke and other solid fuel producers.

Stocks of coal

2.42   Undistributed stocks are those held at collieries and opencast sites. It is not possible to distinguish these two locations in the stock figures. Distributed stocks are those held at power stations and stocking grounds of the major power producing companies (as defined in Chapter 5, paragraph 5.47), coke ovens, low temperature carbonisation plants and patent fuel plants.

Transformation, energy industry use and consumption of solid fuels

2.43   Annex A of this Digest outlines the principles of energy and commodity balances and defines the activities that fall within these parts of the balances. However, the following additional notes relevant to solid fuels are given below:

Transformation: Blast furnaces - Coking coal injected into blast furnaces is shown separately within the balance tables.

Transformation: Low temperature carbonisation plants and patent fuel plants - Coal used at these plants for the manufacture of domestic coke such as Coalite and of briquetted fuels such as Phurnacite and Homefire.

Consumption: Industry - The statistics comprise sales of coal by the nine main coal producers to the iron and steel industry (excluding that used at coke ovens and blast furnaces) and to other industrial sectors and estimated proportions of anthracite and steam coal imports. The figures exclude coal used for industries' own generation of electricity, which appear separately under transformation.

Consumption: Domestic – Some coal is supplied free of charge to retired miners and other retired eligible employees through the National Concessionary Fuel Scheme (NCFS). The concessionary fuel provided in 2005 is estimated at 121 thousand tonnes. This estimate is included in the domestic steam coal and domestic anthracite figures.

Consumption of coke and other manufactured solid fuels - These are disposals from coke ovens to merchants. The figures also include estimated proportions of coke imports.

Coke oven coke (hard coke) and hard coke breeze

2.44   The statistics cover coke produced at coke ovens owned by Corus plc (formerly British Steel), Coal Products Ltd and other producers. Low temperature carbonisation plants are not included (see paragraph 2.47, below). Breeze (as defined in paragraph 2.45) is excluded from the figures for coke oven coke.

2.45   Breeze can generally be described as coke screened below 19 mm (¾ inch) with no fines removed, but the screen size may vary in different areas and to meet the requirements of particular markets. Coke that has been transported from one location to another is usually re-screened before use to remove smaller sizes, giving rise to further breeze.

2.46   In 1998, an assessment using industry data showed that on average over the last five years 91 per cent of imports have been coke and 9 per cent breeze and it is these proportions that have been used for 1998 and subsequent years in Tables 2.4, 2.5, 2.6 and 2.8.

2.47   Other manufactured solid fuels are mainly solid smokeless fuels for the domestic market for use in both open fires and in boilers. A smaller quantity is exported (although exports are largely offset by similar quantities of imports in most years). Manufacture takes place in patented fuel plants and low temperature carbonisation plants. The brand names used for these fuels include Homefire, Phurnacite, Ancit and Coalite.

Blast furnace gas, coke oven gas, benzole and tars

2.48   The following definitions are used in the tables that include these fuels:

Blast furnace gas - includes basic oxygen steel furnace (BOS) gas. Blast furnace gas is the gas produced during iron ore smelting when hot air passes over coke within the blast ovens. It contains carbon monoxide, carbon dioxide, hydrogen and nitrogen. In a basic oxygen steel furnace the aim is not to introduce nitrogen or hydrogen into the steel making process, so pure oxygen gas and suitable fluxes are used to remove the carbon and phosphorous from the molten pig iron and steel scrap. A similar fuel gas is thus produced.

Coke oven gas - is a gas produced during the carbonisation of coal to form coke at coke ovens.

Synthetic coke oven gas - is mainly natural gas that is mixed with smaller amounts of blast furnace and BOS gas to produce a gas with almost the same qualities as coke oven gas. The transfers row of Tables 2.4, 2.5, 2.6 and 2.8 show the quantities of blast furnace gas used for this purpose and the total input of gases to the synthetic coke oven gas process. There is a corresponding outward transfer from natural gas in Chapter 4, Table 4.1.

Benzole - a colourless, liquid, flammable, aromatic hydrocarbon by-product of the iron and steel making process. It is used as a solvent in the manufacture of styrenes and phenols but can also be used as a motor fuel.

Tars - viscous materials usually derived from the destructive distillation of coal, which are by-products of the coke and iron making processes.

Periods covered

2.49   Figures in this chapter (and figures for earlier years given in the tables on the DTI web site) generally relate to periods of 52 weeks or 53 weeks as follows:

Year	53 weeks ended
2000	30 December 2000
	52 weeks ended
2001	29 December 2001
2002	28 December 2002
2003	27 December 2003
2004	25 December 2004
2005	31 December 2005

The 53 week data for 2000 have been adjusted to 52 weeks by omitting data for an average week based on information provided by the largest companies for the first week in April 2000.

2.50   Data for coal used for electricity generation by major power producers follow the electricity industry calendar (see Chapter 5, paragraph 5.58) and coal use by other generators is for the 12 months ending 31 December each year. HM Revenue and Customs data on imports and exports are also for the 12 months ended 31 December each year. Data for coal and coke use in the iron and steel industry, and for gases, benzole and tars produced by the iron and steel industry follow the iron and steel industry calendar (see Chapter 5, paragraph 5.59).

Data collection

2.51   In 2005, aggregate data on coal production were obtained from the Coal Authority. In addition the largest producers (Celtic Energy, Energybuild, Goitre Tower Anthracite, H J Banks, Hall Construction Services Ltd (formerly known as Coal Contractors Limited), J D Flack & Sons Ltd, Scottish Coal Company Ltd and UK Coal plc) have provided data in response to an annual DTI inquiry covering production (deep-mined and opencast), trade, stocks and disposals. The Iron and Steel Statistics Bureau (ISSB) provides DTI with an annual statement of coke and breeze production and use of coal, coke and breeze within that industry. The ISSB is also the source of data on gases produced by the iron and steel industry (coke oven gas, blast furnace gas and basic oxygen steel furnace gas). DTI directly surveys producers of manufactured fuels other than coke or breeze.

2.52   Trade in solid fuels is also covered by using data from HM Revenue and Customs (see Annex G on DTI energy statistics web site). Consumption of coal for electricity generation is covered by data collected by DTI from electricity generators as described in Chapter 5, paragraphs 5.61 to 5.63.

Monthly and quarterly data

2.53   Monthly data on coal production, foreign trade, consumption and stocks are available on DTI's Energy Statistics web site: http://www.dti.gov.uk/energy/statistics/source/coal/page18529.html in monthly Tables 2.4, 2.5, and 2.6. Quarterly commodity balances for coal, coke oven coke, coke breeze and other manufactured solid fuels; and coke oven gas, blast furnace gas, benzole and tars are published in DTI's quarterly statistical bulletin *Energy Trends*. These balances are also available on DTI's Energy Statistics web site. See Annex C for more information about *Energy Trends* and the DTI energy statistics web site.

Statistical differences

2.54   Tables 2.1 to 2.9 each contain a statistical difference term covering the difference between recorded supply and recorded demand. These statistical differences arise for a number of reasons. First, the data within each table are taken from varied sources, as described above, such as producers, intermediate consumers (such as electricity generators), final consumers (namely the iron and steel industry) and HM Revenue and Customs. Second, some of these industries work to different statistical calendars (see paragraphs 2.49 and 2.50, above) and third, some of the figures are estimated either because data in the required detail are not readily available within the industry or because the methods of collecting the data do not cover the smallest members of the industry.

Contact: *Sally Mercer*
Energy Strategy Unit
sally.mercer@dti.gsi.gov.uk
020-7215 2717

2.1 Commodity balances 2005
Coal

Thousand tonnes

	Steam coal	Coking coal	Anthracite	Total
Supply				
Production	..	274	..	20,008
Other sources	..	-	..	490
Imports	37,229	6,551	187	43,968
Exports	-364	-3	-169	-536
Marine bunkers	-	-	-	-
Stock change *(1)*	..	-312	..	-2,129
Transfers	-	-	-	-
Total supply	..	6,510	..	61,801
Statistical difference *(2)*	..	-93	..	-48
Total demand	53,346	6,603	1,900	61,849
Transformation	51,245	6,603	1,558	59,406
Electricity generation	50,792	-	1,292	52,084
Major power producers	49,291	-	1,292	50,582
Autogenerators	1,502	-	-	1,502
Heat generation	453	-	-	453
Petroleum refineries	-	-	-	-
Coke manufacture	-	5,564	-	5,564
Blast furnaces	-	1,039	-	1,039
Patent fuel manufacture and low temperature carbonisation	-	-	266	266
Energy industry use	..	-	..	6
Electricity generation	-	-	-	-
Oil and gas extraction	-	-	-	-
Petroleum refineries	-	-	-	-
Coal extraction	..	-	..	6
Coke manufacture	-	-	-	-
Blast furnaces	-	-	-	-
Patent fuel manufacture	-	-	-	-
Pumped storage	-	-	-	-
Other	-	-	-	-
Losses	-	-	-	-
Final consumption	2,096	-	341	2,437
Industry	1,766	-	25	1,791
Unclassified	-	-	-	-
Iron and steel	-	-	-	-
Non-ferrous metals	..	-	-	41
Mineral products	..	-	-	1,120
Chemicals	..	-	-	141
Mechanical engineering etc	..	-	-	12
Electrical engineering etc	..	-	-	5
Vehicles	..	-	-	54
Food, beverages etc	..	-	-	24
Textiles, leather, etc	..	-	-	70
Paper, printing etc	..	-	-	142
Other industries	..	-	..	182
Construction	-	-	-	-
Transport	-	-	-	-
Air	-	-	-	-
Rail	-	-	-	-
Road	-	-	-	-
National navigation	-	-	-	-
Pipelines	-	-	-	-
Other	..	-	..	646
Domestic	298		316	614
Public administration	..	-	-	15
Commercial	..	-	-	6
Agriculture	..	-	-	9
Miscellaneous	..	-	-	2
Non energy use	-	-	-	-

(1) Stock fall (+), stock rise (-).
(2) Total supply minus total demand.

2.2 Commodity balances 2004
Coal

Thousand tonnes

	Steam coal	Coking coal	Anthracite	Total
Supply				
Production	..	352	..	24,535
Other sources	..	-	-	561
Imports	29,614	6,345	194	36,153
Exports	-440	-9	-172	-622r
Marine bunkers	-	-	-	-
Stock change (1)	..	-206	..	-60r
Transfers	-	-	-	-
Total supply	..	6,482	..	60,567r
Statistical difference (2)	..	+101r	..	+119r
Total demand	52,157r	6,382	1,910	60,462r
Transformation	49,939r	6,382	1,310	57,631r
Electricity generation	49,461r	-	983	50,444r
Major power producers	47,985	-	983	48,968
Autogenerators	1,476r	-	-	1,476r
Heat generation	478r	-	-	478r
Petroleum refineries	-	-	-	-
Coke manufacture	-	5,487	-	5,487
Blast furnaces	-	895	-	895
Patent fuel manufacture and low temperature carbonisation	-	-	327	327
Energy industry use	..	-	..	8
Electricity generation	-	-	-	-
Oil and gas extraction	-	-	-	-
Petroleum refineries	-	-	-	-
Coal extraction	..	-	..	8
Coke manufacture	-	-	-	-
Blast furnaces	-	-	-	-
Patent fuel manufacture	-	-	-	-
Pumped storage	-	-	-	-
Other	-	-	-	-
Losses	-	-	-	-
Final consumption	2,211r	-	599	2,810r
Industry	1,813r	-	33	1,846r
Unclassified	-	-	-	-
Iron and steel	-	-	-	-
Non-ferrous metals	..	-	-	12r
Mineral products	..	-	-	1,127r
Chemicals	..	-	-	148r
Mechanical engineering etc	..	-	-	13r
Electrical engineering etc	..	-	-	5
Vehicles	..	-	-	79r
Food, beverages etc	..	-	-	38r
Textiles, leather, etc	..	-	-	82r
Paper, printing etc	..	-	-	141r
Other industries	..	-	..	203r
Construction	-	-	-	-
Transport	-	-	-	-
Air	-	-	-	-
Rail	-	-	-	-
Road	-	-	-	-
National navigation	-	-	-	-
Pipelines	-	-	-	-
Other	..	-	..	964r
Domestic	375r	-	566	941r
Public administration	..	-	..	9r
Commercial	..	-	..	5r
Agriculture	..	-	..	7r
Miscellaneous	..	-	-	2r
Non energy use	-	-	-	-

(1) Stock fall (+), stock rise (-).

(2) Total supply minus total demand.

2.3 Commodity balances 2003
Coal

Thousand tonnes

	Steam coal	Coking coal	Anthracite	Total
Supply				
Production	..	373	..	27,759
Other sources	..	-	..	520
Imports	25,098	6,474	319	31,891
Exports	-359	-2	-181	-542
Marine bunkers	-		-	-
Stock change (1)	..	+62	..	+3,237r
Transfers	-	-	-	-
Total supply	..	6,907	..	62,865r
Statistical difference (2)		+296	..	-159r
Total demand	54,314r	6,611	2,099	63,039r
Transformation	52,073r	6,611	1,409	60,093r
Electricity generation	51,451	-	1,013r	52,464
Major power producers	49,883	-	1,013r	50,896
Autogenerators	1,568	-	-	1,568
Heat generation	622r	-	-	622r
Petroleum refineries	-	-	-	-
Coke manufacture	-	5,729	-	5,729
Blast furnaces	-	882	-	882
Patent fuel manufacture and low temperature carbonisation	-		396	396
Energy industry use	..	-	..	**6**
Electricity generation	-	-	-	-
Oil and gas extraction	-	-	-	-
Petroleum refineries	-	-	-	-
Coal extraction	..	-	..	6
Coke manufacture	-	-	-	-
Blast furnaces	-	-	-	-
Patent fuel manufacture	-	-	-	-
Pumped storage	-	-	-	-
Other	-	-	-	-
Losses	-	-	-	-
Final consumption	2,235r	-	689	2,924r
Industry	1,785r	-	72	1,857r
Unclassified	-	-	-	-
Iron and steel	-	-	-	-
Non-ferrous metals	..	-	-	13r
Mineral products	..	-	-	1,199r
Chemicals	..	-	-	70r
Mechanical engineering etc	..	-	-	14r
Electrical engineering etc	..	-	-	2
Vehicles	..	-	-	70r
Food, beverages etc	..	-	-	50r
Textiles, leather, etc	..	-	-	86r
Paper, printing etc	..	-	-	128r
Other industries	..	-	..	225r
Construction	-	-	-	-
Transport	-	-	-	-
Air	-	-	-	-
Rail	-	-	-	-
Road	-	-	-	-
National navigation	-	-	-	-
Pipelines	..	-	-	-
Other	..	-	..	1,068r
Domestic	426r	-	617	1,043r
Public administration	..	-	..	12r
Commercial	..	-	..	5r
Agriculture	..	-	..	6
Miscellaneous	..	-	..	2r
Non energy use	-	-	-	-

(1) Stock fall (+), stock rise (-).

(2) Total supply minus total demand.

2.4 Commodity balances 2005
Manufactured fuels

	Thousand tonnes				Benzole and tars *(4)*	Coke oven gas	GWh Blast furnace gas
	Coke oven coke	Coke breeze	Other manuf. solid fuel	Total manuf. solid fuel	Benzole and tars *(4)*	Coke oven gas	Blast furnace gas
Supply							
Production	4,105	259	258	4,622	1,750	9,290	16,199
Other sources	-	-	-	-	-	-	-
Imports	681	240	6	927	-	-	-
Exports	-64	-55	-15	-134	-	-	-
Marine bunkers	-	-	-	-	-	-	-
Stock change *(1)*	-94	-59	+6	-147	-	-	-
Transfers *(2)*	-983	+983	-	-	-	+53	-2
Total supply	**3,645**	**1,369**	**254**	**5,268**	**1,750**	**9,343**	**16,197**
Statistical difference *(3)*	-1	-1	-2	-4	-	+64	-102
Total demand	**3,646**	**1,369**	**256**	**5,272**	**1,750**	**9,279**	**16,298**
Transformation	**3,516**	**551**	-	**4,067**		**2,589**	**9,490**
Electricity generation	-	-	-	-	-	2,170	9,310
Major power producers	-	-	-	-	-	-	-
Autogenerators	-	-	-	-	-	2,170	9,310
Heat generation	-	-	-	-	-	418	179
Petroleum refineries	-	-	-	-	-	-	-
Coke manufacture	-	-	-	-	-		
Blast furnaces	3,516	551	-	4,067	-		
Patent fuel manufacture	-	-	-	-	-	-	-
Low temperature carbonisation	-	-	-	-	-	-	-
Energy industry use	-	-	-	-	-	**5,064**	**4,474**
Electricity generation	-	-	-	-	-	-	-
Oil and gas extraction	-	-	-	-	-		
Petroleum refineries	-	-	-	-	-		
Coal extraction	-	-	-	-	-	-	-
Coke manufacture	-	-	-	-	-	4,321	285
Blast furnaces	-	-	-	-	-	743	4,189
Patent fuel manufacture	-	-	-	-	-	-	-
Pumped storage	-	-	-	-	-	-	-
Other	-	-	-	-	-	-	-
Losses	-	-	-	-	-	441	2,014
Final consumption	**130**	**818**	**256**	**1,204**	**1,750**	**1,185**	**320**
Industry	**95**	**818**	-	**838**	**1,750**	**1,185**	**320**
Unclassified	74	19	-	17	1,750	297	-
Iron and steel	22	799	-	821	-	888	320
Non-ferrous metals	-	-	-	-	-	-	-
Mineral products	-	-	-	-	-	-	-
Chemicals	-	-	-	-	-	-	-
Mechanical engineering, etc	-	-	-	-	-	-	-
Electrical engineering, etc	-	-	-	-	-	-	-
Vehicles	-	-	-	-	-	-	-
Food, beverages, etc	-	-	-	-	-	-	-
Textiles, leather, etc	-	-	-	-	-	-	-
Paper, printing, etc	-	-	-	-	-	-	-
Other industries	-	-	-	-	-	-	-
Construction	-	-	-	-	-	-	-
Transport	-	-	-	-	-	-	-
Other	**35**	-	**256**	**366**	-	-	-
Domestic	34		256	366	-	-	-
Public administration	-	-	-	-	-	-	-
Commercial	-	-	-	-	-	-	-
Agriculture	-	-	-	-	-	-	-
Miscellaneous	-	-	-	-	-	-	-
Non energy use	-	-	-	-	-	-	-

(1) Stock fall (+), stock rise (-).
(2) Coke oven gas and blast furnace gas transfers are for synthetic coke oven gas, see paragraph 2.48.
(3) Total supply minus total demand.

(4) Because of the small number of benzole suppliers, figures for benzole and tars cannot be given separately.

2.5 Commodity balances 2004
Manufactured fuels

	Thousand tonnes					GWh	
	Coke oven coke	Coke breeze	Other manuf. solid fuel	Total manuf. solid fuel	Benzole and tars (4)	Coke oven gas	Blast furnace gas
Supply							
Production	4,038	298	318	4,653r	1,722	9,076	15,770
Other sources	-	-	-	-			
Imports	847r	199r	5	1,051	-	-	-
Exports	-80	-62	-39	-182r	-	-	-
Marine bunkers	-	-	-	-	-	-	-
Stock change (1)	-88	-63	+22r	-129r	-		-
Transfers (2)	-1,012	+1,012	-	-	-	+40	-2
Total supply	**3,704r**	**1,384r**	**305r**	**5,392r**	**1,722**	**9,116**	**15,768**
Statistical difference (3)	-14r	-45r	-14r	-73r	-	+65r	-103r
Total demand	**3,718r**	**1,428r**	**320r**	**5,466r**	**1,722**	**9,051r**	**15,872**
Transformation	**3,569**	**602**	**-**	**4,171**		**1,944r**	**9,370r**
Electricity generation	-	-	-	-	-	1,526r	9,191r
Major power producers	-	-	-	-	-	-	-
Autogenerators	-	-	-	-	-	1,526r	9,191r
Heat generation	-	-	-	-	-	418r	179r
Petroleum refineries	-	-	-	-	-	-	-
Coke manufacture	-	-	-	-		-	-
Blast furnaces	3,569	602	-	4,171	-	-	-
Patent fuel manufacture	-	-	-	-	-	-	-
Low temperature carbonisation	-	-	-	-	-	-	-
Energy industry use	**-**	**-**	**4**	**4**	**-**	**5,273r**	**4,570**
Electricity generation	-	-	-	-	-	-	-
Oil and gas extraction	-	-	-	-	-	-	-
Petroleum refineries	-	-	-	-	-	-	-
Coal extraction	-	-	-	-	-	-	-
Coke manufacture	-	-	-	-	-	4,326	297
Blast furnaces	-	-	-	-	-	948	4,273
Patent fuel manufacture	-	-	4	4	-	-	-
Pumped storage	-	-	-	-	-	-	-
Other	-	-	-	-	-	-	-
Losses	**-**	**-**	**-**	**-**	**-**	**783**	**1,557**
Final consumption	**149r**	**827r**	**316r**	**1,291r**	**1,722**	**1,050r**	**375r**
Industry	**98r**	**827r**	**12**	**936**	**1,722**	**1,050r**	**375r**
Unclassified	76r	39r	12	127r	1,722	265r	-
Iron and steel	22	788	-	810	-	785r	375r
Non-ferrous metals	-	-	-	-	-	-	-
Mineral products	-	-	-	-	-	-	-
Chemicals	-	-	-	-	-	-	-
Mechanical engineering, etc	-	-	-	-	-	-	-
Electrical engineering, etc	-	-	-	-	-	-	-
Vehicles	-	-	-	-	-	-	-
Food, beverages, etc	-	-	-	-	-	-	-
Textiles, leather, etc	-	-	-	-	-	-	-
Paper, printing, etc	-	-	-	-	-	-	-
Other industries	-	-	-	-	-	-	-
Construction	-	-	-	-	-	-	-
Transport	**-**	**-**	**-**	**-**	**-**	**-**	**-**
Other	**51**	**-**	**303**	**354**	**-**	**-**	**-**
Domestic	51	-	303	354	-	-	-
Public administration	-	-	-	-	-	-	-
Commercial	-	-	-	-	-	-	-
Agriculture	-	-	-	-	-	-	-
Miscellaneous	-	-	-	-	-	-	-
Non energy use	**-**	**-**	**-**	**-**	**-**	**-**	**-**

(1) Stock fall (+), stock rise (-).
(2) Coke oven gas and blast furnace gas transfers are for synthetic coke oven gas, see paragraph 2.48.
(3) Total supply minus total demand.

(4) Because of the small number of benzole suppliers, figures for benzole and tars cannot be given separately.

2.6 Commodity balances 2003
Manufactured fuels

	Thousand tonnes					GWh	
	Coke oven coke	Coke breeze	Other manuf. solid fuel	Total manuf. solid fuel	Benzole and tars (4)	Coke oven gas	Blast furnace gas
Supply							
Production	4,286	315	392	4,993	1,773	9,564	15,790
Other sources	-	-	-	-	-	-	-
Imports	929r	49r	6	984	-	-	-
Exports	-74	-64	-55	-193	-	-	-
Marine bunkers	-	-	-	-	-	-	-
Stock change (1)	-60	-83	-	-143	-	-	-
Transfers (2)	-1,095	+1,095	-	-	-	+86	-3
Total supply	3,986r	1,312r	343	5,641	1,773	9,650	15,787
Statistical difference (3)	-19r	-20r	-19	-58	-	+36	-106
Total demand	4,005r	1,332r	362	5,699	1,773	9,614	15,893
Transformation	3,716	530	-	4,246	-	2,909r	9,301r
Electricity generation	-	-	-	-	-	1,854	9,002
Major power producers	-	-	-	-	-	-	-
Autogenerators	-	-	-	-	-	1,854	9,002
Heat generation	-	-	-	-	-	1,055	299
Petroleum refineries	-	-	-	-	-	-	-
Coke manufacture	-	-	-	-	-	-	-
Blast furnaces	3,716	530	-	4,246	-	-	-
Patent fuel manufacture	-	-	-	-	-	-	-
Low temperature carbonisation	-	-	-	-	-	-	-
Energy industry use	-	-	4	4	-	5,630	4,771
Electricity generation	-	-	-	-	-	-	-
Oil and gas extraction	-	-	-	-	-	-	-
Petroleum refineries	-	-	-	-	-	-	-
Coal extraction	-	-	-	-	-	-	-
Coke manufacture	-	-	-	-	-	4,466	432
Blast furnaces	-	-	-	-	-	1,164	4,339
Patent fuel manufacture	-	-	4	4	-	-	-
Pumped storage	-	-	-	-	-	-	-
Other	-	-	-	-	-	-	-
Losses	-	-	-	-	-	457	1,398
Final consumption	289r	802r	358	1,449	1,773	618	423
Industry	160r	802r	17	979	1,773	618	423
Unclassified	113r	7r	17	137	1,773	53	-
Iron and steel	23	795	-	818	-	565	423
Non-ferrous metals	24	-	-	24	-	-	-
Mineral products	-	-	-	-	-	-	-
Chemicals	-	-	-	-	-	-	-
Mechanical engineering, etc	-	-	-	-	-	-	-
Electrical engineering, etc	-	-	-	-	-	-	-
Vehicles	-	-	-	-	-	-	-
Food, beverages, etc	-	-	-	-	-	-	-
Textiles, leather, etc	-	-	-	-	-	-	-
Paper, printing, etc	-	-	-	-	-	-	-
Other industries	-	-	-	-	-	-	-
Construction	-	-	-	-	-	-	-
Transport	-	-	-	-	-	-	-
Other	129	-	341	470	-	-	-
Domestic	129	-	341	470	-	-	-
Public administration	-	-	-	-	-	-	-
Commercial	-	-	-	-	-	-	-
Agriculture	-	-	-	-	-	-	-
Miscellaneous	-	-	-	-	-	-	-
Non energy use	-	-	-	-	-	-	-

(1) Stock fall (+), stock rise (-).
(2) Coke oven gas and blast furnace gas transfers are for synthetic coke oven gas, see paragraph 2.48.
(3) Total supply minus total demand.

(4) Because of the small number of benzole suppliers, figures for benzole and tars cannot be given separately.

2.7 Supply and consumption of coal

Thousand tonnes

	2001	2002	2003	2004	2005
Supply					
Production	31,513	29,539	27,759	24,535r	20,008
Deep-mined	17,347	16,391	15,633	12,542r	9,563
Opencast	14,166	13,148	12,126	11,993	10,445
Other sources (1)	417	450	520	561	490
Imports	35,542	28,686	31,891	36,153	43,968
Exports	-550	-537	-542	-622r	-536
Stock change (2)	-3,392	+501	+3,237r	-60r	-2,129
Total supply	**63,530**	**58,639**	**62,865r**	**60,567r**	**61,801**
Statistical difference (3)	-320	+86	-159r	+119r	-48
Total demand	**63,850**	**58,553**	**63,024r**	**60,448r**	**61,849**
Transformation	**60,072**	**55,427**	**60,093r**	**57,631r**	**59,406**
Electricity generation	50,931	47,741	52,464	50,444r	52,084
Major power producers	49,290	46,145	50,896	48,968	50,582
Autogenerators	1,641	1,596	1,568	1,476r	1,502
Heat generation	750	717	622r	478r	453
Coke manufacture	7,132	5,807	5,729	5,487	5,564
Blast furnaces	764	726	882	895	1,039
Patent fuel manufacture and low temperature carbonisation	496	436	396	327	266
Energy industry use	**10**	**9**	**6**	**8**	**6**
Coal extraction	10	9	6	8	6
Final consumption	**3,768**	**3,117**	**2,925r**	**2,810r**	**2,437**
Industry	**1,826**	**1,809**	**1,857r**	**1,846r**	**1,791**
Unclassified					
Iron and steel	1r	-	-	-	-
Non-ferrous metals	13r	24r	13r	12r	41
Mineral products	1,260r	1,213r	1,199r	1,127r	1,120
Chemicals	35r	61r	70r	148r	141
Mechanical engineering etc	13r	14r	14r	13r	12
Electrical engineering etc	8r	7r	2	5	5
Vehicles	60r	61r	70r	79r	54
Food, beverages etc	42r	45r	50r	38r	24
Textiles, clothing, leather, etc	75r	84r	86r	82r	70
Pulp, paper, printing etc	107r	119r	128r	141r	142
Other industries	213r	181r	225r	203r	182
Construction	-	-	-	-	-
Transport	-	-	-	-	-
Other	**1,942r**	**1,308**	**1,068r**	**964r**	**646**
Domestic	1,874r	1,286	1,043r	941r	614
Public administration	47	7	11r	9r	16
Commercial	6	5	6r	6r	6
Agriculture	5	6	6	7r	9
Miscellaneous	10	2	2	2	2
Non energy use	-	-	-	-	-
Stocks at end of year (4)					
Distributed stocks	15,785r	14,386r	12,007r	12,498r	14,719
Of which:					
Major power producers	13,620	12,542	10,971	11,019	12,696
Coke ovens	1,309	1,148	1,086	1,291	1,604
Undistributed stocks	1,583	2,482	1,624	1,192	1,101
Total stocks	**17,368r**	**16,868r**	**13,631r**	**13,691r**	**15,819**

(1) Estimates of slurry etc. recovered from ponds, dumps, rivers, etc.

(2) Stock fall (+), stock rise (-).

(3) Total supply minus total demand.

(4) Excludes distributed stocks held in merchants' yards, etc., mainly for the domestic market, and stocks held by the industrial sector.

2.8 Supply and consumption of coke oven coke, coke breeze and other manufactured solid fuels

	2001	2002	2003	2004	2005
Coke oven coke					
Supply					
Production	5,306	4,335	4,286	4,038	4,105
Imports	101	226	929r	847r	681
Exports	-176	-272	-74	-80	-64
Stock change (1)	+121	+257	-60	-88	-94
Transfers	-982	-927	-1,095	-1,012	-983
Total supply	**4,370**	**3,620**	**3,986r**	**3,704r**	**3,645**
Statistical difference (2)	-24	-37	-19r	-14r	-1
Total demand	**4,394**	**3,657**	**4,005r**	**3,718r**	**3,646**
Transformation	**3,957**	**3,224**	**3,716**	**3,569**	**3,516**
Blast furnaces	3,957	3,224	3,716	3,569	3,516
Energy industry use	**32**	**17**	**-**	**-**	**-**
Final consumption	**405**	**417**	**289r**	**149r**	**130**
Industry	**338**	**239**	**160r**	**98r**	**96**
Unclassified	181	151	113r	76r	74
Iron and steel	32	29	23	22	22
Non-ferrous metals	125	59	24	-	-
Other	**67**	**178**	**129**	**51**	**34**
Domestic	67	178	129	51	34
Stocks at end of year (3)	**428**	**171**	**230**	**318**	**413**
Coke breeze					
Supply					
Production	210	224	315	298	259
Imports	56	12	49r	199r	240
Exports	-143	-46	-64	-62	-55
Stock change (1)	+8	-14	-83	-63	-59
Transfers	+982	+927	+1,095	+1,012	+983
Total supply	**1,112**	**1,102**	**1,312r**	**1,384r**	**1,369**
Statistical difference (2)	-7	+28	-20r	-45r	-1
Total demand	**1,120**	**1,075**	**1,332r**	**1,428r**	**1,369**
Transformation	**313**	**331**	**530**	**602**	**551**
Coke manufacture	9	-	-	-	-
Blast furnaces	304	331	530	602	551
Energy industry use	**-**	**-**	**-**	**-**	**-**
Final consumption	**807**	**744**	**802r**	**827r**	**818**
Industry	**807**	**744**	**802r**	**827r**	**818**
Unclassified	16	44	7r	39r	19
Iron and steel	791	700	795	788	799
Stocks at end of year (3)	**199**	**213**	**296**	**359**	**418**
Other manufactured solid fuels					
Supply					
Production	487	431	392	318	258
Imports	8	17	6	5r	6
Exports	-75	-67	-55	-39	-15
Stock change (1)	+37	+14	-	+22r	+6
Total supply	**457**	**394**	**343**	**305r**	**254**
Statistical difference (2)	-38	-29	-19	-14r	-2
Total demand	**495**	**424**	**362**	**320r**	**256**
Transformation	**-**	**-**	**-**	**-**	**-**
Energy industry use	**12**	**10**	**4**	**4**	**-**
Patent fuel manufacture	12	10	4	4	-
Final consumption	**483**	**414**	**358**	**316r**	**256**
Industry	**37**	**22**	**17**	**12**	**-**
Unclassified	37	22	17	12	-
Other	**446**	**392**	**341**	**303**	**256**
Domestic	446	392	341	303	256
Stocks at end of year (3)	**66**	**52**	**51**	**30**	**24**

(1) Stock fall (+), stock rise (-).
(2) Total supply minus total demand.
(3) Producers stocks and distributed stocks.

2.9 Supply and consumption of coke oven gas, blast furnace gas, benzole and tars

GWh

	2001	2002	2003	2004	2005
Coke oven gas					
Supply					
Production	11,516	9,549	9,564	9,076	9,290
Imports	-	-	-	-	-
Exports	-	-	-	-	-
Transfers (1)	+68	+104	+86r	+40	+53
Total supply	**11,584**	**9,653**	**9,650**	**9,116**	**9,343**
Statistical difference (2)	+141	+64	+36	+65r	+64
Total demand	**11,443**	**9,589**	**9,614**	**9,051r**	**9,279**
Transformation	**3,365**	**2,973**	**2,909r**	**1,944r**	**2,589**
Electricity generation	1,490	1,486	1,854	1,526r	2,170
Heat generation	1,875	1,486	1,055	418r	418
Other	-	-	-	-	-
Energy industry use	**6,053**	**5,321**	**5,630**	**5,273r**	**5,064**
Coke manufacture	4,720	4,270	4,466	4,326	4,321
Blast furnaces	1,333	1,051	1,164	948	743
Other	-	-	-	-	-
Losses	**231**	**387**	**457**	**783**	**441**
Final consumption	**1,794**	**909**	**618**	**1,050r**	**1,185**
Industry	**1,794**	**909**	**618**	**1,050r**	**1,185**
Unclassified	367	40	53	265r	297
Iron and steel	1,427	869	565	785r	888
Blast furnace gas					
Supply					
Production	14,767	13,130	15,790	15,770	16,199
Imports	-	-	-	-	-
Exports	-	-	-	-	-
Transfers (1)	-3	-4	-3	-2	-2
Total supply	**14,764**	**13,125**	**15,787**	**15,768**	**16,197**
Statistical difference (2)	-100	-92	-106	-103r	-102
Total demand	**14,864**	**13,218**	**15,893**	**15,872**	**16,298**
Transformation	**6,025**	**5,843**	**9,301r**	**9,370r**	**9,490**
Electricity generation (3)	5,493	5,422	9,002	9,191r	9,310
Heat generation	532	422	299	179r	179
Other	-	-	-	-	-
Energy industry use	**4,709**	**4,095**	**4,771**	**4,570**	**4,474**
Coke manufacture	649	510	432	297	285
Blast furnaces	4,060	3,585	4,339	4,273	4,189
Other	-	-	-	-	-
Losses	**965**	**648**	**1,398**	**1,557**	**2,014**
Final consumption	**3,165**	**2,632**	**423**	**375r**	**320**
Industry	**3,165**	**2,632**	**423**	**375r**	**320**
Unclassified	-	-	-	-	-
Iron and steel (3)	3,165	2,632	423	375r	320
Benzole and tars (4)					
Supply					
Production	2,115	1,781	1,773	1,722	1,750
Final consumption (5)	**2,115**	**1,781**	**1,773**	**1,722**	**1,750**
Unclassified	2,115	1,781	1,773	1,722	1,750
Iron and steel	-	-	-	-	-

(1) To and from synthetic coke oven gas, see paragraph 2.48.

(2) Total supply minus total demand.

(3) From 2003, a new method of calculating fuel use for CHP in the iron and steel industry has been used (see paragraph 6.32). This results in more blast furnace gas being allocated to electricity generation and less to final consumption than in previous years. It has not been possible to recalculate CHP use for previous years on this new basis.

(4) Because of the small number of benzole suppliers, figures for benzole and tars cannot be given separately

(5) From 2000 Iron and steel under final consumption has been reclassified due to additional information being received

2.10 Major deep mines in production at 31 March 2006[1]

Licensee	Site	Location
Tower Colliery Ltd	Tower Colliery	Rhondda, Cynon Taff
UK Coal plc(2)	Daw Mill Colliery	Warwickshire
	Harworth Colliery	Nottinghamshire
	Kellingley Colliery	North Yorkshire
	Maltby Colliery	Rotherham, Yorkshire
	Thoresby Colliery	Nottinghamshire
	Welbeck Colliery	Nottinghamshire

(1) In addition there were 5 smaller deep mines in production at 31 March 2006, viz:

Blaentillery Colliery, owned by Blaentillery Mining Ltd, in Torfaen
Eckington Colliery, owned by Eckington Colliery Partnerships, in Derbyshire
Hay Royds Colliery, owned by Hayroyds Colliery LLP, in Yorkshire
Nanthir Colliery, owned by M & W A Anthracite Ltd, in Neath, Port Talbot
Aberpergwm Colliery, owned by Energybuild in Glyn Neath

(2) UK Coal - Rossington Colliery was mothballed in March 2006
*   - Harworth Colliery may also be mothballed later this year*

Source: The Coal Authority

2.11 Opencast sites in production at 31 March 2006[1]

Licensee	Site Name	Location
Aardvark TMC	Skares Road	Cumnock, East Ayrshire
(trading as ATH Resources)	Skares Road Extension	Cumnock, East Ayrshire
	Grievehill	East Ayrshire
ATH Garleffan Ltd	Garleffan	New Cumnock, East Ayrshire
Bryn Bach Coal Ltd	Cwm Yr Onen Colliery Reclamation	Neath, Port Talbot
Celtic Energy Ltd	Margam Opencast	Bridgend
	Nant Helen Extension	Powys
	Selar	Neath Port Talbot
Dynant Fach Colliery Company	Dynant Fawr	Carmarthenshire, Wales
Ecosse Regeneration Ltd	Polkemmet	West Lothian
Energybuild Ltd	Nant Melyn	Neath Port Talbot
	Nant-y-Mynydd	Neath Port Talbot
G M Mining	Kingslaw Site	Kirkcaldy, Fife
H J Banks & Company Ltd	Bankrigg Ltd.	Falkirk
	Delhi Site	Stannington, Northumberland
	Fox Covert	Newcastle
Hall Construction Services Ltd	Albion Extension	Moira, Leicestershire
	Earlseat OCCS	East Wemys, Fife
I & H Brown Ltd	Begg Farm	Kirkcaldy, Fife
	Rosebank	East Wemys, Fife
Kier Minerals Ltd	Greenburn Project	East Ayrshire
Minerals (UK) Ltd	Bwlch Ffos Mining Site	Neath, Port Talbot
Parkhill Estates Ltd	Caughley Quarry	Shropshire
Scottish Coal Company Ltd	Broken Cross & Extension	Lanark, South Lanarkshire
	Chalmerston	East Ayrshire
	Chalmerston North	East Ayrshire
	Glentaggart	South Lanarkshire
	Greenbank (St Ninians)	Nr Kelty, Fife
	House of Water	New Cumnock, East Ayrshire
	Newbigging Farm	Midlothian
	Powharnal	East Ayrshire
	Spireslack	Cumnock, East Ayrshire
Shires Development Ltd	Roundwood Colliery Reclamation Scheme	Yorkshire
UK Coal Mining Ltd	Barugh Bridge	Barnsley, Yorkshire
	Maiden's Hall Extension	Morpeth, Northumberland

(1) There were 35 opencast sites as at 31 March 2006.

Source: The Coal Authority

Chapter 3
Petroleum

Introduction

3.1   This chapter contains commodity balances covering the supply and disposal of primary oils (crude oil and natural gas liquids), feedstocks (including partly processed oils) and petroleum products in the UK in the period 2003 to 2005. These balances are given in Tables 3.1 to 3.6. Additional data have been included in supplementary tables on areas not covered by the format of the balances. This extra information includes details on refinery capacities and aggregates for refinery operations, and extra detail on deliveries into consumption, including breakdowns by country, sector and industry.

3.2   Statistics on supply (covering production, imports and exports) and demand of crude oil, other refinery feedstocks and petroleum products are obtained from the United Kingdom oil industry and the Department of Trade and Industry's Petroleum Production Reporting System.

3.3   The annual figures relate to calendar years or the ends of calendar years. In the majority of tables the data cover the United Kingdom.

3.4   Information on long-term trends (Tables 3.1.1 and 3.1.2) and the annex on the oil and gas resources of the UK (Annex F) are now only available in the internet version of this publication which can be found on DTI's energy statistics web site at
http://www.dti.gov.uk/energy/statistics/publications/dukes/page29812.html. This
information is included in the internet version to provide a more complete picture of the UK oil and gas production sector.

Commodity balances for primary oil (Tables 3.1, 3.2 and 3.3)

3.5   These tables show details of the production, supply and disposals of primary oils (crude oil and natural gas liquids (NGLs)) and feedstocks in 2005, 2004 and 2003. The upper half of the table (supply) equates to the upstream oil industry, covering the supply chain from the production of oil and NGLs, recorded by individual oil terminals and oil fields, to their disposal to export or to UK refineries (see Annex F, Table F.2 on DTI's energy statistics web site). The lower half of the table covers the use of these primary oils, including the amount used as a fuel during the extraction process (ie burned to provide power for drilling and pumping operations) and as inputs into refineries, as recorded by the refineries.   The statistical difference in the tables thus represents the differences between data reported by these different sources and the sites of production and consumption.

3.6   Gross production of crude oil and NGLs in 2005 was 85 million tonnes, a decline of 11 per cent on 2004 and 38 per cent lower than the peak production level of 137 million tonnes in 1999. In 2005 about two-thirds of the United Kingdom's primary oil production was exported with imported crude oil accounting for about two-thirds of refinery intake. Feedstocks (including partly processed oils) made up 11 per cent of total imports of oil in 2005. Total primary oil imports in 2005 were 6 per cent lower than in 2004 at 59 million tonnes, while exports fell by 16 per cent to 54 million tonnes. As a result the UK became a net-importer of primary oils in 2005 for the first time since 1992. Exports in 2005 were 8 per cent lower than imports down from previous years where exports were 3 per cent higher than imports in 2004 and 28 per cent higher in 2003. Further declines in exports and increases in imports will be seen as indigenous production continues to decline. Even so primary oil exports will continue to make a significant contribution to the UK economy (see Annex G on DTI's energy statistics web site). Chart 3.1 illustrates recent trends in production, imports and exports of crude oil, NGLs and feedstocks.

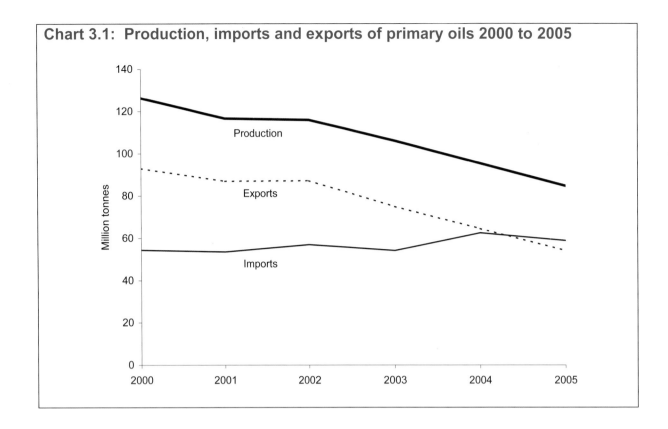

Chart 3.1: Production, imports and exports of primary oils 2000 to 2005

3.7   The UK imports crude oil for various commercial reasons. Primarily, refineries consider the type of crude oil rather than its source origin. Most UK refineries use North Sea 'type' crude and do not differentiate between the UK and Norwegian sectors of the North Sea. Indeed, some UK refiners have production interests in both UK and Norwegian waters so the company may own the imported crude at the point of production. The close proximity of some UK and Norwegian oil fields mean that they may use the same pipeline infrastructure, for example the Norpipe oil terminal in Teesside receives both UK and Norwegian crude from the North Sea. Some crude oils are specifically imported for the heavier hydrocarbons which they contain as these are needed for the manufacture of various petroleum products such as bitumen and lubricating oils. This is in contrast to most North Sea type crude which contains a higher proportion of the lighter hydrocarbon fuels resulting in higher yields of products such as motor spirit and other transport fuels.

3.8   Chart 3.2 compares the level of imports and exports of crude oil, NGLs and feedstocks with those for petroleum products over the period 2000 to 2005. Production from the United Kingdom Continental Shelf peaked in 1999 but has been in general decline since. Crude oil exports have fallen in line with the decline in production whilst imports have risen steadily. This resulted in the UK being a net importer of crude oil in 2005. Exports of petroleum products declined from 1998 to 2001 but have subsequently increased while imports of products have followed a similar pattern to that of crude imports by steadily increasing. The UK is still a net exporter of petroleum products and the significant refinery infrastructure suggests that it will continue to be so for sometime. Additional analysis of the exports and imports of oil products is given in paragraphs 3.14 to 3.18 and the long term trends internet section (3.1.2 to 3.1.9) and additional details about trends in UK oil production are given in Annex F on DTI's energy statistics web site.

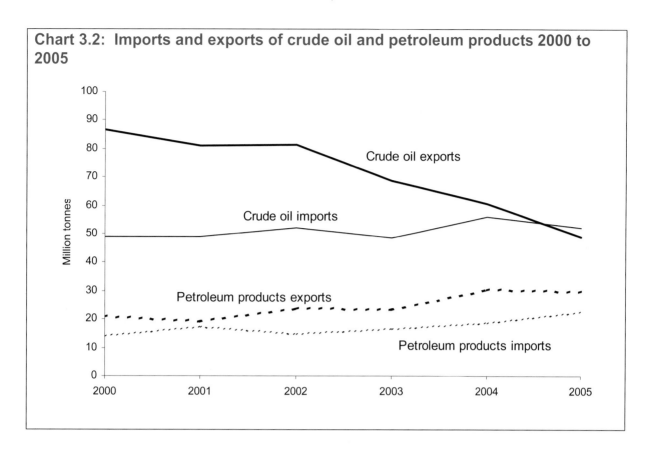

Chart 3.2: Imports and exports of crude oil and petroleum products 2000 to 2005

3.9   The energy balances in Table 3.1 show that the overall statistical difference in the primary oil balance for 2005 to be minus 66 thousand tonnes. This means that the total quantities of crude oil and NGLs reported as being produced by the individual UK production fields are 66 thousand tonnes less than the totals reported by UK oil companies as being received by refineries or going for export. The reasons for this are discussed later in paragraphs 3.35 to 3.39.

Commodity balances - Petroleum products (Tables 3.4 to 3.6)

3.10   These tables show details of the production, supply and disposals of petroleum products into the UK market in 2005, 2004 and 2003. The upper half of the table represents the supply side and calculates overall availability of the various products in the UK by combining production at refineries with trade (imports and exports), stock changes, product transfers and deliveries to international marine bunkers. The lower half of the table reports the demand side and covers the uses made of the differing products, including the uses made within refineries as fuels in the refining process and details of the amounts reported by oil companies within the UK as delivered for final consumption.

Supply of petroleum products

3.11   Total petroleum products output from UK refineries in 2005 was 86 million tonnes, which was 4 per cent lower than the level in 2004 but 2 per cent higher than the 2003 level. The fluctuations in refinery output have tended to result from routine maintenance work rather than the upgrading of facilities.

3.12 In terms of output of individual products, production of aviation turbine fuel, burning oil and motor spirit all decreased by 8 per cent in 2005 compared to 2004 while gas/diesel oil production fell by half a per cent. These falls were partially offset by increased production of liquid petroleum gases (propane and butane) and petroleum coke, which both increased by 13 per cent.

3.13 UK domestic production of individual petroleum products is increasingly no longer aligned with the domestic market demand. While the UK has surplus production of motor spirit and fuel oil, it produces insufficient aviation turbine fuel. Production of aviation turbine fuel has fallen in recent years, primarily due to the fact that aviation turbine fuel and gas/diesel oil are extracted from the same fraction of crude oil (middle distillates), though to different quality criteria. Therefore, as the demand for gas/diesel oil and other middle distillates has increased, there is less of this fraction of the crude oil processed at refineries available for production of aviation turbine fuel. More information on refinery capacity in the UK and refinery capacity utilisation is given in paragraphs 3.40 and 3.41.

3.14 The UK has been a net exporter of oil products every year since 1974, with the exception of 1984 due to the effects of the industrial action in the coal-mining sector. Exports of petroleum products were 30 million tonnes in 2005, 2 per cent lower than in 2004 but 27 per cent higher than in 2003. Imports of oil products into the UK were 23 million tonnes in 2005, which were 21 per cent higher than in 2004 and 37 per cent higher than in 2003. Overall, the UK net exports were 7 million tonnes in 2005, down from the almost 12 million tonnes reported in 2004 but at a similar level to that reported in 2003.

3.15 The United States remains one of the key markets for UK exports of oil products, with 6.7 million tonnes being exported there in 2005. These exports made up 23 per cent of total UK exports of oil products in 2005, with the other main countries receiving UK exports of petroleum products being Ireland, the Netherlands, France, Spain, Germany and Belgium. The main sources of the UK's imports of petroleum products in 2005 were Norway, the Netherlands, Saudi Arabia, France, Kuwait, Estonia and Latvia (source: International Energy Agency (IEA)).

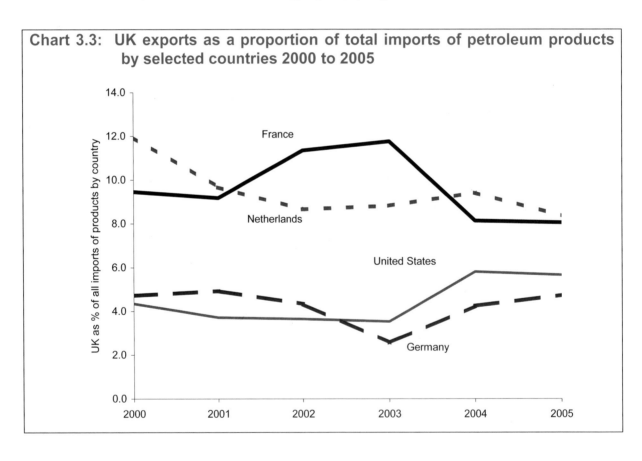

Chart 3.3: UK exports as a proportion of total imports of petroleum products by selected countries 2000 to 2005

3.16 Chart 3.3 shows how the UK has penetrated selected overseas markets for its petroleum products. UK supplied 6 per cent of the total volume of US imports of petroleum products in 2005 (mostly in the form of motor spirit) and 8, 8½ and 5 per cent respectively of the total imports of petroleum products into France, the Netherlands and Germany (mostly as gas oil for heating, motor spirit and fuel oil). The UK regularly supplies the vast majority of total oil products imported into Ireland (mostly motor spirit and DERV fuel for transport, and gas oil and burning oil for heating).

3.17 Differences in product types explain why the UK imports petroleum products when there is an overall surplus available for export. Exports in 2005 were mainly made up of motor spirit (6½ million tonnes), gas/diesel oil (6 million tonnes) and fuel oil (8½ million tonnes) whereas imports consisted of aviation turbine fuel (9 million tonnes), motor spirit (2½ million tonnes) and gas/diesel oil (5 million tonnes). Imports take place to cover specific periods of heavy demand within the UK such as seasonal high demand or to cover production shortfalls in refinery shutdowns for maintenance.

3.18 For gas/diesel oil, exports from the UK tend to be of lower grades for use as heating fuels while imports tend to be of higher-grade gas/diesel oil with a low sulphur content. With the introduction of low sulphur DERV fuel and motor spirit into the UK market and the required increased production capacity at UK refineries for these fuels, UK imports of these products increased to meet the shortfall. As noted above, aviation turbine fuel is imported simply because the UK cannot make enough of it to meet demand since it is derived from the same sort of hydrocarbons as gas/diesel oil, and as such there is a physical limit to how much can be made from the amount of oil processed in the UK.

3.19 More information on the structure of refineries in the UK and trends in imports and exports of crude oil and oil products is given in the long-term trends section on DTI's energy statistics web site (Table 3.1.1).

3.20 In 2005, 10 per cent of UK production of fuel oil and 3 per cent of gas oil/diesel production went into international marine bunkers, totalling 2 million tonnes of products, 2 per cent of total UK refinery production in the year. These are fuel sales destined for consumption on ocean going vessels and therefore cannot be classified as being consumed within the UK. Correspondingly these quantities are treated in a similar way to exports in the commodity balances. It should be noted that these quantities do not include deliveries of fuels for use in UK coastal waters, which are counted as UK consumption and are given in the figures of the transport section of the commodity balances.

3.21 Details are given in the balances of stocks of products held within the UK either at refineries or oil distribution centres such as coastal oil terminals (undistributed stocks). In addition, some information is available on stocks of oil products held by major electricity generators (distributed stocks). However, these figures exclude any details of stocks held by distributors of fuels or stocks held at retail sites, such as petrol stations. The figures for stocks in the balances also solely relate to those stocks currently present in the UK and specifically exclude any stocks that might be held by UK oil companies in other countries under bilateral agreements.

3.22 In order for the UK to be prepared for any oil emergency, companies supplying oil products into final consumption in the UK are obligated by the UK Government to maintain a certain level of stocks of oil products used as fuels. As part of this, oil companies are allowed to hold stocks in other EU countries subject to bilateral agreements between governments and count these stocks towards their stocking obligations. The stocks figures in Table 3.10 take account of these bilateral stocks (see paragraphs 3.63 to 3.66) to give a true picture of the amount of stocks available to the UK.

Consumption of petroleum products

3.23 The text in the following section examines the data given on the consumption of oil products in the period 2003 to 2005. The main sectors of consumers will be looked at first (going down the tables) before the data for individual products (going across the tables) are considered.

3.24 Table 3.4 shows how overall deliveries of petroleum products into consumption in the UK in 2005, including those used by the UK refining industry as fuels within the refining process and all other uses, totalled 81 million tonnes. This was 2 per cent higher than in 2004 and 5 per cent higher than in 2003. Between 1996 and 2002, deliveries have been on a declining trend, which since 2002 has turned upwards.

3.25 From the tables, one of the most significant changes in deliveries of products in recent years has been the decline in use for electricity generation. (See long term trends, Table 3.1.2 on DTI's energy statistics web site). This change is primarily a result of major electricity producers using natural gas as their fuel of choice for electricity generation rather than oil-based fuels. This trend is also reflected in the declining level of usage by auto-producers of electricity over the period, despite the growth in auto-generation of electricity by industry as a whole and in the significant declining use in heat generation. However, since 2004 oil products used for electricity generation bucked this downward trend and increased from 536 thousand tonnes in 2003 to 650 thousand tonnes in 2005. Part of this increase may result from the high level of gas prices in 2004 and particularly in late 2005. Whilst the 10 per cent increase in 2005 from 2004 and 21 per cent increase from 2003 appear significant, use of oil products for fuel generation in 2005 was still 33 per cent below the level seen in 2001.

3.26 The data included under the blast furnaces heading of the Transformation sector represents fuel oil used in the manufacture of iron and steel which is directly injected into blast furnaces, as opposed to being used as a fuel to heat the blast furnaces. The fuel used for the latter (mostly gas oil) is included under the blast furnaces heading of the Energy Industry Use sector.

3.27 Other figures in the Energy Industry Use sector relate to uses within the UK refining industry in the manufacture of oil products. These are products either used as fuels during refining processes or products used by the refineries themselves as opposed to being sold to other consumers. It excludes any fuels used for the generation of electricity since these amounts are included in the Transformation sector totals. Given the interest in the total amounts of fuels used within refineries, Table 3.7 includes data on total refinery fuel usage (i.e. including that used in the generation of electricity) over the period 2001 to 2005. The data under the other headings of the Energy Industry Use sector represent fuels used by the gas supply industry.

3.28 Final consumption of oil products in 2005, i.e. excluding any uses by the energy industries themselves or for transformation purposes, amounted to 74½ million tonnes, 1½ million tonnes higher than in 2004 and 3½ million tonnes higher than in 2003.   Chart 3.4 shows the breakdown of consumption for energy uses by each sector in 2005.

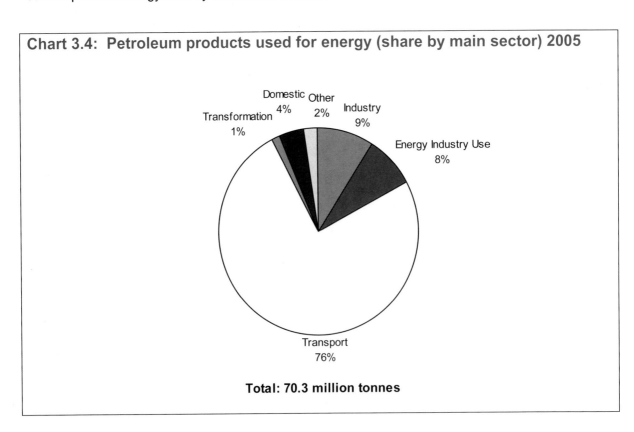

Chart 3.4: Petroleum products used for energy (share by main sector) 2005

Domestic 4% Other 2% Industry 9% Transformation 1% Energy Industry Use 8% Transport 76%

Total: 70.3 million tonnes

3.29   The total amount of oil products used by industry was in decline in the middle-1990s due to industry moving away from using oil products as an energy source. In the three-year period 1998 to 2000 oil use by industry was fairly constant before increasing by ½ million tonnes in 2001 to almost 6 million tonnes and falling back to just over 6 million tonnes in 2002. Since then industrial usage has grown again climbing progressively from 5½ million tonnes in 2003, to just over 6 million tonnes in 2004 and to 6½ million tonnes in 2005.

3.30   Transport sector consumption in 2005 was 2 per cent higher than in 2004 and 5 per cent higher than in 2003. The increase in the transport sector consumption has largely been driven by increased use of aviation fuels that were up by 5½ per cent in 2005 when compared to 2004 while consumption of road fuels increased by ½ per cent. Total transport usage in 2005 was almost 53 million tonnes and accounted for 71 per cent of total final consumption of oil products. In contrast, final energy consumption by sectors other than transport and industry increased by 3 per cent in 2005 compared with 2004.

3.31   Consumption of non-energy products increased towards 11 million tonnes in 2005, up by 1 per cent when compared to 2004 with non-energy products making up 14 per cent of final consumption of oil products. Additional detail on the non-energy uses of oil products, by product and by type of use where such information is available, is given in Table 3C and paragraphs 3.55 to 3.61 later in this text.

3.32   Final consumption is dominated by three individual products; aviation turbine fuel, motor spirit and gas/diesel oil that between them made up 77 per cent of total final consumption in 2005. These three products are predominantly used as transport fuels although some gas oil is used for power generation and domestic heating. Changes in the consumption of aviation fuel are discussed in more detail in paragraphs 3.52 to 3.54 below while more detailed information on consumption of road fuels over the period 2001 to 2005 is given in Table 3.8 and discussed in paragraphs 3.42 to 3.51.

3.33   In 2005 total final consumption of fuel oil was just over 1 million tonnes, down by 9 per cent on 2004. This was mainly due to a decrease in industrial usage of 19 per cent between 2004 and 2005 with an additional fall of 22 per cent in fuel oil used for heat generation for sale to third parties. These decreases were partially offset with increased transport consumption in national navigation and increased use of fuel oil for electricity generation within the transformation part of the balance up by 17 per cent between 2004 and 2005. Further detail on the consumption of fuel oil broken down by grade is given in Table 3.8.

3.34   Tables 3.4 to 3.6 include estimates for the use of gas for road vehicles. These estimates were based on information on the amounts of duty received by HM Revenue and Customs from the tax on gas used as a road fuel. It is estimated that some 120 thousand tonnes of gas (mostly butane or propane) was used in road vehicles in the UK in 2005. Although this is a very small use when compared to overall consumption of these fuels and the total consumption of fuels for road transport, the consumption of these gases for road transport has risen five-fold since 2000.

Supply and disposal of products (Table 3.7)

3.35   This table brings together the commodity balances for primary oils and for petroleum products into a single overall balance table.

3.36   The statistical difference for primary oils in the table includes own use in onshore terminals and gas separation plants, losses, platform and other field stock changes. Another factor is the time lag that can exist between production and loading onto tankers being reported at an offshore field and the arrival of these tankers at onshore refineries and oil terminals. This gap is usually minimal and works such that any effect of this at the start of a month is balanced by a similar counterpart effect at the end of a month. However, there can be instances where the length of this interval is considerable and, if it happens at the end of a year, there can be significant effects on the statistical differences seen for the years involved.

3.37   With the downstream sector, the statistical differences can similarly be used to assess the validity and consistency of the data. From the tables, these differences are generally a very small proportion of the totals involved.

3.38   Paragraphs 3.71 to 3.82 provide details on the reasons why statistical differences occur for the upstream and downstream sectors.

3.39   Following the identification of some discrepancies in the reporting of refinery production data in 2001, significant changes have been made to the downstream oil data reporting system that culminated in the launch of a revised system in 2005.

Refinery capacity

3.40   Data for refinery capacity as at the end of 2005 are presented in Table 3A, with the location of these refineries illustrated in Map 3A.   These figures are collected annually by the Department of Trade and Industry from individual oil companies.   Capacity per annum for each refinery is derived by applying the rated capacity of the plant per day when on-stream by the number of days the plant was on stream during the year.   Fluctuations in the number of days the refinery is active are usually the main reasons for annual changes in the level of capacity.   Reforming capacity covers catalytic reforming, and cracking/conversion capacity covers processes for upgrading residual oils to lighter products, eg catalytic, thermal or hydro-cracking, visbreaking and coking.

Table 3A: UK refinery processing capacity as at end 2005 [1]

| | Million tonnes per annum | | |
(Symbols relate to Map 3A)	Distillation	Reforming	Cracking and Conversion
❶ Stanlow - Shell UK Ltd	11.5	1.5	3.8
❷ Fawley - ExxonMobil Co. Ltd	16.3	4.2	3.0
❸ Coryton - BP Ltd	8.8	1.8	3.4
❹ Grangemouth - Ineos Refining Ltd	10.0	1.9	3.3
❺ Lindsey Oil Refinery Ltd South Killingholme - Total (UK)	10.9	1.5	4.1
❻ Pembroke - Texaco Refining Co. Ltd	10.1	1.5	6.1
❼ Killingholme - Conoco Ltd	10.2	2.2	9.2
❽ Milford Haven - Total (UK) / Murco Pet. Ltd	5.3	0.8	1.9
❾ North Tees - Petroplus International Ltd	5.0	-	-
① Harwich - Petrochem Carless Ltd	0.7	-	-
② Eastham - Eastham Refinery Ltd	1.1	-	-
③ Dundee (Camperdown) - Nynas UK AB	0.7	-	-
Total all refineries	**90.6**	**15.4**	**34.8**

(1) Rated design capacity per day on stream multiplied by the average number of days on stream.

Map 3A: Distribution of UK refineries active as at end 2005
Symbols relate to refinery details given in Table 3A

3.41 At the end of 2005 the UK had 9 major refineries operating, with three minor refineries in existence. Distillation capacity in the UK at the end of 2005 was 90.6 million tonnes, 1.4 million tonnes lower than at the end of 2004. Total UK reforming capacity at the end of 2005 was 15.4 million tonnes, an increase of 1.2 million tonnes over 2004 while cracking and conversion capacity was 1.7 million tonnes lower at 34.8 million tonnes.

Additional information on inland deliveries of selected products (Table 3.8)

3.42 This table gives details for consumption of motor spirit, gas oil/diesel and fuel oils given in the main commodity balance tables for the period 2001 to 2005. It includes information on retail and commercial deliveries of motor spirit and DERV fuel that cannot be accommodated within the structure of the commodity balances but which are of interest. The table also includes additional details of the quantities of motor spirit and DERV fuel sold collectively by hypermarket and supermarket companies in the UK.

3.43 Motor spirit deliveries in 2005 were 4 per cent down compared to 2004, and 6 per cent lower than in 2003. In contrast, deliveries of DERV fuel were 5 per cent higher in 2005 compared to 2004, which in turn was 9 per cent higher than in 2003. The differing trends of continued decline in motor spirit deliveries and rising DERV deliveries led to DERV deliveries surpassing motor spirit for the first time in 2005 in terms of weight. (DERV is a heavier fuel than motor spirit so that in volume terms, motor spirit deliveries were still higher).

3.44 Chart 3.5 shows how consumption of DERV fuel has steadily increased from 2001 to surpass deliveries of motor spirit in 2005. This is a result of a long-term shift to diesel engine vehicles. The chart also shows the reduction in the consumption of motor spirit in the UK, which has been an overall downward trend since 1990. Consumption of motor spirit in 2005 was 22 per cent lower than the peak of 24 million tonnes in 1990.

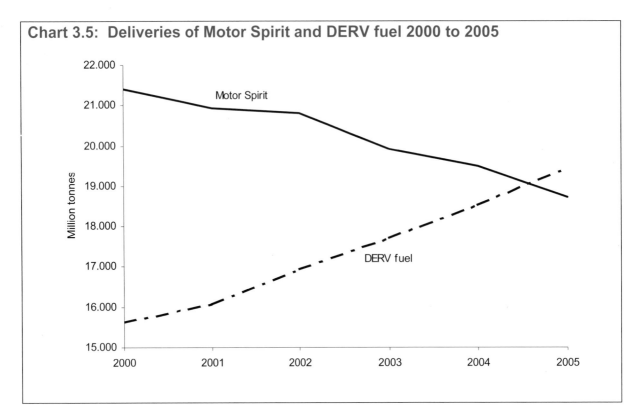

Chart 3.5: Deliveries of Motor Spirit and DERV fuel 2000 to 2005

3.45   Several factors are behind the differing trends seen for motor spirit and DERV fuel. For a number of years, the number of diesel-engined vehicles in use in the UK has been increasing. Diesel vehicles are more fuel-efficient than their petrol equivalents. In the National Travel Survey carried out by the Department for Transport, diesel-engined cars averaged 39 miles per gallon of fuel, compared with 30 miles per gallon for petrol-engined cars. Traditionally the greater fuel-efficiency of diesel vehicles had been at the expense of higher purchase prices and a performance deficit when compared to petrol-engined equivalents. More recently, the purchase prices for diesel and petrol engined vehicles have become more equivalent while improved technology has substantially reduced the performance deficit.

3.46   The price differential between DERV fuel and motor spirit has affected the relative demands for the two road fuels. In the early 1990s there was a significant price differential that worked in favour of using DERV fuel. For example, the average retail price for a litre of 4-star petrol in 1990 was 44.87 pence compared to 40.48 pence for a litre of DERV fuel, representing a 10 per cent saving. By December 2005, average retail prices for a litre of the most common grade of motor spirit purchased (ultra low sulphur petrol (ULSP)) and DERV fuel were 87.5 and 91.7 pence per litre respectively. In the mid 1990s, the policy on DERV taxation was changed for environmental reasons and the level of tax was increased to remove the favourable price differential. It is thought that the removal of the favourable differential significantly reduced the rate of transfer from petrol to diesel engine vehicles in recent years compared to what would have otherwise occurred.

3.47   Chart 3.6 illustrates how demand for DERV fuel has increased since 1992 based on information from NETCEN (see paragraph 3.89 below). The most significant increase has been for use in cars and taxis, up by 350 per cent since 1992 and their share of overall DERV demand being more than 2½ times that of 1992. DERV consumption in goods vehicles (both light and heavy) has also increased substantially, up by 62 per cent in total and reflecting more general growth in the economy. The use in light goods vehicles more than doubled between 1992 and 2005, a far larger increase than the use in heavy goods vehicles that increased by 42 per cent. This led to an increase in the share of total demand accounted for by light good vehicles while the heavy goods vehicles share decreased. This shows the change in the market towards the lighter goods vehicles. Bus and coach use has remained flat at around 1.3 million tonnes a year, meaning their share of demand has decreased.

Chart 3.6: Demand for DERV fuel

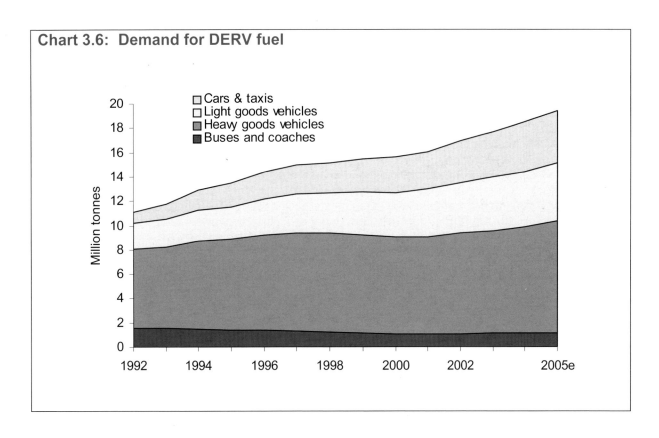

3.48   Chart 3.7 illustrates the switch from petrol to diesel engines in terms of private vehicle licence registrations and new vehicle registrations based on DVLA data. It contains details of vehicle licence registrations for private cars during each year for the period 1995 to 2005, broken down by type of engine. Whilst the number of petrol engined vehicles licensed only grew by 11 per cent, the number of diesel engined vehicles licensed has increased nearly 195 per cent in the same period. For new vehicles, the diesel engined vehicle share has risen from 19 per cent in 1995 to 38 per cent in 2005. Vehicles under 3 years old are generally thought to be responsible for most vehicle mileage.

Chart 3.7: Private car registrations by type of engine 1995 to 2005

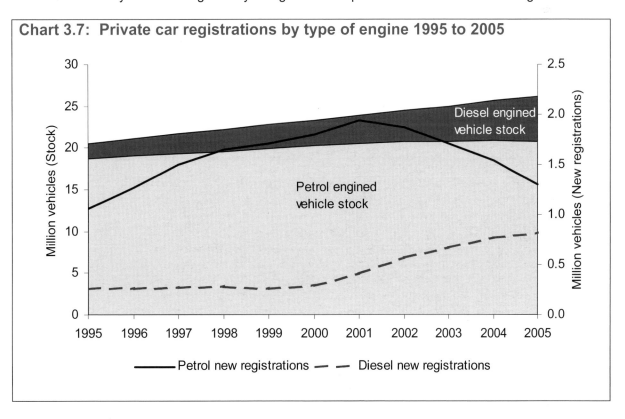

3.49   The chart also illustrates that while the motor spirit consumption has steadily declined, the actual number of petrol engine vehicles on the road has been increasing. This suggests that the average fuel efficiency of the UK petrol vehicle stock has improved. The improvement in vehicle efficiency is partly due to the switch from leaded to unleaded petrol. The large differential between the price of a litre of leaded and unleaded motor spirit helped encourage motorists to switch from leaded to unleaded petrol. In addition, the implementation of the Auto-Oil Directive banned the general sale of leaded petrol (4-star) from 1st January 2000 giving a final push for motorists to switch to unleaded fuels. The switch to unleaded petrol provided an impetus for people to change their vehicles to newer ones. The resultant reduction in the age of the vehicle stock has probably further reduced overall motor spirit consumption, as newer vehicles tend to be more fuel efficient due to improved technology.

3.50   Sales by super/hypermarkets have taken an increasing share of retail deliveries (ie deliveries to dealers) of motor spirit and DERV fuel in recent years as Table 3B shows. These figures have been derived from a survey of super/hypermarket companies to collect details of their sales of motor spirit and DERV fuel. The share of total deliveries (i.e. including deliveries direct to commercial consumers) is also shown.

Table 3B: Super/hypermarkets share of retail deliveries, 2001 to 2005

per cent

	Motor spirit		DERV fuel	
	Share of retail	Share of total (1)	Share of retail	Share of total (1)
2001	28.2	27	20.8	10
2002	29.3	29	22.7	11
2003	30.7	30	23.6	12
2004	32.9	32	26.0	13
2005	37.5	36	28.9	14

(1) Total deliveries include deliveries direct to commercial consumers.

3.51   The increases seen in recent years represent an increase in sales by super/hypermarket companies although the percentage shares are also affected by the decline in the overall deliveries of motor spirit in the UK seen in these years as mentioned earlier. Hypermarket deliveries of motor spirit increased by 9 per cent from 2004 and their DERV deliveries increased by 25 per cent. For motor spirit in particular, the hypermarkets are being noticeably successful at increasing or at least maintaining their sales as overall consumption declines.

Aviation fuel

3.52   Data in Tables 3.4 to 3.6 show the changing amounts of aviation turbine fuel (ATF) kerosene being consumed in the UK between 2003 and 2005. The long-term trends section on the Internet discusses the trend seen since 1970 in the use of ATF kerosene in the UK. Overall, deliveries in the UK in 2005 were 5 per cent higher than in 2004.

3.53   Chart 3.8 shows annual deliveries of ATF kerosene in the UK over the last decade. ATF consumption increased steadily until 1997 and then rapidly until 2000. The September 11th terrorist attacks on the United States had a significant impact on the global aviation industry and reversed the trend for a period lasting more than twelve months. The increase in ATF deliveries since 2002 illustrates the subsequent recovery of the global aviation industry.

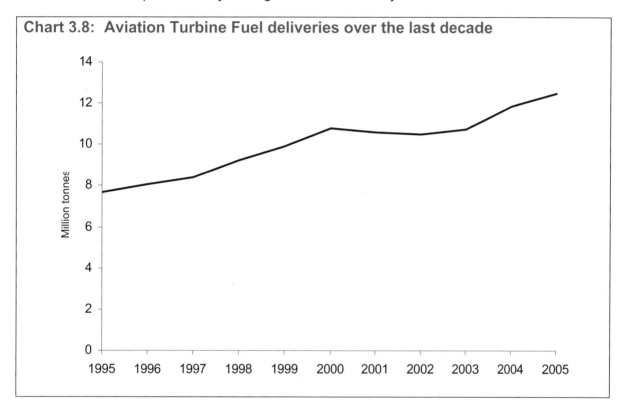

Chart 3.8: Aviation Turbine Fuel deliveries over the last decade

3.54   Chart 3.9 shows the aviation industry's activities over the last ten years split by the domestic and international passenger uplifts and cargo delivery categories. It is clear to see that the events of September 11th 2001 had varied effects on the different sections of the industry. International air passenger movements suffered a fall in the rate of growth, while domestic flights appear to be largely unaffected. The most significant effect however is clearly visible within the cargo division of the industry, which saw a fall of 21 per cent in 2001. The differing ways in which the demand for the industry's separate services reacted to the terrorist attack implies that rather than causing a reluctance of passengers in the UK to fly, the negative effect on the economy, causing cargo demand to fall, had the greatest impact. Since 2001 the cargo division has steadily grown and in 2005 was similar to the level seen in 2000.

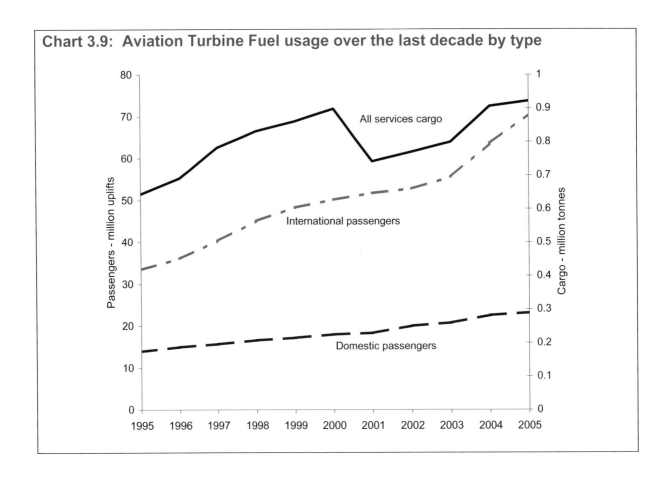

Chart 3.9: Aviation Turbine Fuel usage over the last decade by type

Additional information on inland deliveries for non-energy uses

3.55 Table 3C below summarises additional data on the non–energy uses made of the total deliveries of oil products included as the bottom line in the commodity balances in Tables 3.4 to 3.6. It provides extra information on the uses of lubricating oils and greases by use and details of products used as petro-chemical feedstocks.

3.56 All inland deliveries of lubricating oils and petroleum coke have been classified as non-energy use only. However, some deliveries are used for energy purposes but it is difficult to estimate energy use figures for these products with any degree of accuracy, hence no such estimates appear in the commodity balance tables.

3.57 For lubricating oils, about 50 per cent of inland deliveries each year are lost as a film on manufactured goods, loss due to evaporation, consumed during use (i.e. burnt within engines) or for products like process oils and white oils, the oil becomes part of the product. Work done by the Department for Environment, Food and Rural Affairs (DEFRA) suggests that each year about 50 per cent of inland deliveries become available as waste or used lubricating oil. Some 85 per cent of the waste/used lubricating oil (ie some 320 thousand tonnes) is centrally collected and processed for reuse as Recovered Fuel Oil. The remaining 15 per cent of the waste is probably burnt locally in small space heaters. Studies have shown that the UK's 85 per cent collection rate of used lubricating oils is one of the highest in Europe.

3.58 For petroleum coke, more information is available allowing more accurate estimates to be made. It has been possible to analyse the data available for the imports of petroleum coke to identify which type of company is importing the product. This work has shown that a significant proportion of petroleum coke imports each year are made by energy companies, such as power generators or fuels merchants, with another substantial proportion being imported by cement manufacturers. Whilst it cannot be certain that these imports are being used as a fuel, information on the use of petroleum coke in cement manufacture suggests that it is.

Table 3C: Additional information on inland deliveries for non-energy uses, 2003 to 2005

Thousand tonnes

	2003	2004	2005
Feedstock for petroleum chemical plants:			
Propane	835	1,106	1,328
Butane	789	680	901
Other gases	1,810	1,661	1,767
Total gases	3,434	3,447	3,996
Naphtha (LDF)	2,332	2,029	1,916
Middle Distillate Feedstock (MDF)	287	249	229
Other products	-	-	-
Total feedstock	6,053	5,725	6,141
Lubricating oils and grease:			
Aviation	3	3	5
Industrial	522	560	503
Marine	40	28	27
Motors	288	310	209
Agricultural	15	14	7
Fuel oil sold as lubricant	-	-	-
Total lubricating oils and grease	868	914	750
Other non-energy products:			
Industrial spirit/white spirit	147	281	284
Bitumen	1,959	1,991	1,906
Petroleum wax	57	50	72
Petroleum coke	880	1,146	1,042
Miscellaneous products	449	476	484
Total non-energy use	10,411	10,584	10,678

3.59   Using imports data, estimates have been constructed which show that around 1 million tonnes of petroleum coke were imported for inland deliveries in 2005. Around 343 thousand tonnes of petroleum coke were estimated to have been imported in 2004 for energy uses (for electricity generation, use as a fuel in the manufacture of cement, sold as a solid fuel or to be used in the manufacture of other solid fuels). Estimates of imports for energy uses rose in 2005 to 404 thousand tonnes or 42 per cent of total supplies.

3.60   Analysis of the data on the quantity and value of imports of petroleum coke into the UK from HM Revenue and Customs provides some estimates for the cost of imports and gives some indication of the prices being paid. These are only indicative of the prices being paid in the port of importation and do not include the extra transport costs from the port to the final destination that would be part of more rigorous price estimate. Details of these estimates are included in Annex G on trade in fuels, as part of Table G.3 on the DTI energy statistics web site. A breakdown has been made by grade of petroleum coke and type of use for imports into the UK, which is given in Table 3D below. Calcined petroleum coke is virtually pure carbon and as such is more valuable than non-calcined (otherwise known as "green") petroleum coke, as shown by the higher price per tonne it commands and the fact that it is not used simply as a fuel.

Table 3D: Estimated £ per tonne for imports of petroleum coke into the UK

	Non-calcined ("green") petroleum coke			Calcined petroleum coke
	Energy	Non-energy	Total	Non-energy
2002	18.0	37.9	26.2	131.0
2003	22.2	28.9	25.9	122.7
2004	22.5	35.0	29.9	120.6
2005	30.8	35.3	32.9	131.1

3.61   Petroleum coke is a relatively low energy content fuel, having a calorific value of 35.8 GJ per tonne, compared with an average for petroleum products of 45.9 GJ per tonne and 43.5 GJ per tonne for fuel oil. It is, however, higher than coal (25.6 GJ per tonne) and in certain areas is competing with coal as a fuel. It has the advantage of being a very cheap fuel, since it is often regarded as a waste product rather than a specific output from the refining process. Compared to imports of coal, prices of petroleum coke per GJ were about 60 per cent lower in 2005.

Inland deliveries by country (Table 3.9)

3.62   This table shows deliveries in England and Wales, Scotland, and Northern Ireland for 2003 to 2005. The figures for deliveries for energy use show an increase in use in England and Wales with decreases for Scotland and Northern Ireland. Energy use in England and Wales rose by 3 per cent between 2004 and 2005 partly due to an increase of 5 per cent in deliveries of DERV that offset falling motor spirit deliveries (down by 4 per cent). Between 2004 and 2005 motor spirit deliveries in Scotland fell by 3 per cent while DERV rose by 3½ per cent leading to an overall 4 per cent fall in energy deliveries. By contrast energy deliveries in Northern Ireland fell by 11 per cent, mainly due to a 17 per cent decrease in burning oil deliveries while at the same time DERV deliveries were up 4 per cent. Driven by demand for feedstock in the petrochemical industry, non-energy use deliveries rose in England and Wales by 4½ per cent but fell in Scotland by 8 per cent. Non-energy use in Northern Ireland is substantially lower than other parts of the UK due to lack of a significant local petrochemical industry.

Stocks of oil (Table 3.10)

3.63   This table shows stocks of crude oil, feedstocks (including partly processed oils) and products (in detail) at the end of each year. Stocks of crude oil and feedstocks increased in 2005, with increases in stocks held at offshore facilities and refineries offsetting a decrease in stocks held at terminals. Stocks of petroleum products at the end of 2005 were 5 per cent lower than a year earlier. The total stocks of crude oil and products held by UK companies at the end of 2005 were equivalent to approximately 98½ days of UK consumption.

3.64   The UK holds emergency stocks of oil to help reduce the adverse impact on the UK of any disruptions of supplies of oil arising from domestic or international incidents. EU legislation (EC Directive 98/93) requires EU member states to hold oil stocks equivalent to 90 days worth of average daily consumption calculated from the previous calendar year. These stocks are held purely to deal with oil supply emergencies, not to manage or affect prices. The UK, as a producer, receives a derogation of 25 per cent on its obligation and is only required to hold stocks equivalent to 67½ days of consumption.

3.65   To meet this obligation the UK government requires companies supplying oil products into final consumption in the UK to maintain a certain level of emergency stocks of oil products as fuels. As part of this, oil companies are allowed to hold stocks in other EU countries subject to bilateral agreements between governments, and count these stocks towards their stocking obligations. The stock figures in Table 3.10 take account of these stocks to give a true picture of the amount of stocks available to the UK.

3.66   The system was tested in September 2005 following Hurricane Katrina in the USA, when the International Energy Agency and EU agreed that member states should make a total of 2 million barrels of oil a day available to the market over a period of 30 days to help counter the impact of the hurricane on world production and markets. The total contribution sought from the UK was of 2.2 million barrels, or 280 thousand tonnes, and in the event UK companies were able to make available about 3 million barrels, or 380 thousand tonnes.

Technical notes and definitions

3.67   These notes and definitions are in addition to the technical notes and definitions covering all fuels and energy as a whole in Chapter 1, paragraphs 1.24 to 1.56. For notes on the commodity balances and definitions of the terms used in the row headings see the Annex A, paragraphs A.7 to A.42. While the data in the printed and bound copy of this Digest cover only the most recent 5 years, these notes also cover data for earlier years that are available on the DTI web site.

Indigenous production
3.68   The term indigenous is used throughout this chapter and includes oil from the UK Continental Shelf both offshore and onshore.

Deliveries
3.69   These are deliveries into consumption, as opposed to being estimates of actual consumption or use. They are split between inland deliveries and deliveries to marine bunkers. Inland deliveries will not necessarily be consumed in the United Kingdom (eg aviation fuels).

Sources of data
3.70   The majority of the data included in the text and tables of this chapter are derived from the DTI's Downstream Oil Reporting System (DORS), which replaced the UK Petroleum Industry Association (UKPIA) reporting system in 2005. Data relating to the inland operations of the UK oil industry (ie information on the supply, refining and distribution of oil in the UK) are collected from companies. The data format and coverage have been designed to meet most of the needs of both government and the industry itself. Each member of UKPIA and a number of other contributing companies provides returns on its refining activities and deliveries of various products to the internal UK market. This information is supplemented whenever necessary to allow for complete coverage within the statistics, with separate exercises carried out on special topics (for example, the work on super/hypermarkets referred to in paragraph 3.50) or with the use of additional data (such as trade data from HM Revenue and Customs to cover import activity by non-reporting companies).

Statistical differences
3.71   In Tables 3.1 to 3.7, there are headings titled "statistical differences". These are differences between the separately observed figures for production and delivery of crude oil and products during the path of their movement from the point of production to the point of consumption.

3.72   The statistical differences headings listed in the primary oil commodity balances (Tables 3.1 to 3.3) are differences between the separately observed and reported figures for production from onshore or offshore fields and supply to the UK market that cannot be accounted for by any specific factors. Primarily they result from inaccuracies in the meters at various points along offshore pipelines. These meters vary slightly in their accuracy within accepted tolerances, giving rise to both losses and gains when the volumes of oil flowing are measured. Errors may also occur when non-standard conditions are used to meter the oil flow.

3.73   Another technical factor that can contribute to the statistical differences relates to the recording of quantities at the producing field (which is the input for the production data) and at oil terminals and refineries, since they are in effect measuring different types of oil. Terminals and refineries are able to measure a standardised, stabilised crude oil, ie with its water content and content of NGLs at a standard level and with the amounts being measured at standard conditions. However, at the producing field they are dealing with a "live" crude oil that can have a varying level of water and NGLs within it. While offshore companies report live crude at field, the disposals from oil terminals and offshore loading fields are reported as stabilised crude oil. This effectively assumes that terminal disposals are stabilised crude production figures. These changes were introduced in the 2002 edition of this Digest.

3.74   Part of the overall statistical difference may also be due to problems with the correct reporting of individual NGLs at the production site and at terminals and refineries. It is known that there is some mixing of condensate and other NGLs in with what might otherwise be stabilised crude oil before it enters the pipeline. This mixing occurs as it removes the need for separate pipeline systems for transporting the NGLs and it also allows the viscosity of the oil passing down the pipeline to be varied as necessary. While the quantity figures recorded by terminals are in terms of stabilised crude oil, with the NGL component removed, there may be situations where what is being reported does not comply with this requirement.

3.75 Refinery data are collated from details of individual shipments received and made by each refinery and terminal operating company. Each year there are thousands of such shipments, which may be reported separately by two or three different companies involved in the movement. While intensive work is carried out to check these returns, it is possible that some double counting of receipts may occur.

3.76 Temperature, pressure and natural leakage also contribute to the statistical differences. In addition, small discrepancies can occur between the estimated calorific values used at the field and the more accurate values measured at the onshore terminal where data are shown on an energy basis. The statistical differences can also be affected by rounding or clerical errors or unrecorded losses, such as leakage. Other contributory factors are inaccuracies in the reporting of the amounts being disposed of to the various activities listed, including differences between the quantities reported as going to refineries and the actual amounts passing through refineries.

3.77 Similarly, the data under the statistical difference headings in Tables 3.4 to 3.6 are the differences between the deliveries of petroleum products to the inland UK market reported by the supplying companies and estimates for such deliveries. These estimates are calculated by taking the output of products reported by refineries and then adjusting it by the relevant factors (such as imports and exports of the products, changes in the levels of stocks etc).

3.78 It may be thought that such differences should not exist as the data underlying both the observed deliveries into the UK market and the individual components of the estimates (i.e. production, imports, exports and stocks) come from the same source (the oil companies). While it is true that each oil company provides data on its own activities in each area, there are separate areas of operation within the companies that report their own part of the overall data. Table 3E below illustrates this.

Table 3E: Sources of data within oil companies

Area covered	Source
Refinery production	Refinery
Imports and exports	Refinery, logistics departments, oil traders
Stocks	Refinery, crude and product terminals, major storage and distribution sites
Final deliveries	Sales, marketing and accounts departments

3.79 Each individual reporting source will have direct knowledge of its own data. For example, refineries will know what they produce and how much leaves the refinery gate as part of routine monitoring of the refinery operations. Similarly other data such as sales to final consumers or imports and exports will be closely monitored. Companies will ensure that each component set of data reported is as accurate as possible but their reporting systems may not be integrated, meaning that internal consistency checks across all reported data cannot be made. Each part of a company may also work to different timings as well, which may further add to the degree of differences seen.

3.80 The main area where there is known to be a problem is with the "Transfers" heading in the commodity balances. The data reported under this heading have two components. Firstly there is an allowance for reclassification of products within the refining process. For example, butane can be added to motor spirit to improve the octane rating, aviation turbine fuel could be reclassified as domestic kerosene if its quality deteriorates, and much of the fuel oil imported into the UK is further refined into other petroleum products. Issues can arise with product flows between different reporting companies, for example when company A delivers fuel oil to company B who report a receipt of a feedstock. Secondly, and in addition to these inter-product transfers, the data also include an allowance to cover the receipt of backflows of products from petrochemical plants that are often very closely integrated with refineries (for example, Ineos' refinery at Grangemouth is right next to the petrochemical plant). A deduction for these backflows thus needs to be included under the "Transfers" heading so that calculated estimates reflect net output and are thus more comparable with the basis of the observed deliveries data.

3.81 However, there is scope for error in the recording of these two components. With inter-product transfers, the data are recorded within the refinery during the refining and blending processes where the usual units used to record the changes are volumes rather than masses. Different factors apply for each product when converting from a volume to mass basis, as shown by the conversion factors given in Annex A of this Digest. Thus, a balanced transfer in volume terms may not be equivalent when converted to a mass basis. This is thought to be the main source of error within the individual product balances.

3.82 With the backflows data, the scope for error results from the recording of observed deliveries data being derived from sales data on a "net" basis and will therefore exclude the element of backflows data as received at the refinery. For example, these could be seen simply as an input of fuel oils to be used as a feedstock and thus recorded as an input without their precise nature being recorded – in effect a form of double-counting. This relationship between the petrochemical sector and refineries is thought to be one of the main sources of error in the overall oil commodity balances.

Imports and exports
3.83 The information given under the headings "imports" and "exports" in this chapter are the figures recorded by importers and exporters of oil. They can differ in some cases from the import and export figures provided by HM Revenue and Customs that are given in Annex G on the Internet. Such differences arise from timing differences between actual and declared movements but also result from the Customs figures including re-exports. These are products that may have originally entered the UK as imports from another country and been stored in the UK prior to being exported back out of the UK, as opposed to having been actually produced in the UK.

Marine bunkers
3.84 This covers deliveries to ocean going and coastal vessels under international bunker contracts. Other deliveries to fishing, coastal and inland vessels are excluded.

Crude and process oils
3.85 These are all feedstocks, other than distillation benzene, for refining at refinery plants. Gasoline feedstock is any process oil whether clean or dirty which is used as a refinery feedstock for the manufacture of gasoline or naphtha. Other refinery feedstock is any process oil used for the manufacture of any other petroleum products.

Refineries
3.86 Refineries distilling crude and process oils to obtain petroleum products. This excludes petrochemical plants, plants only engaged in re-distilling products to obtain better grades, crude oil stabilisation plants and gas separation plants.

Products used as fuel (energy use)
3.87 The following paragraphs define the product headings used in the text and tables of this chapter. The products are used for energy in some way, either directly as a fuel or as an input into electricity generation.

Refinery fuel - Petroleum products used as fuel at refineries.

Ethane – A naturally gaseous straight-chain hydrocarbon (C_2H_6) in natural gas and refinery gas streams. Primarily used, or intended to be used, as a chemical feedstock.

Propane - Hydrocarbon containing three carbon atoms(C_3H_8), gaseous at normal temperature but generally stored and transported under pressure as a liquid. Used mainly for industrial purposes but also as transport LPG and some domestic heating and cooking.

Butane - Hydrocarbon containing four carbon atoms(C_4H_{10}), otherwise as for propane. Additionally used as a constituent of motor spirit to increase vapour pressure and as a chemical feedstock.

Naphtha (Light distillate feedstock) - Petroleum distillate boiling predominantly below 200°C.

Aviation spirit - All light hydrocarbon oils intended for use in aviation piston-engine power units, including bench testing of aircraft engines.

Motor spirit - Blended light petroleum components used as fuel for spark-ignition internal-combustion engines other than aircraft engines:

(i) Premium unleaded grade - all finished motor spirit, with an octane number (research method) not less than 95.

(ii) Super premium unleaded grade - finished motor spirit, with an octane number (research method) not less than 97.

(iii) Lead Replacement Petrol (LRP) – finished motor spirit with an octane number (research method) not less than 97. This is usually Super Premium Unleaded containing a valve seat protection additive.

Aviation turbine fuel (ATF) - All other turbine fuel intended for use in aviation gas-turbine power units and including bench testing of aircraft engines.

Burning oil (kerosene or "paraffin") - Refined petroleum fuel, intermediate in volatility between motor spirit and gas oil, used primarily for heating. White spirit and kerosene used for lubricant blends are excluded.

Gas/diesel oil - Petroleum fuel having a distillation range immediately between kerosene and light-lubricating oil:

(i) **DERV (Diesel Engined Road Vehicle) fuel** - automotive diesel fuel for use in high speed, compression ignition engines in vehicles subject to Vehicle Excise Duty.

(ii) **Gas oil** - used as a burner fuel in heating installations, for industrial gas turbines and as for DERV (but in vehicles not subject to Vehicle Excise Duty e.g. agriculture vehicles, fishing vessels, construction equipment).

(iii) **Marine diesel oil** - heavier type of gas oil suitable for heavy industrial and marine compression-ignition engines.

Fuel oil - Heavy petroleum residue blends used in atomising burners and for heavy-duty marine engines (marine bunkers, etc.) with heavier grades requiring pre-heating before combustion. Excludes fuel oil for grease making or lubricating oil and fuel oil sold as such for road making.

Products not used as fuel (non-energy use)

3.88 The following paragraphs define the product headings used in the text and tables of this chapter, which are used for non-energy purposes.

Feedstock for petroleum chemical plants - All petroleum products intended for use in the manufacture of petroleum chemicals. This includes middle distillate feedstock of which there are several grades depending on viscosity. The boiling point ranges between 200°C and 400°C. (A deduction has been made from these figures equal to the quantity of feedstock used in making the conventional petroleum products that are produced during the processing of the feedstock. The output and deliveries of these conventional petroleum products are included elsewhere as appropriate.)

White spirit and specific boiling point (SBP) spirits – These are refined distillate intermediates with a distillation in the naphtha / kerosene range. **White spirit** has a boiling range of about 150°C to 200°C and is used as a paint or commercial solvent. **SBP spirit** is also known as **Industrial spirit** and has a wider boiling range that varies up to 200°C dependent upon its eventual use. It has a variety of uses that vary from use in seed extraction, rubber solvents and perfume.

Lubricating oils (and grease) - Refined heavy distillates obtained from the vacuum distillation of petroleum residues. Includes liquid and solid hydrocarbons sold by the lubricating oil trade, either alone or blended with fixed oils, metallic soaps and other organic and/or inorganic bodies. A certain percentage of inland deliveries are re-used as a fuel (see paragraphs 3.55 to 3.61).

Bitumen - The residue left after the production of lubricating oil distillates and vacuum gas oil for upgrading plant feedstock. Used mainly for road making and building construction purposes. Includes other petroleum products such as creosote and tar mixed with bitumen for these purposes and fuel oil sold specifically for road making.

Petroleum wax - Includes paraffin wax, which is a white crystalline hydrocarbon material of low oil content normally obtained during the refining of lubricating oil distillate, paraffin scale, slack wax, microcrystalline wax and wax emulsions. Used for candle manufacture, polishes, food containers, wrappings etc.

Petroleum cokes - Carbonaceous material derived from hydrocarbon oils, uses for which include metallurgical electrode manufacture. Quantities of imports of this product are used as a fuel, primarily in the manufacture of cement (see paragraphs 3.55 to 3.61).

Miscellaneous products - Includes aromatic extracts, defoament solvents and other minor miscellaneous products.

Main classes of consumer

3.89 The following are definitions of the main groupings of users of petroleum products used in the text and tables of this chapter.

Electricity generators - Petroleum products delivered for use by major power producers and other companies for electricity generation including those deliveries to the other industries listed below which are used for autogeneration of electricity (Tables 3.4 to 3.6). This includes petroleum products used to generate electricity at oil refineries and is recorded in the Transformation sector, as opposed to other uses of refinery fuels that are recorded in the Energy Industry Use sector. These numbers may not necessarily be the same as those reported in the **Electricity** chapter (Chapter 5), which gives **consumption** of petroleum products by electricity generators. Differences occur because delivered fuel may be put to stock and not used immediately.

Agriculture - Deliveries of fuel oil and gas oil/diesel for use in agricultural power units, dryers and heaters. Burning oil for farm use.

Iron and steel - Deliveries of petroleum products to steel works and iron foundries. This is now based on information from the Iron and Steel Statistics Bureau.

Other industries - The industries covered correspond to the industrial groups shown in Table 1E excluding Iron and Steel of Chapter 1.

National navigation - Fuel oil and gas/diesel oil delivered, other than under international bunker contracts, for fishing vessels, UK oil and gas exploration and production, coastal and inland shipping and for use in ports and harbours.

Railways - Deliveries of fuel oil, gas/diesel oil and burning oil to railways now based on estimates produced by the National Environmental Technology Centre (NETCEN) as part of their work to compile the UK Greenhouse Gas Inventory.

Air transport - Total inland deliveries of aviation turbine fuel and aviation spirit. The figures cover deliveries of aviation fuels in the United Kingdom to international and other airlines, British and foreign governments (including armed services) and for private flying. In order to compile the UK Greenhouse Gas Inventory, NETCEN need to estimate how aviation fuel usage splits between domestic and international consumption. Information from NETCEN suggests that virtually all aviation spirit is used domestically while just 6 per cent of civilian aviation turbine fuel use is for domestic consumption.

Road transport - Deliveries of motor spirit and DERV fuel for use in road vehicles of all kinds. Again as part of their work to compile the UK emissions inventory, NETCEN has constructed estimates for the consumption of road transport fuels by different vehicle classes and these are shown in Table 3F. The table shows the increasing share of DERV used by cars and light goods vehicles (vans).

Table 3F: Estimated consumption of road transport fuels by vehicle class

	1990	1995	2000	2004
Motor spirit:				
Cars and taxis	90%	92%	95%	97%
Light goods vehicles	9%	7%	5%	3%
Motor cycles etc	1%	1%	1%	1%
DERV:				
Cars and taxis	6%	14%	19%	22%
Light goods vehicles	15%	20%	23%	25%
Heavy goods vehicles	64%	55%	51%	47%
Buses and coaches	14%	10%	7%	6%

Source: NETCEN

As part of the 2003 Energy White Paper remit to provide more regional data, DTI commissioned NETCEN to provide estimates for regional and local use of road transport fuels. This work was first published in the June 2005 edition of Energy Trends with figures for 2002 and 2003 and has been updated in the June 2006 edition of Energy Trends to include figures for 2004: http://www.dti.gov.uk/energy/statistics/index.html.

Domestic - Fuel oil and gas oil delivered for central heating of private houses and other dwellings and deliveries of kerosene (burning oil) and liquefied petroleum gases for domestic purposes (see Tables 3.4 to 3.6).

Public services - Deliveries to national and local government premises (including educational, medical and welfare establishments and British and foreign armed forces) of fuel oil and gas oil for central heating and of kerosene (burning oil).

Miscellaneous - Deliveries of fuel oil and gas oil for central heating in premises other than those classified as domestic or public.

Monthly and quarterly data

3.90 Monthly or quarterly aggregate data for certain series presented in this chapter are available. This information can be obtained free of charge by following the links given at the energy statistics section of the DTI web site, at: http://www.dti.gov.uk/energy/statistics/index.html.

Contact: *Martin Young*
               martin.young@dti.gsi.gov.uk
               020-7215 5184

               Clive Evans
               clive.evans@dti.gsi.gov.uk
               020-7215 5189

               Kelly Adams
               kelly.adams@dti.gsi.gov.uk
               020-7215 2712

3.1 Commodity balances 2005[1]

Primary oil

Thousand tonnes

	Crude oil	Ethane	Propane	Butane	Condensate	Total NGL	Feedstock	Total primary oil
Supply								
Production	77,179	1,414	2,181	1,648	2,300	7,543	-	84,721
Other sources	-	-	-	-	-	-	-	-
Imports	52,211	-	-	-	-	-	6,675	58,886
Exports	-48,879	-14	-1,204	-760	-1,249	-3,227	-1,992	-54,098
Marine bunkers	-	-	-	-	-	-	-	-
Stock change (2)	-277	..	..	..	..	+73	-180	-385
Transfers	-	-1,397	-857	-500	-632	-3,386	+332	-3,054
Total supply	**80,233**	..	..	..	..	**1,002**	**4,835**	**86,070**
Statistical difference (3)(4)	+12	..	..	..	..	+9	-87	-66
Total demand (4)	**80,221**	..	..	..	..	**993**	**4,922**	**86,135**
Transformation (4)	**80,221**	..	..	..	..	**993**	**4,922**	**86,135**
Electricity generation	-	-	-	-	-	-	-	-
Major power producers	-	-	-	-	-	-	-	-
Autogenerators	-	-	-	-	-	-	-	-
Heat generation	-	-	-	-	-	-	-	-
Petroleum refineries	80,221	..	..	..	..	993	4,922	86,135
Coke manufacture	-	-	-	-	-	-	-	-
Blast furnaces	-	-	-	-	-	-	-	-
Patent fuel manufacture	-	-	-	-	-	-	-	-
Other	-	-	-	-	-	-	-	-
Energy industry use	-	-	-	-	-	-	-	-
Electricity generation	-	-	-	-	-	-	-	-
Oil & gas extraction	-	-	-	-	-	-	-	-
Petroleum refineries	-	-	-	-	-	-	-	-
Coal extraction	-	-	-	-	-	-	-	-
Coke manufacture	-	-	-	-	-	-	-	-
Blast furnaces	-	-	-	-	-	-	-	-
Patent fuel manufacture	-	-	-	-	-	-	-	-
Pumped storage	-	-	-	-	-	-	-	-
Other	-	-	-	-	-	-	-	-
Losses	-	-	-	-	-	-	-	-

(1) As there is no use made of primary oils and feedstocks by industries other than the oil and gas extraction and petroleum refining industries, other industry headings have not been included in this table. As such, this table is a summary of the activity of what is known as the Upstream oil industry.

(2) Stock fall (+), stock rise (-).

(3) Total supply minus total demand.

(4) Figures for total demand for the individual NGLs (and thus for the statistical differences as well) are not availble.

3.2 Commodity balances 2004[1]
Primary oil

	Crude oil	Ethane	Propane	Butane	Condensate	Total NGL	Feedstock	Total primary oil
Supply								
Production	87,516	1,473	2,441	1,863	2,081	7,858	-	95,374
Other sources	-	-	-	-	-	-	-	-
Imports	55,858	-	-	-	-	-	6,659	62,516
Exports	-60,724	-10	-1,265	-639	-774	-2,688	-1,091	-64,504
Marine bunkers	-	-	-	-	-	-	-	-
Stock change (2)	-136	..	..	..	..	-53	+55	-133
Transfers	-	-1,417	-828	-645	-835	-3,724	+181	-3,543
Total supply	**82,513**	..	..	..	..	**1,392**	**5,804**	**89,710**
Statistical difference (3)(4)	+341	..	..	..	..	+35	-487	-111
Total demand (4)	**82,173**	..	..	..	..	**1,357**	**6,291**	**89,821**
Transformation (4)	**82,173**	..	..	..	..	**1,357**	**6,291**	**89,821**
Electricity generation	-	-	-	-	-	-	-	-
Major power producers	-	-	-	-	-	-	-	-
Autogenerators	-	-	-	-	-	-	-	-
Heat generation	-	-	-	-	-	-	-	-
Petroleum refineries	82,173	..	..	..	..	1,357	6,291	89,821
Coke manufacture	-	-	-	-	-	-	-	-
Blast furnaces	-	-	-	-	-	-	-	-
Patent fuel manufacture	-	-	-	-	-	-	-	-
Other	-	-	-	-	-	-	-	-
Energy industry use	-	-	-	-	-	-	-	-
Electricity generation	-	-	-	-	-	-	-	-
Oil & gas extraction	-	-	-	-	-	-	-	-
Petroleum refineries	-	-	-	-	-	-	-	-
Coal extraction	-	-	-	-	-	-	-	-
Coke manufacture	-	-	-	-	-	-	-	-
Blast furnaces	-	-	-	-	-	-	-	-
Patent fuel manufacture	-	-	-	-	-	-	-	-
Pumped storage	-	-	-	-	-	-	-	-
Other	-	-	-	-	-	-	-	-
Losses	-	-	-	-	-	-	-	-

(1) As there is no use made of primary oils and feedstocks by industries other than the oil and gas extraction and petroleum refining industries, other industry headings have not been included in this table. As such, this table is a summary of the activity of what is known as the Upstream oil industry.
(2) Stock fall (+), stock rise (-).
(3) Total supply minus total demand.
(4) Figures for total demand for the individual NGLs (and thus for the statistical differences as well) are not availble.

3.3 Commodity balances 2003[1]
Primary oil

Thousand tonnes

	Crude oil	Ethane	Propane	Butane	Condensate	Total NGL	Feedstock	Total primary oil
Supply								
Production	97,835	1,531	2,578	1,999	2,130	8,238	-	106,073
Other sources	-	-	-	-	-	-	-	-
Imports	48,589	-	-	-	-	-	5,588	54,177
Exports	-68,823	-24	-1,785	-917	-978	-3,703	-2,372	-74,898
Marine bunkers	-	-	-	-	-	-	-	-
Stock change (2)	+486	..	..	..	..	-5	-11	+469
Transfers	-	-1,509	-628	-524	-	-2,661	+1,653	-1,008
Total supply	**78,086**	..	..	..	..	**1,869**	**4,859**	**84,814**
Statistical difference (3)(4)	**+778**	..	..	..	..	**+596**	**-1,145**	**+229**
Total demand (4)	**77,309**	..		..	..	**1,273**	**6,004**	**84,585**
Transformation (4)	**77,309**	..	..	..	..	**1,273**	**6,004**	**84,585**
Electricity generation	-	-	-	-	-	-	-	-
Major power producers	-	-	-	-	-	-	-	-
Autogenerators	-	-	-	-	-	-	-	-
Heat generation	-	-	-	-	-	-	-	-
Petroleum refineries	77,309	..	..	..	..	1,273	6,004	84,585
Coke manufacture	-	-	-	-	-	-	-	-
Blast furnaces	-	-	-	-	-	-	-	-
Patent fuel manufacture	-	-	-	-	-	-	-	-
Other	-	-	-	-	-	-	-	-
Energy industry use	**-**	**-**	**-**	**-**	**-**	**-**	**-**	**-**
Electricity generation	-	-	-	-	-	-	-	-
Oil & gas extraction	-	-	-	-	-	-	-	-
Petroleum refineries	-	-	-	-	-	-	-	-
Coal extraction	-	-	-	-	-	-	-	-
Coke manufacture	-	-	-	-	-	-	-	-
Blast furnaces	-	-	-	-	-	-	-	-
Patent fuel manufacture	-	-	-	-	-	-	-	-
Pumped storage	-	-	-	-	-	-	-	-
Other	-	-	-	-	-	-	-	-
Losses	**-**	**-**	**-**	**-**	**-**	**-**	**-**	**-**

(1) As there is no use made of primary oils and feedstocks by industries other than the oil and gas extraction and petroleum refining industries, other industry headings have not been included in this table. As such, this table is a summary of the activity of what is known as the Upstream oil industry.
(2) Stock fall (+), stock rise (-).
(3) Total supply minus total demand.
(4) Figures for total demand for the individual NGLs (and thus for the statistical differences as well) are not availble.

3.4 Commodity balances 2005
Petroleum products

	Ethane	Propane	Butane	Other gases	Naphtha	Aviation spirit	Motor spirit	White Spirit & SBP	Aviation turbine fuel
Supply									
Production	5	1,944	518	2,996	3,023	32	22,620	136	5,167
Other sources	1,397	857	500	-	632	-	-	-	-
Imports	-	281	502	137	1,380	13	2,377	224	9,083
Exports	-	-748	-550	-	-3,167	-3	-6,586	-63	-1,397
Marine bunkers	-	-	-	-	-	-	-	-	-
Stock change (2)	-	+8	+13	+1	+63	-2	+366	-15	+96
Transfers	-	-5	+2	-3	+32	+14	-4	+3	-343
Total supply	1,402	2,337	986	3,130	1,964	53	18,772	285	12,606
Statistical difference (3)	-57	-184	-85	-6	+45	+1	+41	-0	+109
Total demand	1,459	2,521	1,071	3,136	1,919	52	18,731	284	12,497
Transformation	-	-	-	182	-	-	-	-	-
Electricity generation	-	-	-	182	-	-	-	-	-
Major power producers	-	-	-	-	-	-	-	-	-
Autogenerators	-	-	-	182	-	-	-	-	-
Heat generation	-	-	-	-	-	-	-	-	-
Petroleum refineries	-	-	-	-	-	-	-	-	-
Coke manufacture	-	-	-	-	-	-	-	-	-
Blast furnaces	-	-	-	-	-	-	-	-	-
Patent fuel manufacture	-	-	-	-	-	-	-	-	-
Other	-	-	-	-	-	-	-	-	-
Energy industry use	5	38	-	2,569	3	-	-	-	-
Electricity generation	-	-	-	-	-	-	-	-	-
Oil & gas extraction	-	-	-	-	-	-	-	-	-
Petroleum refineries	5	38	-	2,569	3	-	-	-	-
Coal extraction	-	-	-	-	-	-	-	-	-
Coke manufacture	-	-	-	-	-	-	-	-	-
Blast furnaces	-	-	-	-	-	-	-	-	-
Patent fuel manufacture	-	-	-	-	-	-	-	-	-
Pumped storage	-	-	-	-	-	-	-	-	-
Other	-	-	-	-	-	-	-	-	-
Losses	-	-	-	-	-	-	-	-	-
Final consumption	1,454	2,483	1,071	384	1,916	52	18,731	284	12,497
Industry	71	631	161	-	-	-	-	-	-
Unclassified	71	631	161	-	-	-	-	-	-
Iron & steel	-	-	-	-	-	-	-	-	-
Non-ferrous metals	-	-	-	-	-	-	-	-	-
Mineral products	-	-	-	-	-	-	-	-	-
Chemicals	-	-	-	-	-	-	-	-	-
Mechanical engineering, etc	-	-	-	-	-	-	-	-	-
Electrical engineering, etc	-	-	-	-	-	-	-	-	-
Vehicles	-	-	-	-	-	-	-	-	-
Food, beverages, etc	-	-	-	-	-	-	-	-	-
Textiles, leather, etc	-	-	-	-	-	-	-	-	-
Paper, printing etc	-	-	-	-	-	-	-	-	-
Other industries	-	-	-	-	-	-	-	-	-
Construction	-	-	-	-	-	-	-	-	-
Transport	-	120	-	-	-	52	18,731	-	12,497
Air	-	-	-	-	-	52	-	-	12,497
Rail	-	-	-	-	-	-	-	-	-
Road	-	120	-	-	-	-	18,731	-	-
National navigation	-	-	-	-	-	-	-	-	-
Pipelines	-	-	-	-	-	-	-	-	-
Other	-	404	9	-	-	-	-	-	-
Domestic	-	289	9	-	-	-	-	-	-
Public administration	-	-	-	-	-	-	-	-	-
Commercial	-	-	-	-	-	-	-	-	-
Agriculture	-	115	-	-	-	-	-	-	-
Miscellaneous	-	-	-	-	-	-	-	-	-
Non energy use (4)	1,383	1,328	901	384	1,916	-	-	284	-

(1) Includes marine diesel oil
(2) Stock fall (+), stock rise (-).
(3) Total supply minus total demand.
(4) For further details on non-energy usage see paragraphs 3.55 to 3.61.

3.4 Commodity balances 2005 (continued)
Petroleum products

Burning oil	Gas/ Diesel Oil (1)	Fuel oils	Lubri -cants	Bitu -men	Petroleum wax	Petroleum coke	Misc. products	Total Products	
									Supply
3,325	28,691	11,728	936	1,912	98	1,867	1,005	86,003	Production
-	-	-	-	-	-	-	-	3,386	Other sources
407	4,921	1,528	424	216	28	947	42	22,511	Imports
-282	-6,314	-8,452	-709	-242	-33	-570	-606	-29,722	Exports
-	889	1,166	-	-	-	-	-	2,055	Marine bunkers
+24	+284	+136	+73	+1	-20	-26	+45	+1,046	Stock change (2)
+333	-262	-92	-	+24	-8	-	-22	-333	Transfers
3,807	26,431	3,681	725	1,911	65	2,217	464	80,837	**Total supply**
-63	-8	+143	-25	+5	-6	-31	-20	-140	**Statistical difference (3)**
3,870	26,438	3,538	750	1,906	72	2,249	484	80,977	**Total demand**
-	75	723	-	-	-	-	-	980	**Transformation**
-	66	402	-	-	-	-	-	650	Electricity generation
-	37	215	-	-	-	-	-	252	Major power producers
-	29	187	-	-	-	-	-	398	Autogenerators
-	9	52	-	-	-	-	-	61	Heat generation
-	-	-	-	-	-	-	-	-	Petroleum refineries
-	-	-	-	-	-	-	-	-	Coke manufacture
-	-	269	-	-	-	-	-	269	Blast furnaces
-	-	-	-	-	-	-	-	-	Patent fuel manufacture
-	-	-	-	-	-	-	-	-	Other
1	206	1,573	-	-	-	1,207	-	5,602	**Energy industry use**
-	-	-	-	-	-	-	-	-	Electricity generation
-	-	-	-	-	-	-	-	-	Oil & gas extraction
1	206	1,573	-	-	-	1,207	-	5,602	Petroleum refineries
-	-	-	-	-	-	-	-	-	Coal extraction
-	-	-	-	-	-	-	-	-	Coke manufacture
-	-	-	-	-	-	-	-	-	Blast furnaces
-	-	-	-	-	-	-	-	-	Patent fuel manufacture
-	-	-	-	-	-	-	-	-	Pumped storage
-	-	-	-	-	-	-	-	-	Other
-	-	-	-	-	-	-	-	-	**Losses**
3,869	26,158	1,242	750	1,906	72	1,042	484	74,395	**Final Consumption**
1,490	3,286	786	-	-	-	-	-	6,424	**Industry**
1,490	-	-	-	-	-	-	-	2,352	Unclassified
-	-	14	-	-	-	-	-	14	Iron & steel
-	28	22	-	-	-	-	-	50	Non-ferrous metals
-	197	1	-	-	-	-	-	198	Mineral products
-	109	72	-	-	-	-	-	181	Chemicals
-	90	19	-	-	-	-	-	109	Mechanical engineering etc
-	26	7	-	-	-	-	-	33	Electrical engineering etc
-	109	19	-	-	-	-	-	128	Vehicles
-	259	39	-	-	-	-	-	298	Food, beverages etc
-	93	9	-	-	-	-	-	101	Textiles, leather, etc
-	51	29	-	-	-	-	-	81	Paper, printing etc
-	2,164	539	-	-	-	-	-	2,704	Other industries
-	159	16	-	-	-	-	-	175	Construction
12	21,140	355	-	-	-	-	-	52,908	**Transport**
-	-	-	-	-	-	-	-	12,549	Air
12	784	-	-	-	-	-	-	796	Rail
-	19,436	-	-	-	-	-	-	38,287	Road
-	920	355	-	-	-	-	-	1,274	National navigation
-	-	-	-	-	-	-	-	-	Pipelines
2,368	1,503	101	-	-	-	-	-	4,385	**Other**
2,344	141	-	-	-	-	-	-	2,782	Domestic
12	443	50	-	-	-	-	-	505	Public administration
-	315	36	-	-	-	-	-	351	Commercial
12	192	5	-	-	-	-	-	324	Agriculture
-	413	10	-	-	-	-	-	423	Miscellaneous
-	229	-	750	1,906	72	1,042	484	10,678	**Non energy use (4)**

3.5 Commodity balances 2004
Petroleum products

	Ethane	Propane	Butane	Other gases	Naphtha	Aviation spirit	Motor spirit	White Spirit & SBP	Aviation turbine fuel
Supply									
Production	15	1,794	376	3,012	3,176	31	24,589	100	5,615
Other sources	1,417	828	645	-	835	-	-	-	-
Imports	-	245	245	34	871	19	2,175	210	7,658
Exports	-	-621	-411	-	-2,940	-8	-7,334	-62	-758
Marine bunkers	-	-	-	-	-	-	-	-	-
Stock change (2)	-	-15	-19	-	-109	+1	-40	+2	-112
Transfers	-	-37	+42	-1	+79	-	-11	+23	-345
Total supply	1,432	2,193	879	3,045	1,911	44	19,380	273	12,059
Statistical difference (3)	-7	-26	-36	+59	-125	-6	-105	-8	+197
Total demand	1,439	2,219	914	2,986	2,036	49	19,484	281	11,862
Transformation	-	-	-	181r	-	-	-	-	-
Electricity generation	-	-	-	181r	-	-	-	-	-
Major power producers	-	-	-	181r	-	-	-	-	-
Autogenerators	-	-	-	-	-	-	-	-	-
Heat generation	-	-	-	-	-	-	-	-	-
Petroleum refineries	-	-	-	-	-	-	-	-	-
Coke manufacture	-	-	-	-	-	-	-	-	-
Blast furnaces	-	-	-	-	-	-	-	-	-
Patent fuel manufacture	-	-	-	-	-	-	-	-	-
Other	-	-	-	-	-	-	-	-	-
Energy industry use	15	19	-	2,492r	7	-	-	-	-
Electricity generation	-	-	-	-	-	-	-	-	-
Oil & gas extraction	-	-	-	-	-	-	-	-	-
Petroleum refineries	15	19	-	2,492r	7	-	-	-	-
Coal extraction	-	-	-	-	-	-	-	-	-
Coke manufacture	-	-	-	-	-	-	-	-	-
Blast furnaces	-	-	-	-	-	-	-	-	-
Patent fuel manufacture	-	-	-	-	-	-	-	-	-
Pumped storage	-	-	-	-	-	-	-	-	-
Other	-	-	-	-	-	-	-	-	-
Losses	-	-	-	-	-	-	-	-	-
Final consumption	1,424	2,200	914	313	2,029	49	19,484	281	11,862
Industry	76	592	190	-	-	-	-	-	-
Unclassified	76	592	190	-	-	-	-	-	-
Iron & steel	-	-	-	-	-	-	-	-	-
Non-ferrous metals	-	-	-	-	-	-	-	-	-
Mineral products	-	-	-	-	-	-	-	-	-
Chemicals	-	-	-	-	-	-	-	-	-
Mechanical engineering, etc	-	-	-	-	-	-	-	-	-
Electrical engineering, etc	-	-	-	-	-	-	-	-	-
Vehicles	-	-	-	-	-	-	-	-	-
Food, beverages, etc	-	-	-	-	-	-	-	-	-
Textiles, leather, etc	-	-	-	-	-	-	-	-	-
Paper, printing etc	-	-	-	-	-	-	-	-	-
Other industries	-	-	-	-	-	-	-	-	-
Construction	-	-	-	-	-	-	-	-	-
Transport	-	112	-	-	-	49	19,484	-	11,862
Air	-	-	-	-	-	49	-	-	11,862
Rail	-	-	-	-	-	-	-	-	-
Road	-	112	-	-	-	-	19,484	-	-
National navigation	-	-	-	-	-	-	-	-	-
Pipelines	-	-	-	-	-	-	-	-	-
Other	-	391	45	-	-	-	-	-	-
Domestic	-	285	45	-	-	-	-	-	-
Public administration	-	-	-	-	-	-	-	-	-
Commercial	-	-	-	-	-	-	-	-	-
Agriculture	-	106	-	-	-	-	-	-	-
Miscellaneous	-	-	-	-	-	-	-	-	-
Non energy use (4)	1,348	1,106	680	313	2,029	-	-	281	-

(1) Includes marine diesel oil
(2) Stock fall (+), stock rise (-).
(3) Total supply minus total demand.
(4) For further details on non-energy usage see paragraphs 3.55 to 3.61.

3.5 Commodity balances 2004 (continued)
Petroleum products

Burning oil	Gas/ Diesel Oil (1)	Fuel oils	Lubri -cants	Bitu -men	Petroleum wax	Petroleum coke	Misc. products	Total Products	
									Supply
3,613	28,839	12,988	1,136	2,196	94	1,645	607	89,828	Production
-	-	-	-	-	-		-	3,724	Other sources
360	4,216	612r	530	227	29	1,081	32	18,545r	Imports
-413	-6,623	-8,936	-750	-336	-41	-598	-438	-30,270	Exports
-	1,073	1,012	-	-	-		-	2,085	Marine bunkers
-58	-268	-46	-14	-11	-2	+31	+370	-289	Stock change (2)
+413	-393	-19	-3	+22	-36	-	+63	-203	Transfers
3,915	24,698	3,586r	900	2,098	44	2,160	634	79,250r	**Total supply**
-35	-30	-158	-15	+108	-7	+2	+158	-34	**Statistical difference (3)**
3,950	24,729	3,744r	914	1,991	50	2,157	476	79,284r	**Total demand**
-	75r	694r	-	-	-	-	-	951r	**Transformation**
-	67r	345r	-	-	-	-	-	593r	Electricity generation
-	11	136	-	-	-	-	-	328r	Major power producers
-	56r	209r	-	-	-	-	-	265r	Autogenerators
-	9	52r	-	-	-	-	-	61r	Heat generation
-	-	-	-	-	-	-	-	-	Petroleum refineries
-	-	-	-	-	-	-	-	-	Coke manufacture
-	-	297	-	-	-	-	-	297	Blast furnaces
-	-	-	-	-	-	-	-	-	Patent fuel manufacture
-	-	-	-	-	-	-	-	-	Other
-	192	1,681	-	-	-	1,012	-	5,419r	**Energy industry use**
-	-	-	-	-	-	-	-	-	Electricity generation
-	-	-	-	-	-	-	-	-	Oil & gas extraction
-	192	1,680	-	-	-	1,012	-	5,417r	Petroleum refineries
-	-	-	-	-	-	-	-	-	Coal extraction
-	-	1	-	-	-	-	-	1	Coke manufacture
-	-	-	-	-	-	-	-	-	Blast furnaces
-	-	-	-	-	-	-	-	-	Patent fuel manufacture
-	-	-	-	-	-	-	-	-	Pumped storage
-	-	-	-	-	-	-	-	-	Other
-	-	-	-	-	-	-	-	-	**Losses**
3,950	24,461r	1,368r	914	1,991	50	1,146	476	72,915r	**Final Consumption**
1,465	2,854r	972r	-	-	-	-	-	6,150r	**Industry**
1,465	-	-	-	-	-	-	-	2,324	Unclassified
-	2	31	-	-	-	-	-	33	Iron & steel
-	27	23r	-	-	-	-	-	49r	Non-ferrous metals
-	171	15	-	-	-	-	-	186	Mineral products
-	116	73r	-	-	-	-	-	189r	Chemicals
-	90	18	-	-	-	-	-	108	Mechanical engineering etc
-	22	13r	-	-	-	-	-	35r	Electrical engineering etc
-	79	22r	-	-	-	-	-	101	Vehicles
-	261	58	-	-	-	-	-	319	Food, beverages etc
-	58	10	-	-	-	-	-	68	Textiles, leather, etc
-	27	28	-	-	-	-	-	55	Paper, printing etc
-	1,858r	680r	-	-	-	-	-	2,538r	Other industries
-	143	-	-	-	-	-	-	143	Construction
12	20,142r	266	-	-	-	-	-	51,927r	**Transport**
-	-	-	-	-	-	-	-	11,911	Air
12	784r	-	-	-	-	-	-	796r	Rail
-	18,514	-	-	-	-	-	-	38,110	Road
-	844r	266	-	-	-	-	-	1,110	National navigation
-	-	-	-	-	-	-	-	-	Pipelines
2,472	1,216	130	-	-	-	-	-	4,254	**Other**
2,448	160r	-	-	-	-	-	-	2,938r	Domestic
12	394	60r	-	-	-	-	-	465r	Public administration
-	341	44	-	-	-	-	-	385	Commercial
12	122	5	-	-	-	-	-	245	Agriculture
-	200r	21r	-	-	-	-	-	221r	Miscellaneous
-	249	-	914	1,991	50	1,146	476	10,584	**Non energy use (4)**

3.6 Commodity balances 2003
Petroleum products

	Ethane	Propane	Butane	Other gases	Naphtha	Aviation spirit	Motor spirit	White Spirit & SBP	Aviation turbine fuel
Supply									
Production	11	1,620	679	2,891	3,516	26	22,627	104	5,277
Other sources	1,509	628	524	-	-	-	-	-	-
Imports	-	194	172	-	782	12	2,022	34	7,346
Exports	-	-328	-16	-7	-2,461	-5	-5,603	-	-587
Marine bunkers	-	-	-	-	-	-	-	-	-
Stock change *(2)*	-	+5	+22	+1	-74	-1	-88	+4	-100
Transfers	-9	-254	-703	-196	+742	-1	+454	-	-1,347
Total supply	**1,510**	**1,865**	**679**	**2,688**	**2,506**	**31**	**19,412**	**141**	**10,588**
Statistical difference *(3)*	-60	-180	-311	-40	+161	-15	-506	-6	-176
Total demand	**1,571**	**2,046**	**990**	**2,728r**	**2,345**	**46**	**19,918**	**147**	**10,765**
Transformation	-	1	-	229r	-	-	-	-	-
Electricity generation	-	1	-	229r	-	-	-	-	-
Major power producers	-	-	-	229r	-	-	-	-	-
Autogenerators	-	1	-	-	-	-	-	-	-
Heat generation	-	-	-	-	-	-	-	-	-
Petroleum refineries	-	-	-	-	-	-	-	-	-
Coke manufacture	-	-	-	-	-	-	-	-	-
Blast furnaces	-	-	-	-	-	-	-	-	-
Patent fuel manufacture	-	-	-	-	-	-	-	-	-
Other	-	-	-	-	-	-	-	-	-
Energy industry use	**9**	**19**	**-**	**2,176r**	**13**	**-**	**-**	**-**	**-**
Electricity generation	-	-	-	-	-	-	-	-	-
Oil & gas extraction	-	-	-	-	-	-	-	-	-
Petroleum refineries	9	19	-	2,176r	13	-	-	-	-
Coal extraction	-	-	-	-	-	-	-	-	-
Coke manufacture	-	-	-	-	-	-	-	-	-
Blast furnaces	-	-	-	-	-	-	-	-	-
Patent fuel manufacture	-	-	-	-	-	-	-	-	-
Pumped storage	-	-	-	-	-	-	-	-	-
Other	-	-	-	-	-	-	-	-	-
Losses	-	-	-	-	-	-	-	-	-
Final consumption	**1,562**	**2,027**	**990**	**323**	**2,332**	**46**	**19,918**	**147**	**10,765**
Industry	**75**	**690**	**154**	**-**	**-**	**-**	**-**	**-**	**-**
Unclassified	75	690	154	-	-	-	-	-	-
Iron & steel	-	-	-	-	-	-	-	-	-
Non-ferrous metals	-	-	-	-	-	-	-	-	-
Mineral products	-	-	-	-	-	-	-	-	-
Chemicals	-	-	-	-	-	-	-	-	-
Mechanical engineering, etc	-	-	-	-	-	-	-	-	-
Electrical engineering, etc	-	-	-	-	-	-	-	-	-
Vehicles	-	-	-	-	-	-	-	-	-
Food, beverages, etc	-	-	-	-	-	-	-	-	-
Textiles, leather, etc	-	-	-	-	-	-	-	-	-
Paper, printing etc	-	-	-	-	-	-	-	-	-
Other industries	-	-	-	-	-	-	-	-	-
Construction	-	-	-	-	-	-	-	-	-
Transport	**-**	**104**	**-**	**-**	**-**	**46**	**19,918**	**-**	**10,765**
Air	-	-	-	-	-	46	-	-	10,765
Rail	-	-	-	-	-	-	-	-	-
Road	-	104	-	-	-	-	19,918	-	-
National navigation	-	-	-	-	-	-	-	-	-
Pipelines	-	-	-	-	-	-	-	-	-
Other	**-**	**397**	**48**	**-**	**-**	**-**	**-**	**-**	**-**
Domestic	-	294	47	-	-	-	-	-	-
Public administration	-	-	-	-	-	-	-	-	-
Commercial	-	-	-	-	-	-	-	-	-
Agriculture	-	103	-	-	-	-	-	-	-
Miscellaneous	-	-	-	-	-	-	-	-	-
Non energy use *(4)*	**1,487**	**835**	**789**	**323**	**2,332**	**-**	**-**	**147**	**-**

(1) Includes marine diesel oil
(2) Stock fall (+), stock rise (-).
(3) Total supply minus total demand.
(4) For further details on non-energy usage see paragraphs 3.55 to 3.61.

3.6 Commodity balances 2003 (continued)
Petroleum products

Thousand tonnes

Burning oil	Gas/ Diesel Oil (1)	Fuel oils	Lubri -cants	Bitu -men	Petroleum wax	Petroleum coke	Misc. products	Total Products	
									Supply
3,521	27,579	11,517	576	1,925	460	1,630	569	84,529	Production
-	-	-	-	-	-		-	2,661	Other sources
327	3,503	394r	570	249	21	834	13	16,472r	Imports
-556	-5,528	-6,385	-678	-329	-46	-566	-228	-23,323	Exports
-	897	867	-	-	-	-	-	1,764	Marine bunkers
+36	-27	-3	+46	-9	+3	+17	-94	-262	Stock change (2)
+151	-625	+136	+454	+43	-375	-22	-100	-1,652	Transfers
3,479	24,006	4,792r	968	1,879	64	1,893	160	76,661r	**Total supply**
-90	-231	+1,230	+101	-80	+7	-5	-289	-492	**Statistical difference (3)**
3,569	24,237	3,562r	868	1,959	57	1,898	449	77,153r	**Total demand**
-	47	639r	-	-	-	-	-	916r	**Transformation**
-	29	277r	-	-	-	-	-	536r	Electricity generation
-	17	83	-	-	-	-	-	329r	Major power producers
-	12	194r	-	-	-	-	-	207r	Autogenerators
-	18	133	-	-	-	-	-	151r	Heat generation
-	-	-	-	-	-	-	-	-	Petroleum refineries
-	-	-	-	-	-	-	-	-	Coke manufacture
-	-	229	-	-	-	-	-	229	Blast furnaces
-	-	-	-	-	-	-	-	-	Patent fuel manufacture
-	-	-	-	-	-	-	-	-	Other
-	200	2,024	-	-	-	1,018	-	5,458	**Energy industry use**
-	-	-	-	-	-	-	-	-	Electricity generation
-	-	-	-	-	-	-	-	-	Oil & gas extraction
-	199	2,022	-	-	-	1,018	-	5,456	Petroleum refineries
-	-	-	-	-	-	-	-	-	Coal extraction
-	-	1	-	-	-	-	-	1	Coke manufacture
-	-	-	-	-	-	-	-	-	Blast furnaces
-	-	-	-	-	-	-	-	-	Patent fuel manufacture
-	-	-	-	-	-	-	-	-	Pumped storage
-	-	-	-	-	-	-	-	-	Other
-	-	-	-	-	-	-	-	-	**Losses**
3,569	23,990	899r	868	1,959	57	880	449	70,779r	**Final Consumption**
839	3,213r	707r	-	-	-	-	-	5,678r	**Industry**
839	-	-	-	-	-	-	-	1,758	Unclassified
-	1	17	-	-	-	-	-	19	Iron & steel
-	21	24r	-	-	-	-	-	45r	Non-ferrous metals
-	206	17r	-	-	-	-	-	223r	Mineral products
-	111	73r	-	-	-	-	-	184r	Chemicals
-	113	27r	-	-	-	-	-	140r	Mechanical engineering etc
-	13	13r	-	-	-	-	-	26r	Electrical engineering etc
-	69	24r	-	-	-	-	-	93r	Vehicles
-	154	52r	-	-	-	-	-	206r	Food, beverages etc
-	78	24r	-	-	-	-	-	102r	Textiles, leather, etc
-	21	32r	-	-	-	-	-	53r	Paper, printing etc
-	2,133r	401r	-	-	-	-	-	2,534r	Other industries
-	293	3	-	-	-	-	-	295	Construction
12	19,543r	50	-	-	-	-	-	50,438r	**Transport**
-	-	-	-	-	-	-	-	10,810	Air
12	746r	-	-	-	-	-	-	758r	Rail
-	17,712	-	-	-	-	-	-	37,735	Road
-	1,085	50	-	-	-	-	-	1,135	National navigation
-	-	-	-	-	-	-	-	-	Pipelines
2,717	947	142r	-	-	-	-	-	4,251r	**Other**
2,693	163	6	-	-	-	-	-	3,204	Domestic
12	283	75r	-	-	-	-	-	370r	Public administration
-	258	43r	-	-	-	-	-	301r	Commercial
12	173	4	-	-	-	-	-	292	Agriculture
-	70	14	-	-	-	-	-	84	Miscellaneous
-	287	-	868	1,959	57	880	449	10,411	**Non energy use (4)**

3.7 Supply and disposal of petroleum[1]

	2001	2002	2003	2004	2005
Primary oils (Crude oil, NGLs and feedstocks)					
Indigenous production *(2)*	116,678	115,944	106,073	95,374	84,721
Imports	53,551	56,968	54,177	62,516	58,886
Exports *(3)*	-86,930	-87,144	-74,898	-64,504	-54,098
Transfers - Transfers to products *(4)*	-3,575	-3,294	-2,661	-3,724	-3,386
Product rebrands (5)	+4,328	+1,739	+1,653	+181	+332
Stock change *(6)*	-614	+143	+469	-133	-385
Use during production *(7)*	-	-	-	-	-
Calculated refinery throughput *(8)*	83,438	84,356	84,814	89,710	86,070
Overall statistical difference *(9)*	+96	-428	+229	-111	-66
Actual refinery throughput	**83,343**	**84,784**	**84,585**	**89,821**	**86,135**
Petroleum products					
Losses in refining process *(10)*	1,233r	788	56	-7r	132
Refinery gross production *(11)*	82,109	83,996	84,529	89,828	86,003
Transfers - Transfers to products *(4)*	+3,575	+3,295	2,661	+3,724	+3,386
Product rebrands *(5)*	-4,328	-1,739	-1,652	-203	-333
Imports	17,234r	14,900r	16,472r	18,545r	22,511
Exports *(12)*	-19,088	-23,444	-23,323	-30,270	-29,722
Marine bunkers	-2,274	-1,913	-1,764	-2,085	-2,055
Stock changes *(6)* - Refineries	-583	+1,238	-233	-232	+1,043
Power generators	-15	-12	-29	-57	+3
Calculated total supply	76,631r	76,321r	76,661r	79,250r	80,837
Statistical difference *(9)*	+217	+86	-492	-34	-140
Total demand *(4)*	**76,413r**	**76,233r**	**77,153r**	**79,284r**	**80,977**
Of which:					
Energy use	67,526r	66,561r	66,742r	68,700r	70,299
Of which, for electricity generation *(13)*	971	671	536r	593r	650
total refinery fuels *(13)*	5,059	5,677	5,456r	5,417r	5,602
Non-energy use	8,887	9,673	10,411	10,584	10,678

(1) Aggregate monthly data on oil production, trade, refinery throughput and inland deliveries are available - see paragraph 3.90 and Annex C.
(2) Crude oil plus condensates and petroleum gases derived at onshore treatment plants.
(3) Includes NGLs, process oils and re-exports.
(4) Disposals of NGLs by direct sale (excluding exports) or for blending.
(5) Product rebrands (inter-product blends or transfers) represent petroleum products received at refineries/ plants as process for refinery or cracking unit operations.
(6) Impact of stock changes on supplies. A stock fall is shown as (+) as it increases supplies, and vice-versa for a stock rise (-).
(7) Own use in onshore terminals and gas separation plants. These figures ceased to be available from January 2001 with the advent of the new PPRS system.
(8) Equivalent to the total supplies reported against the upstream transformation sector in Tables 3.1 to 3.3.
(9) Supply greater than (+) or less than (-) recorded throughput or disposals.
(10) Calculated as the difference between actual refinery throughput and gross refinery production.
(11) Includes refinery fuels.
(12) Excludes NGLs.
(13) Figures cover petroleum used to generate electricity by all major power producers and by all other generators, including petroleum used to generate electricity at refineries. These quantities are also included in the totals reported as used as refinery fuel, so there is thus some overlap in these figures.

3.8 Additional information on inland deliveries of selected products[1][2][3]

Thousand tonnes

	2001	2002	2003	2004	2005
Motor spirit					
Retail deliveries (4)					
Hypermarkets (5)					
Leaded premium / Lead Replacement Petrol (6)	213	138	92	66	22
Super premium unleaded	24	33	39	53	108
Premium unleaded	5,498	5,764	5,803	6,019	6,580
Total hypermarkets	5,735	5,934	5,935	6,138	6,710
Refiners/other traders					
Leaded premium / Lead Replacement Petrol (6)	624	263	91	8	2
Super premium unleaded	396	673	822	757	816
Premium unleaded	13,602	13,404	12,488	11,776	10,374
Total Refiners/other traders	14,622	14,340	13,400	12,541	11,193
Total retail deliveries					
Leaded premium / Lead Replacement Petrol (6)	838	401	183	74	25
Super premium unleaded	420	706	861	810	924
Premium unleaded	19,100	19,167	18,291	17,795	16,954
Total retail deliveries	20,358	20,274	19,335	18,679	17,903
Commercial consumers (7)					
Leaded premium / Lead Replacement Petrol (6)	34	19	19	14	1
Super premium unleaded	9	17	22	26	16
Premium unleaded	538	499	542	765	811
Total commercial consumers	581	535	583	805	828
Total motor spirit	**20,939**	**20,809**	**19,918**	**19,484**	**18,731**
Unleaded as % of Total motor spirit	95.8	98.0	99.0	99.5	99.9
Gas oil/diesel oil					
DERV fuel:					
Retail deliveries (4):					
Hypermarkets (5)	1,633	1,854	2,135	2,474	3,091
Refiners/other traders	6,214	6,300	6,922	7,043	7,588
Total retail deliveries	7,846	8,153	9,057	9,517	10,679
Commercial consumers (7)	8,213	8,774	8,655	8,997	8,757
Total DERV fuel	16,059	16,927	17,712	18,514	19,436
Other gas oil (8)	6,959r	6,099	6,325r	6,022	6,797
Total gas oil/diesel oil	**23,018r**	**23,026**	**24,037r**	**24,536**	**26,233**
Fuel oils (9)					
Light	55	84	169	214	124
Medium	609r	636r	582r	961r	881
Heavy	1,914r	1,001r	788r	888r	960
Total fuel oils	**2,578r**	**1,721r**	**1,539r**	**2,062r**	**1,965**

(1) Aggregate monthly data for inland deliveries of oil products are available - see paragraph 3.90 and Annex C.
(2) The end use section analyses are based partly on recorded figures and on estimates. They are intended for general guidance only. See also the notes in the main text of this chapter.
(3) For a full breakdown of the end-uses of all oil products, see Commodity Balances in Tables 3.4 to 3.6.
(4) Retail deliveries - deliveries to garages, etc. mainly for resale to final consumers.
(5) Data for sales by super and hypermarket companies are collected via a separate reporting system, but are consistent with the main data collected from UKPIA member companies - see paragraph 3.70
(6) Sales of Leaded Petrol ceased on 31 December 1999.
(7) Commercial consumers - direct deliveries for use in consumer's business.
(8) Includes marine diesel oil.
(9) Inland deliveries excluding that used as a fuel in refineries, but including that used for electricity generation by major electricity producers and other industries.

3.9 Inland deliveries by country[(1)]

Thousand tonnes

	England and Wales [(2)]			Scotland			Northern Ireland		
	2003	2004	2005	2003	2004	2005	2003	2004	2005
Energy use									
Gases for gasworks & other uses									
Butane and propane	1,186	1,090	1,072	80	97	96	23	30	36
Other gases	151r	100r	124	153r	157r	130	-	-	-
Aviation spirit	41	35	44	3	12	7	1	2	1
Motor spirit:									
Dealers	17,962	17,352	16,617	1,026	980	950	347	348	336
Commercial consumers	518	738	773	40	42	39	25	25	16
Total motor spirit	18,480	18,090	17,391	1,066	1,022	989	372	373	351
Kerosenes									
Aviation turbine fuel	10,102	11,091	11,832	592	691	596	71	79	70
Burning oil	2,352	2,698	2,843	298	247	195	918	1,004	832
Gas oil/diesel oil									
DERV fuel	16,310	17,064	17,932	1,110	1,094	1,134	292	356	371
Other (3)	4,872	4,727	5,399	693	620	791	474	427	378
Fuel oils	1,316r	1,666r	1,788	134r	300r	122	88r	97r	54
Total products used as energy (4)	**54,915r**	**56,672r**	**58,481**	**4,129r**	**4,241r**	**4,119**	**2,241r**	**2,369r**	**2,097**
Non-energy use									
Feedstock for petroleum chemical plants	4,829	4,402	4,906	2,552	2,945	2,760	-	-	-
Industrial/white spirit	147	281	284	-	-	-	-	-	-
Lubricating oils	835	878	730	29	32	17	4	5	3
Bitumen	1,634	1,684	1,627	217	199	178	108	107	101
Petroleum wax	57	50	72	-	-	-	-	-	-
Total products used as non-energy (5)	**7,501**	**7,296**	**7,620**	**2,798**	**3,176**	**2,955**	**111**	**112**	**104**
Total all products	**61,496r**	**62,962r**	**66,100**	**6,928r**	**7,417r**	**7,074**	**2,352r**	**2,480r**	**2,202**

(1) Excludes products used as a fuel within refineries that are included in Tables 3.4 to 3.6.
(2) Includes the Channel Islands and the Isle of Man.
(3) Includes deliveries of marine diesel oil.
(4) Includes deliveries of LPG road transport fuel.
(5) Includes deliveries of miscellaneous products and petroleum coke.

3.10 Stocks of crude oil and petroleum products at end of year[1]

					Thousand tonnes
	2001	2002	2003	2004	2005
Crude and process oils					
Refineries *(2)*	4,183	4,508	4,670	4,440	4,875
Terminals *(3)*	2,526	2,126	1,509	1,261	1,129
Offshore *(4)*	828	760	741	736	798
Total crude and process oils *(5)*	7,637	7,504	7,140	6,648	7,067
Petroleum products					
Ethane	6	6	6	6	6
Propane	188	108	103	119	111
Butane	105	117	95	113	100
Other petroleum gases	-	2	2	1	-
Naphtha	424	404	478	575	511
Aviation spirit	4	2	3	2	4
Motor spirit	1,375	1,280	1,487	1,503	1,047
White spirit & SBP	35	33	29	29	44
Aviation turbine fuel	779	510	610	759	663
Burning oil	292	300	265	310	292
Gas/Diesel oil *(6)*	2,232	2,363	2,765	2,721	2,956
Fuel oils	1,180	1,196	1,237	987	1,057
Lubricating oils	202	214	166	182	109
Bitumen	215	192	212	205	204
Petroleum wax	9	15	12	12	33
Petroleum coke	318	302	285	254	280
Miscellaneous products	1,097	670	778	197	151
Total all products	8,461	7,712	8,533	7,975	7,567
Of which : net bilateral stocks *(7)*	514	1,008	1,500	1,545	1,587

(1) Aggregate monthly data on the level of stocks of crude oil and oil products are available - see paragraph 3.90 and Annex C.
(2) Stocks of crude oil, NGLs and process oils at UK refineries.
(3) Stocks of crude oil and NGLs at UKCS pipeline terminals.
(4) Stocks of crude oil in tanks and partially loaded tankers at offshore fields.
(5) Includes process oils held abroad for UK use approved by bilateral agreements.
(6) Includes middle distillate feedstock and marine diesel oil.
(7) The difference between stocks held abroad for UK use under approved bilateral agreements and the equivalent stocks held in the UK for foreign use.

Chapter 4
Natural gas

Introduction

4.1   This chapter presents figures on the production, transmission and consumption of natural gas and colliery methane. Three tables are presented and a map showing the gas transmission system in Great Britain is included (page 107). The commodity balances for natural gas and colliery methane form the first table (Table 4.1). This is followed by a 5 year table showing the supply, transmission and consumption of these gases as a time series (Table 4.2). A more detailed examination of the various stages of natural gas from gross production through to consumption is given in Table 4.3. Long term trends commentary and table on production and consumption of gas back to 1970 is to be found on the DTI Energy Statistics web site at:

http://www.dti.gov.uk/energy/statistics/publications/dukes/page29812.html

4.2   Petroleum gases are covered in Chapter 3. Gases manufactured in the coke making and iron and steel making processes (coke oven gas and blast furnace gas) appear in Chapter 2. Biogases (landfill gas and sewage gas) are part of Chapter 7. Details of net selling values of gas for the domestic sector are to be found in Chapter 1.

The gas supply industry Great Britain

4.3   When British Gas was privatised in 1986, it was given a statutory monopoly over supplies of natural gas (methane) to premises taking less than 732,000 kWh (25,000 therms) a year. Under the Oil and Gas (Enterprise) Act 1982, contract customers taking more than this were able to buy their gas from other suppliers but no other suppliers entered the market until 1990.

4.4   In 1991, the Office of Fair Trading (OFT) followed up an examination of the contract market by the Monopolies and Mergers Commission (MMC) that had taken place in 1988. It reviewed progress towards a competitive market and found that the steps taken in 1988 had been ineffective in encouraging self-sustaining competition. British Gas undertook in March 1992 to allow competitors to take by 1995 at least 60 per cent of the contract market above 732,000 kWh (25,000 therms) a year (subsequently redefined as 45 per cent of the market above 73,200 kWh (2,500 therms)); to release to competitors the gas necessary to achieve this; and to establish a separate transport and storage unit with regulated charges. At the same time, the Government took powers in the 1992 Competition and Service (Utilities) Act to reduce or remove the tariff monopoly, and in July 1992 it lowered the tariff threshold to 73,200 kWh.

4.5   Difficulties in implementing the March 1992 undertakings led to further references to the MMC. As a result of the new recommendations made by the MMC in 1993, the President of the Board of Trade decided in December 1993 to require full internal separation of British Gas's supply and transportation activities, but not divestment, and to accelerate removal of the tariff monopoly to April 1996, with a phased opening of the domestic market by the regulator over the following two years.

4.6   In November 1995 the Gas Bill received Royal Assent, clearing the way for the extension of competition into the domestic gas supply market on a phased basis between 1996 and 1998. This was carried out in stages between April 1996 and May 1998. By December 2005, nearly 9.3 million gas consumers (44 per cent) were no longer supplied by British Gas. Table 4A gives market penetration in more detail, by local distribution zone (LDZ). For all types of domestic customer it is in the markets in Northern England and Wales that new suppliers have had most success. At the end of Q4 2005, British Gas had lost around 39 per cent of the credit and 51 per cent of the direct debit market compared to 33 per cent of the pre-payment market. It should be noted that historically British Gas's pre-payment prices have tended to be below the average of new suppliers; however in 2004 and 2005 average new suppliers pre-payment prices were below that of British Gas. At the end of 2005, 43 suppliers were licensed to supply gas to domestic customers.

Table 4A: Domestic gas market penetration (in terms of percentage of customers supplied) by local distribution zone and payment type, fourth quarter of 2005

Region	British Gas Trading			Non-British Gas		
	Credit	Direct Debit	Prepayment	Credit	Direct Debit	Prepayment
Wales	49	48	45	51	52	55
Northern	54	40	54	46	60	46
Scotland	58	47	80	42	53	20
North West	61	52	78	39	48	22
East Midlands	61	48	67	39	52	33
Eastern	61	49	68	39	51	32
South East	61	48	67	39	52	33
Southern	61	42	64	39	58	36
North East	62	51	66	38	49	34
North Thames	65	61	73	35	39	27
South Western	65	50	64	35	50	36
West Midlands	70	55	74	30	45	26
Great Britain	61	49	67	39	51	33

4.7   Following the 1995 Act, the business of British Gas was fully separated into two corporate entities. The supply and shipping businesses were devolved to a subsidiary, British Gas Trading Limited, while the transportation business (Transco) remained within British Gas plc. In February 1997, Centrica plc was demerged from British Gas plc (which was itself renamed as BG plc) completing the division of the business into two independent entities. Centrica became the holding company for British Gas Trading, British Gas Services, the Retail Energy Centres and the company producing gas from the North and South Morecambe fields. BG plc comprised the gas transportation and storage business of Transco, along with British Gas's other exploration and production, international downstream, research and technology and property activities. In October 2000 BG plc demerged into two separately listed companies, of which Lattice Group plc was the holding company for Transco, while BG Group plc included the international and gas storage businesses. On 21 October 2002 Transco and the National Grid Company merged to form National Grid.

4.8   From 1 October 2001, under the Utilities Act, gas pipeline companies have been able to apply for their own national Gas Transporter Licences so that they can compete with Transco. In some areas low pressure spur networks had already been developed by new transporters competing with Transco to bring gas supplies to new customers (mainly domestic). In addition, some very large loads (above 60 GWh) are serviced by pipelines operated independently, some by North Sea producers.

4.9   By the end of 1994, competitors had exceeded the target 45 per cent of the market above 73,200 kWh (2,500 therms) but virtually all of this was in the firm gas market. From 1995 British Gas's competitors made inroads into the interruptible market but in 2005 Centrica's share of the industrial and commercial market declined slightly to 10 per cent. At the end of 2005, there were about 40 suppliers active in the UK gas market, but some companies own or part own more than one supplier. The structure of the gas industry in Great Britain as it stood at the end of 2005 is shown in Chart 4.1.

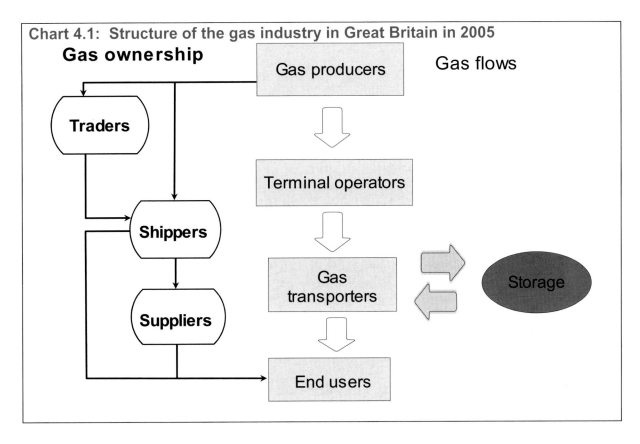

Chart 4.1: Structure of the gas industry in Great Britain in 2005

Regional analysis

4.10   Table 4B gives the number of consumers with a gas demand below 73,200 kWh per year in 2004 and the total number of gas consumers. It covers customers receiving gas from the national transmission system. The below 73,200 kWh category covers both domestic and small business customers and it was this section of the market that was progressively opened up to competition between April 1996 and May 1998. In previous years the regions shown in the table were Transco's 13 local distribution zones (LDZs), but data are now available for Government Office Regions and so this information has been substituted. Note that the data are for 2004.

Table 4B: Consumption by gas customers by region in 2004

| Government Office Region | Consumption by customers below 73,200 kWh (2,500 therms) annual demand | | Consumption by all customers | |
	Number of consumers (thousands)	Gas sales 2004 (GWh)	Number of consumers (thousands)	Gas sales 2004 (GWh)
Wales	1001	20,735	1,017	43,092
Scotland	1,679	35,194	1,714	63,251
North East	994	21,073	1,011	34,987
North West	2,656	55,314	2,708	96,393
Yorkshire and the Humber	1,928	39,582	1,968	75,269
East Midlands	1,538	31,845	1,568	54,213
West Midlands	1,922	39,715	1,961	69,028
East of England	1,785	37,021	1,820	60,206
Greater London	2,871	57,080	2,939	91,635
South East	2,850	59,401	2,915	93,103
South West	1,568	29,180	1,598	47,149
Great Britain	20,791	426,140	21,219	728,326

Source: National Grid

4.11   In December 2005, DTI published in Energy Trends and on the DTI web site (http://www.dti.gov.uk/energy/statistics/regional/index.html) gas consumption data at both regional and local level. The local level data are at "NUTS4" level (see article in December 2005 Energy Trends for definition) and the regional data at "NUTS1" level. Data for 2001, 2002, 2003 and 2004 are presented on the web site but only 2004 data appear in the article. Domestic sector sales were shown separately from commercial and industrial sales. Numbers of consumers were also given. The 2001, 2002 and 2003 data on the web site replaced figures for those years that had been published in December 2004. It is planned to update the analysis to cover 2005 and release these figures in January 2007.

Northern Ireland

4.12   Before 1997, Northern Ireland did not have a public natural gas supply. The construction of a natural gas pipeline from Portpatrick in Scotland to Northern Ireland was completed in 1996 and provided the means of establishing such a system. The primary market is Ballylumford power station, which was purchased by British Gas in 1992 and converted from oil to gas firing (with a heavy fuel oil back up). The onshore line has been extended to serve wider industrial, commercial and domestic markets and this extension is continuing. In 2005, 81 per cent of all gas supplies in Northern Ireland were used to generate electricity.

Competition

4.13   Paragraphs 4.3 to 4.12 above referred to the developments in recent years in opening up the non-domestic market to competition. About three-quarters of this market (by volume) in the United Kingdom was opened to competition at the end of 1982 and the remainder in August 1992 (with the reduction in the tariff threshold). As mentioned above, however, no other suppliers entered the market until 1990. After 1990 there was a rapid increase in the number of independent companies supplying gas, although from 1999 there were signs of some consolidation and in recent years sales of gas have become more concentrated in the hands of the largest companies in the domestic, industrial and commercial sectors. This came about through larger companies absorbing smaller suppliers and through mergers between already significant suppliers. However, in 2005 competition appears to have increased among suppliers and has coincided with rising gas prices. The three largest suppliers now jointly account for 76 per cent of sales to domestic customers, whereas in 2004 the proportion was 79 per cent. For the industrial sector the share of the largest three suppliers fell from 63 per cent in 2004 to 52½ per cent in 2005. For commercial sector sales, in 2005 the three largest suppliers accounted for 64 per cent of sales, down from 69 per cent in 2004.

Commodity balances for gas (Table 4.1)

4.14   In 2004 the UK became a net importer of gas for the first time since 1996 with imports of natural gas 18.9 TWh higher than exports. In 2005 these net imports had increase to 77.1 TWh and accounted for 7 per cent of total natural gas supply. Imports and exports of natural gas are described in greater detail below in paragraph 4.19.

4.15   Although demand for natural gas is traditionally less than supply because of the various measurement differences described in paragraphs 4.44 to 4.47, in 2005 they broadly balanced each other, the difference being only 0.1 per cent.

4.16   In 2005, 30½ per cent of natural gas demand was for electricity generation (transformation sector), ½ per cent more than in 2004. A further 7½ per cent was consumed for heating purposes within the energy industries. 1 per cent was accounted for by distribution losses within the gas network. (For an explanation of the items included under losses, see paragraphs 4.44 to 4.47.) Of the remaining 61 per cent, 2 per cent was transformed into heat for sale to a third party, 13½ per cent was accounted for by the industrial sector with the chemicals industry (excluding natural gas for petrochemical feedstocks), food and paper making industries being the largest consumers. The chemicals sector accounted for over a quarter of the industrial consumption of natural gas.

4.17   Sales of gas to households (domestic sector) produced 35 per cent of gas demand, while public administration (including schools and hospitals) consumed 4½ per cent of total demand, which was more than was sold to the chemicals sector. The commercial, agriculture and miscellaneous sectors together took up 5 per cent. Non-energy use of gas accounted for the remaining 1 per cent. As Table 4C below shows, non-energy use of gas is small (and decreasing in proportion terms) relative to total use (see the technical notes section, paragraph 4.37, for more details on non-energy use of gas).

Table 4C: Non-energy use: share of natural gas demand

	Continental shelf and onshore natural gas
2001	1.0%
2002	1.0%
2003	0.9%
2004	0.9%
2005	0.9%

4.18   Care should be exercised in interpreting the figures for individual industries in these commodity balance tables. As companies switch contracts between gas suppliers, it has not been possible to ensure consistent classification between and within industry sectors and across years. The breakdown of final consumption includes a substantial amount of estimated data. For about 7 per cent of consumption the allocation to consuming sector is estimated.

4.19   Imports of natural gas from the Norwegian sector of the North Sea began to decline in the late 1980s as output from the Frigg field tailed off. Frigg finally ceased production in October 2004. The interconnector linking the UK's transmission network with Belgium via a Bacton to Zeebrugge pipeline began to operate in October 1998. Since 1998 there was an increase in imports brought about by inflows through the Bacton to Zeebrugge interconnector and by November 2005 its imports capacity had almost doubled from 8.5 bcm/y to 16.5 bcm/y. In July 2005 imports of liquefied natural gas (LNG) commenced at the Isle of Grain import/storage facility, the first time LNG had been imported to the UK since the early 1980's. Exports to mainland Europe from the United Kingdom's share of the Markham field began in 1992 with Windermere's output being added in 1997. Exports to the Republic of Ireland started in 1995. Exports of natural gas exceeded imports for the first time in 1997 and grew rapidly to peak in 2003 before falling by 35½ per cent in 2004 to a lower level than imports. In 2005 exports of natural gas were 45½ per cent lower than the 2003 peak.

4.20   Chart 4.2 shows the increase in indigenous production and consumption of natural gas over the past five years and relative size of net exports.

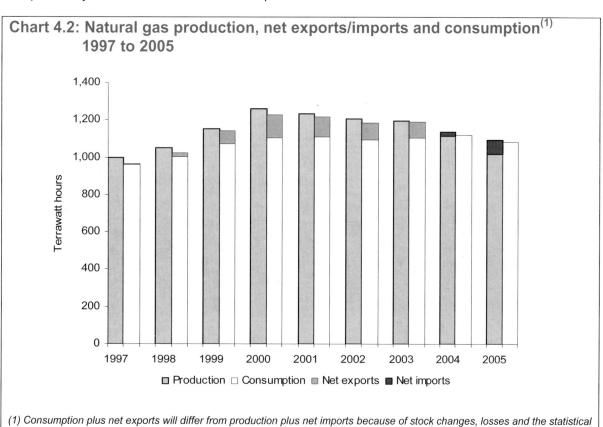

Chart 4.2: Natural gas production, net exports/imports and consumption[1] 1997 to 2005

(1) Consumption plus net exports will differ from production plus net imports because of stock changes, losses and the statistical difference item.

Supply and consumption of natural gas and colliery methane (Table 4.2)

4.21   This table summarises the production and consumption of gas from these sources in the United Kingdom over the last 5 years.

4.22   As Chart 4.3 shows, the growth in consumption for electricity generation has dominated the growth in natural gas consumption over the last 10 years. Most of this gas was used in Combined Cycle Gas Turbine (CCGT) stations, although the use of gas in dual fired conventional steam stations was a growth area in 1997 and 1998. However, gas use for electricity generation fell by 4½ per cent in 2001 as higher gas prices made it more difficult for gas fired stations to compete with large coal fired stations. This was reversed by a 5½ per cent growth in 2002 when gas prices eased but fell again in 2003 by 1½ per cent. Higher gas prices again meant that at times some generators found it more profitable to sell gas than use it for generation, particularly given plentiful supplies of inexpensive coal. In 2004 gas use for generation rose by 5 per cent as newly built power stations came on stream. Gas use then fell by 2 per cent in 2005 as prices paid by generators rose substantially in the second half of the year. In 2005 the transformation sector as a whole accounted for over 32½ per cent of gas demand – half a percentage point higher than in 2004.

4.23   Since 2000, industrial use of gas has been on a downward trend apart from a small recovery in 2003. In 2005, the decline continued across all major industrial sectors, except in electrical engineering, which showed a 5 per cent rise. Overall industrial demand fell by 4 per cent in 2005. At the same time there was a 4 per cent increase in gas used for heat that was then sold to other companies and such sales were particularly marked in the paper and printing sector. If heat use and total industrial use are combined then the decrease in gas use in 2005 is 3 per cent. Use by the public administration sector and the commercial sector were 3 and 7 per cent lower, respectively, in 2005 than in 2004. Consumption in the energy industries other than electricity (and heat) generation fell by 4 per cent.

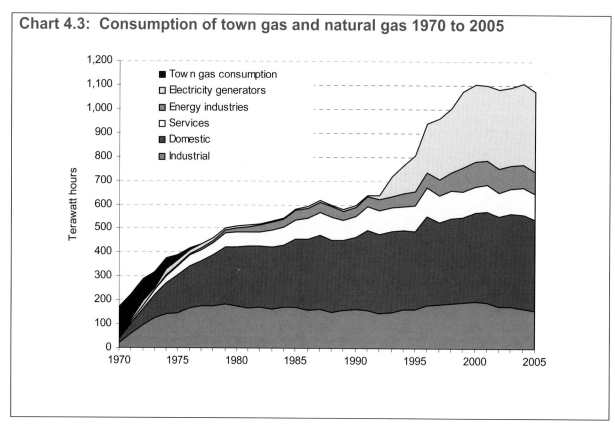

Chart 4.3: Consumption of town gas and natural gas 1970 to 2005

4.24   Gas use in the domestic sector is particularly dependent on winter temperatures and in 2005 the average temperature over the winter months was marginally higher than in 2004 but February 2005 was colder than average, as was November and December 2005. However, rising gas prices during 2005, particularly in the second half of the year, had an impact on demand, reducing domestic sector consumption by 3½ per cent in 2005.

4.25   Maximum daily demand for natural gas through the National Transmission System in winter 2005/06 was 4,286 GWh on 30th January 2006. On that day natural gas demand in Northern Ireland was 62 GWh. This total maximum daily demand was 14 per cent lower than January 2003's record level.

4.26   It is estimated that sales of gas supplied on an interruptible basis accounted for around 20 per cent of total gas sales in 2005; roughly the same as in 2004.

UK continental shelf and onshore natural gas (Table 4.3)

4.27   Table 4.3 shows the flows for natural gas from production through transmission to consumption. The footnotes to the table give more information about each table row. This table departs from the standard balance methodology and definitions in order to maintain the link with past data and with monthly data given in DTI's energy statistics web site (see paragraph 4.43). The relationship between total UK gas consumption shown in this table and total demand for gas given in the balance tables (4.1 and 4.2) is illustrated for 2005 as follows:

		GWh
Total UK consumption (Table 4.3)		1,004,697
plus Producers' own use		73,652
plus Operators' own use		6,555
equals		
"Consumption of natural gas" (see paragraph 4.34)		1,084,904
plus Other losses and metering differences (upstream)		-
plus Downstream losses - leakage assessment	5,260)	7,809
- own use gas	425)	
- theft	2,124)	
plus Metering differences (transmission)		2,880
equals		
Total demand for natural gas (Tables 4.1 and 4.2)		1,095,593

4.28   Gross production of natural gas rose steadily since indigenous production began in 1967 and peaked in 2000 at 1.26 TWh, but has since fallen steadily as reserves on the UKCS deplete. In 2005 natural gas production was 19 per cent lower than the 2000 peak. Gas available at UK terminals has remained fairly constant over this period mainly due to the changes in exports and imports described in paragraph 4.19. Producers' and operators' own use of gas have tended to change in proportion to the volumes of gas produced and transmitted. Gas input into the transmission system fell by 3.4 per cent between 2004 and 2005 while output of natural gas fell 2.9 per cent. Output from the transmission system fell by less than the input because of stock draw and metering differences.

4.29   For a discussion of the various losses and statistical differences terms in this table, see paragraphs 4.44 to 4.47 in the technical notes and definitions section below. The statistical difference between output from the National Transmission System and total UK consumption has been disaggregated using information obtained from Transco on leakage from local distribution zone pipes, theft and use regarded as own use by pipeline operators. The convention used is set out in paragraph 4.47.

4.30   Losses and metering differences attributable to the information provided on the upstream gas industry are zero from 2001 onwards because these data are no longer reported in the revised Petroleum Production Reporting System. This simplified system for reporting the production of crude oil, NGLs and natural gas in the UK was implemented from 1st January 2001; it reduced the burden on the respondents and improved the quality of data reported on gas production.

4.31   Table 4.3 now includes two rows showing gas stocks and gas storage capacity at the end of the year. Storage data are not currently available before 2004. The 2005 stocks and storage data have been sourced from National Grid's weekly brief and 2005 Ten Year Statement.

Technical notes and definitions

4.32   These notes and definitions are in addition to the technical notes and definitions covering all fuels and energy as a whole in Chapter 1, paragraphs 1.24 to 1.57. For notes on the commodity balances and definitions of the terms used in the row headings see Annex A, paragraphs A.7 to A.42. While the data in the printed and bound copy of this Digest cover only the most recent 5 years, these notes also cover data for earlier years that are available on the DTI web site.

Definitions used for production and consumption

4.33   **Natural gas** production in Tables 4.1 and 4.2 relates to the output of indigenous methane at land terminals and gas separation plants (includes producers' and processors' own use). For further explanation, see Annex F, paragraph F.19 on DTI's Energy Statistics web site under 'Production of oil and gas' - http://www.dti.gov.uk/energy/statistics/publications/dukes/page29812.html.   Output of the Norwegian share of the Frigg and Murchison fields is included under imports. A small quantity of onshore produced methane (other than colliery methane) is also included.

4.34   Table 4.3 shows production, transmission and consumption figures for UK continental shelf and onshore natural gas. Production includes waste and own use for drilling, production and pumping operations, but excludes gas flared. Gas available in the United Kingdom excludes waste, own use for drilling etc, stock change, and includes imports net of exports. Gas transmitted (input into inland transmission systems) is after stock change, own use, and losses at inland terminals. The amount consumed in the United Kingdom differs from the total gas transmitted by the gas supply industry, because of losses in transmission, differences in temperature and pressure between the points at which the gas is measured, delays in reading meters and consumption in the works, offices, shops, etc of the undertakings. The figures include an adjustment to the quantities billed to consumers to allow for the estimated consumption remaining unread at the end of the year.

4.35   **Colliery methane** production is colliery methane piped to the surface and consumed at collieries or transmitted by pipeline to consumers. As the output of deep-mined coal declines so does the production of colliery methane, unless a use can be found for gas that was previously vented. The supply of methane from coal measures that are no longer being worked or from drilling into coal measures is licensed under the same legislation as used for offshore gas production.

4.36   **Transfers** of natural gas include natural gas use within the iron and steel industry for mixing with blast furnace gas to form a synthetic coke oven gas. For further details see paragraph 2.48 in Chapter 2.

4.37   **Non-energy gas**: Non-energy use is gas used as feedstock for petrochemical plants in the chemical industry as raw material for the production of ammonia (an essential intermediate chemical in the production of nitrogen fertilisers) and methanol. The contribution of liquefied petroleum gases (propane and butane) and other petroleum gases is shown in Tables 3.4 to 3.6 of Chapter 3. Firm data for natural gas are not available, but estimates for 2001 to 2005 are shown in Table 4.2 and estimates for 2003 to 2005 in Table 4.1 Estimates for the years up to 2004 have been obtained from the National Atmospheric Emissions Inventory (NAEI); 2005 data are DTI extrapolations.

Sectors used for sales/consumption

4.38   For definitions of the various sectors used for sales and consumption analyses see Chapter 1 paragraphs 1.52 to 1.56 and Annex A, paragraphs A.31 to A.42. However, **miscellaneous** has a wider coverage than in the commodity balances of other fuels. This is because some gas supply companies are unable to provide a full breakdown of the services sector and the gas they supply to consumers is allocated to miscellaneous when there is no reliable basis for allocating it elsewhere. See also paragraph 4.41, below, for information on the source of the sectoral data for consumption of gas.

Data collection

4.39   Production figures are generally obtained from returns made under the Department of Trade and Industry's Petroleum Production Reporting System (PPRS) and from other sources. DTI obtain data on the transmission of natural gas from National Grid (who operate the National Transmission System) and from other pipeline operators. Data on consumption are based on returns from gas suppliers and UKCS producers who supply gas directly to customers.

4.40   The production data are for the United Kingdom (including natural gas from the UKCS - offshore and onshore). The restoration of a public gas supply to parts of Northern Ireland in 1997 (see paragraph 4.12 means that all tables in this chapter (except Tables 4A and 4B) cover the UK.

4.41   DTI carry out an annual survey of gas suppliers to obtain details of gas sales to the various categories of consumer. Estimates are included for the suppliers with the smallest market share since the DTI inquiry covers only the largest suppliers (ie those with more than about a ½ per cent share of the UK market up to 1997 and those known to supply more than 1,750 GWh per year for 1998 onwards). For 2000 and subsequent years, gas consumption for the iron and steel sector is based on data provided by the Iron and Steel Statistics Bureau (ISSB) rather than gas suppliers since gas suppliers were over estimating their sales to this sector. The difference between the ISSB and gas suppliers figures has been re-allocated to other sectors using the results of the Office for National Statistics' Purchases Inquiry.

Period covered
4.42   Figures generally relate to years ended 31 December. However, before 2004 data for natural gas for electricity generation relate to periods of 52 weeks as set out in Chapter 5, paragraphs 5.58 and 5.59.

Monthly and quarterly data
4.43   Monthly data on natural gas production and supply are available from the DTI's Energy Statistics web site http://www.dti.gov.uk/energy/statistics/source/gas/page18525.html in monthly Table 4.2. A quarterly commodity balance for natural gas (which includes consumption data) is published in DTI's quarterly statistical bulletin *Energy Trends* and is also available from quarterly Table 4.1 at DTI's Energy Statistics web site. See Annex C for more information about *Energy Trends* and the DTI Energy Statistics web site.

Statistical and metering differences
4.44   In Table 4.3 there are several headings that refer to statistical or metering differences. These arise because measurement of gas flows, in volume and energy terms, takes place at several points along the supply chain. The main sub-headings in the table represent the instances in the supply chain where accurate reports are made of the gas flows at that particular key point in the supply process. It is possible to derive alternative estimates of the flow of gas at any particular point by taking the estimate for the previous point in the supply chain and then applying the known losses and gains in the subsequent part of the supply chain. The differences seen when the actual reported flow of gas at any point and the derived estimate are compared are separately identified in the table wherever possible, under the headings statistical or metering differences.

4.45   The differences arise from several factors:-

- Limitations in the accuracy of meters used at various points of the supply chain. While standards are in place on the accuracy of meters, there is a degree of error allowed which, when large flows of gas are being recorded, can become significant.

- Differences in the methods used to calculate the flow of gas in energy terms. For example, at the production end, rougher estimates of the calorific value of the gas produced are used which may be revised only periodically, rather than the more accurate and more frequent analyses carried out further down the supply chain. At the supply end, although the calorific value of gas shows day-to-day variations, for the purposes of recording the gas supplied to customers a single calorific value is used. Until 1997 this was the lowest of the range of calorific values for the actual gas being supplied within each LDZ, resulting in a "loss" of gas in energy terms. In 1997 there was a change to a "capped flow-weighted average" algorithm for calculating calorific values resulting in a reduction in the losses shown in the penultimate row of Table 4.3. This change in algorithm, along with improved meter validation and auditing procedures, also reduced the level of the "metering differences" row within the downstream part of Table 4.3.

- Differences in temperature and pressure between the various points at which gas is measured. Until February 1997 British Gas used "uncorrected therms" on their billing system for tariff customers when converting from a volume measure of the gas used to an energy measure. This made their supply figure too small by a factor of 2.2 per cent, equivalent to about 1 per cent of the wholesale market.

- Differences in the timing of reading meters. While National Transmission System meters are read daily, customers' meters are read less frequently (perhaps only annually for some domestic customers) and profiling is used to estimate consumption. Profiling will tend to underestimate consumption in a strongly rising market.

- Other losses from the system, for example, theft through meter tampering by consumers.

4.46   The headings in Table 4.3 show where, in the various stages of the supply process, it has been possible to identify these metering differences as having an effect. Usually they are aggregated with other net losses as the two factors cannot be separated. Whilst the factors listed above can give rise to either losses or gains, losses are more common. However, the negative downstream gas metering difference within the transmission system in 2003 was an anomaly that was investigated by National Grid during 2004. They concluded that this unaccounted for element of National Transmission System shrinkage was due to an exceptional run of monthly negative figures between February and June 2003 within what is usually a variable but mainly positive series. However, after a comprehensive investigation of this exceptional period no causal factors were identified. It is probable that the meter error or errors that caused this issue were corrected during the validation of metering. The investigation has enabled the size of the negative metering difference in 2003 to be reduced compared with that reported here in 2004.

4.47   The box below shows how in 2005 the wastage, losses and metering differences figures in Table 4.3 are related to the losses row in the balance Tables 4.1 and 4.2. It should be noted that losses from 2001 onwards are lower than in earlier years because figures for losses and metering differences in the upstream gas industry are no longer available (see above):

Table 4.3	GWh
Upstream gas industry:	
Other losses and metering differences	-
Downstream gas industry:	
Transmission system metering differences	2,880
Leakage assessment	5,260
Own use gas	425
Theft	2,124
Tables 4.1 and 4.2	
Losses	10,689

Similarly the statistical difference row in Tables 4.1 and 4.2 is made up of the following components in 2005:

Table 4.3	GWh
Statistical difference between gas available from upstream and gas input to downstream	-2,164
plus Downstream gas industry:	
Distribution losses and metering differences	2,801
Tables 4.1 and 4.2	
Statistical difference	637

Contact: Sally Mercer   Jim Logan
        Downstream Gas   Upstream Gas
        Energy Strategy Unit   Energy Strategy Unit
        sally.mercer@dti.gsi.gov.uk   jim.logan@dti.gsi.gov.uk
        020 7215 2717   020 7215 2711

The National Gas Transmission System 2005

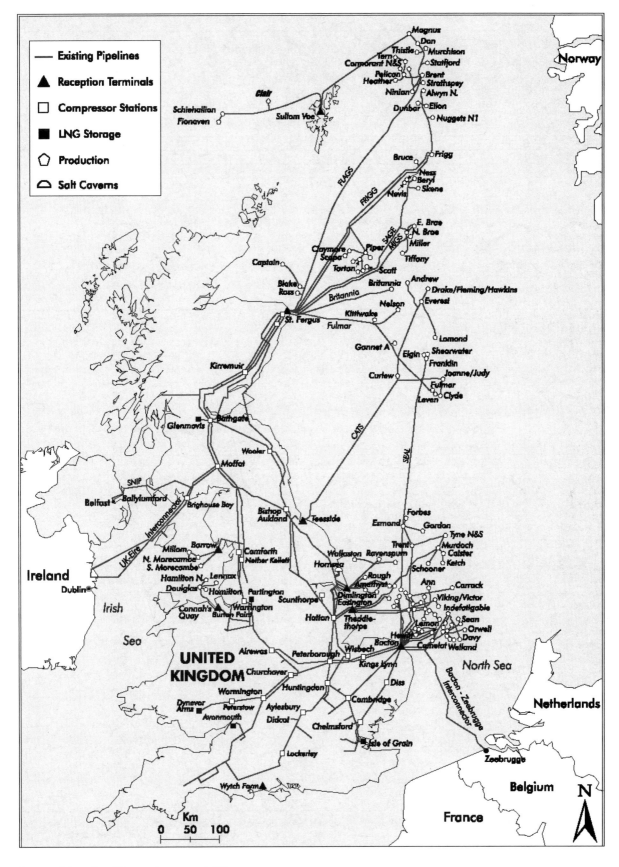

Source: International Energy Agency and DTI

4.1 Commodity balances

Natural gas

	2003			2004			2005		
	Natural gas	Colliery methane	Total Natural gas	Natural gas	Colliery methane	Total Natural gas	Natural gas	Colliery methane	Total Natural gas
Supply									
Production	1,196,115	915	1,197,030	1,115,744	810	1,116,554	1,017,813	757	1,018,570
Other sources	-	-	-	-	-	-	-	-	-
Imports	86,298	-	86,298	133,035	-	133,035	173,328	-	173,328
Exports	-177,039	-	-177,039	-114,111	-	-114,111	-96,181	-	-96,181
Marine bunkers	-	-	-	-	-	-	-	-	-
Stock change (1)	+3,532	-	+3,532	-6,235	-	-6,235	+1,321	-	+1,321
Transfers (2)	-82	-	-82	-39	-	-39	-51	-	-51
Total supply	**1,108,824**	**915**	**1,109,739**	**1,128,395r**	**810**	**1,129,205r**	**1,096,231**	**757**	**1,096,988**
Statistical difference (3)	+748r	-	+748r	+806r	-	+806r	+637	-	+637
Total demand	**1,108,076r**	**915**	**1,108,991r**	**1,127,588r**	**810**	**1,128,398r**	**1,095,594**	**757**	**1,096,351**
Transformation	**343,757r**	**653**	**344,410r**	**360,403r**	**595**	**360,998r**	**353,917**	**588**	**354,505**
Electricity generation	323,927r	653	324,580r	340,516r	595	341,111r	333,246	588	333,834
Major power producers	284,662	-	284,662	304,495	-	304,495	295,643	-	295,643
Autogenerators	39,265r	653	39,918r	36,022r	595	36,617r	37,603	588	38,191
Heat generation (4)	19,830		19,830	19,886r		19,886r	20,671		20,671
Petroleum refineries	-	-	-	-	-	-	-	-	-
Coke manufacture	-	-	-	-	-	-	-	-	-
Blast furnaces	-	-	-	-	-	-	-	-	-
Patent fuel manufacture	-	-	-	-	-	-	-	-	-
Other	-	-	-	-	-	-	-	-	-
Energy industry use	**88,720**	**187**	**88,907**	**86,906r**	**150**	**87,056r**	**84,051**	**114**	**84,165**
Electricity generation	-	-	-	-	-	-	-	-	-
Oil and gas extraction	76,837	-	76,837	76,899	-	76,899	73,652	-	73,652
Petroleum refineries	2,773	-	2,773	1,797r	-	1,797r	1,987	-	1,987
Coal extraction	-	187	187	-	150	150	-	114	114
Coke manufacture	1	-	1	-	-	-	-	-	-
Blast furnaces	539	-	539	728	-	728	941	-	941
Patent fuel manufacture	-	-	-	-	-	-	-	-	-
Pumped storage	-	-	-	-	-	-	-	-	-
Other	8,570	-	8,570	7,482	-	7,482	7,472	-	7,472
Losses (5)	**6,217r**	-	**6,217r**	**8,174**	-	**8,174**	**10,690**	-	**10,690**
Final consumption	**669,382r**	**75**	**669,457r**	**672,106r**	**65**	**672,171r**	**646,935**	**55**	**646,990**
Industry	**166,142**	**75**	**166,217**	**153,609r**	**65**	**153,674r**	**148,683**	**55**	**148,738**
Unclassified	-	75	75	-	65	65	-	55	55
Iron and steel	10,327	-	10,327	9,715r	-	9,715r	8,410	-	8,410
Non-ferrous metals	4,781r	-	4,781r	3,199r	-	3,199r	3,145	-	3,145
Mineral products	14,105r	-	14,105r	13,401r	-	13,401r	12,876	-	12,876
Chemicals	45,048r	-	45,048r	41,942r	-	41,942r	41,422	-	41,422
Mechanical Engineering, etc	9,126r	-	9,126r	8,609r	-	8,609r	8,474	-	8,474
Electrical engineering, etc	4,395r	-	4,395r	4,110r	-	4,110r	4,322	-	4,322
Vehicles	11,621r	-	11,621r	10,228r	-	10,228r	9,896	-	9,896
Food, beverages, etc	28,799r	-	28,799r	28,232r	-	28,232r	27,694	-	27,694
Textiles, leather, etc	7,901r	-	7,901r	7,120r	-	7,120r	6,750	-	6,750
Paper, printing, etc	15,898r	-	15,898r	13,878r	-	13,878r	13,071	-	13,071
Other industries	11,126r	-	11,126r	10,244r	-	10,244r	10,021	-	10,021
Construction	3,015r	-	3,015r	2,931r	-	2,931r	2,602	-	2,602
Transport	-	-	-	-	-	-	-	-	-
Air	-	-	-	-	-	-	-	-	-
Rail	-	-	-	-	-	-	-	-	-
Road (6)	-	-	-	-	-	-	-	-	-
National navigation	-	-	-	-	-	-	-	-	-
Pipelines	-	-	-	-	-	-	-	-	-
Other	**493,219r**	-	**493,219r**	**508,476r**	-	**508,476r**	**488,532**	-	**488,532**
Domestic	386,486	-	386,486	396,411	-	396,411	381,879	-	381,879
Public administration	44,362	-	44,362	50,934r	-	50,934r	49,385	-	49,385
Commercial	39,537	-	39,537	37,574r	-	37,574r	34,960	-	34,960
Agriculture	2,324	-	2,324	2,355	-	2,355	2,201	-	2,201
Miscellaneous	20,510r	-	20,510r	21,202r	-	21,202r	20,107	-	20,107
Non energy use	**10,021**	-	**10,021**	**10,021**	-	**10,021**	**9,721**	-	**9,721**

(1) Stock fall (+), stock rise (-).
(2) Natural gas used in the manufacture of synthetic coke oven gas.
(3) Total supply minus total demand.
(4) Heat generation data are not available before 1999. For earlier years gas used to generate heat for sale is allocated to final consumption by sector
(5) See paragraphs 4.44 to 4.47.
(6) See footnote 5 to Table 4.2.

4.2 Supply and consumption of natural gas and colliery methane[1]

GWh

	2001	2002	2003	2004	2005
Supply					
Production	1,231,263	1,205,405	1,197,030	1,116,554	1,018,570
Imports	30,464	60,493	86,298	133,035	173,328
Exports	-138,330	-150,731	-177,039	-114,111	-96,181
Stock change (2)	-661	-7,356	+3,532	-6,235	+1,321
Transfers	-65	-99	-82	-39	-51
Total supply	**1,122,671**	**1,107,712**	**1,109,739**	**1,129,205r**	**1,096,988**
Statistical difference (3)	+2,079	+1,779	+748r	+806r	+637
Total demand	**1,120,592**	**1,105,933**	**1,108,991r**	**1,128,398r**	**1,096,351**
Transformation	**336,525**	**351,856**	**344,410r**	**360,998r**	**354,505**
Electricity generation	312,939	329,847	324,580r	341,111r	333,834
Major power producers	276,764	291,264	284,662	304,495	295,643
Autogenerators	36,175	38,583	39,918r	36,617r	38,191
Heat generation	23,586	22,009	19,830	19,886r	20,671
Other	-	-	-	-	-
Energy industry use	**91,451**	**91,260**	**88,907**	**87,056r**	**84,165**
Electricity generation	-	-	-	-	-
Oil and gas extraction	78,457	79,364	76,837	76,899	73,652
Petroleum refineries	4,189	3,350	2,773	1,797r	1,987
Coal extraction	211	196	187	150	114
Coke manufacture	9	-	1	-	-
Blast furnaces	375	222	539	728	941
Other	8,210	8,128	8,570	7,482	7,472
Losses (4)	**8,863**	**9,666**	**6,217r**	**8,174**	**10,690**
Final consumption	**683,753**	**653,151**	**669,457r**	**672,171r**	**646,990**
Industry	**179,843**	**165,166**	**166,217**	**153,674r**	**148,738**
Unclassified	105	90	75	65	55
Iron and steel	8,502	8,791	10,327	9,715r	8,410
Non-ferrous metals	5,663	5,255	4,781r	3,199r	3,145
Mineral products	15,565	14,136	14,105r	13,401r	12,876
Chemicals	50,064	44,277	45,048r	41,942r	41,422
Mechanical engineering, etc	9,656	9,273	9,126r	8,609r	8,474
Electrical engineering, etc	5,022	4,615	4,395r	4,110r	4,322
Vehicles	12,035	11,521	11,621r	10,228r	9,896
Food, beverages, etc	29,697	28,884	28,799r	28,232r	27,694
Textiles, leather, etc	7,966	7,837	7,901r	7,120r	6,750
Paper, printing, etc	16,569	15,452	15,898r	13,878r	13,071
Other industries	15,741	11,731	11,126r	10,244r	10,021
Construction	3,258	3,304	3,015r	2,931r	2,602
Transport	-	-	-	-	-
Road (5)	-	-	-	-	-
Other	**492,537**	**477,205**	**493,219r**	**508,476r**	**488,532**
Domestic	379,426	376,372	386,486	396,411	381,879
Public administration	46,232	42,998	44,362	50,934r	49,385
Commercial	37,098	36,224	39,537	37,574r	34,960
Agriculture	2,329	2,346	2,324	2,355	2,201
Miscellaneous	27,452	19,265	20,510r	21,202r	20,107
Non energy use	**11,373**	**10,780**	**10,021**	**10,021**	**9,721**

(1) Colliery methane figures included within these totals are as follows:

	2001	2002	2003	2004	2005
Total production	**730**	**692**	**915**	**810**	**757**
Electricity generation	418	406	653	595	588
Coal extraction	207	196	187	150	114
Other industries	105	90	75	65	55
Total consumption	**730**	**692**	**915**	**810**	**757**

(2) Stock fall (+), stock rise (-).

(3) Total supply minus total demand.

(4) For an explanation of what is included under losses, see paragraphs 4.44 to 4.47.

(5) A small amount of natural gas is consumed by road transport, but gas use in this sector is predominantly of petroleum gas, hence road use of gas is reported in the petroleum products balances in Chapter 3.

4.3 UK continental shelf and onshore natural gas production and supply[1]

GWh

	2001	2002	2003	2004	2005
Upstream gas industry:					
Gross production (2)	1,230,533	1,204,713	1,196,115	1,115,744	1,017,813
Minus Producers' own use (3) (18)	78,457	79,364	76,837	76,899	73,652
Exports	138,330	150,731	177,039	114,111	96,181
Stock change (pipelines) (4) (18)	-	-	-	-	-
Waste (5) (18)	-	-	-	-	-
Other losses and metering differences (6)(7)(18)	-	-	-	-	-
Plus Imports of gas	30,464	60,493	86,298	133,035	173,328
Gas available at terminals (8)	1,044,210	1,035,111	1,028,537	1,057,769	1,021,308
Minus Statistical difference (7)	-690	-125	-1,391	-1,538	-2,164
Downstream gas industry:					
Gas input into the national transmission system (9)	1,044,900	1,035,236	1,029,928	1,059,307	1,023,472
Minus Operators' own use (10)	6,549	7,017	7,475	6,560	6,555
Stock change (storage sites) (11)	661	7,356	-3,532	6,235	-1,321
Metering differences (7)	1,798	1,821	-874	137	2,880
Gas output from the national transmission system (12)	1,035,892	1,019,042	1,026,859	1,046,375	1,015,358
Minus Leakage assessment (13)	4,436	5,283	4,452	5,414	5,260
Own use gas (14)	438	427	439	437	425
Theft (15)	2,190	2,134	2,197	2,186	2,124
Transfers (16)	65	99	82	39	51
Statistical difference and metering differences (7)	2,770	1,884	2,138r	2,345r	2,801
Total UK consumption (17)	**1,025,991**	**1,009,213**	**1,017,547r**	**1,035,955r**	**1,004,697**
Stocks of gas (at end year)	26,741	34,097	30,565	36,800	35,479
Storage capacity (19)				45,309	47,815

(1) For details of where to find monthly updates of natural gas production and supply see paragraph 4.43.

(2) Includes waste and producers' own use, but excludes gas flared.

(3) Gas used for drilling, production and pumping operations.

(4) Gas held within the UKCS pipeline system. As sections are opened and closed between fields, gas moves in and out of the system, hence it is regarded as a change in stocks.

(5) Gas vented from oil and gas platforms as part of the production process. With effect from 1999 gas vented has been deducted from the Gross Production figure.

(6) Losses due to pipeline leakage.

(7) Measurement of gas flows, in volume and energy terms, occurs at several points along the supply chain. As such, differences are seen between the actual recorded flow through any one point and estimates calculated for the flow of gas at that point. More detail on the reasons for these differences is given in the technical notes and definitions section of this chapter, paragraphs 4.44 to 4.47.

(8) The volume of gas available at terminals for consumption in the UK as recorded by the terminal operators. The percentage of gas available for consumption in the UK from indigenous sources in 2005 was 83.0 per cent, compared with 87.4 per cent in 2004.

(9) Gas received as reported by the pipeline operators. The pipeline operators include National Grid, who run the national pipeline network, and other pipelines that take North Sea gas supplies direct to consumers.

(10) Gas consumed by pipeline operators in pumping operations and on their own sites.

(11) Stocks of gas held in specific storage sites, either as liquefied natural gas, pumped into salt cavities or stored by pumping the gas back into an offshore field. Stock rise (+), stock fall (-).

(12) Including public gas supply, direct supplies by North Sea producers, third party supplies and stock changes.

(13) This is a National Grid assessment of leakage through the local distribution system based on the National Leakage Reduction Monitoring Model.

(14) Equivalent to about 0.06 per cent of LDZ throughput this is an assessment of the energy used to counter the effects of gas cooling on pressure reduction.

(15) Calculated by National Grid as 0.3 per cent of LDZ throughput, this is theft before the gas reaches customer meters.

(16) Transfers are the use within the iron and steel industry for use in the manufacture of synthetic coke oven gas.

(17) See paragraph 4.27 for an explanation of the relationship between these "Total UK consumption" figures and "Total demand" shown within the balance tables.

(18) A simplified PPRS reporting system was introduced in January 2001 requiring less data from respondents - see paragraph 4.30.

(19) Data compiled by DTI from individual storage site information. Converted from billion cubic metres to GWh assuming 10.992 kWh per cubicmetre. See paragraph 4.31.

Chapter 5
Electricity

Introduction

5.1   This Chapter presents statistics on electricity from generation through to sales. In addition, statistics on generating capacity, on fuel used for generation and on load factors and efficiencies are included along with a map showing the transmission system in Great Britain and the location of the main power stations page 121).

5.2   Commodity balances for electricity, for each of the last three years, form the introductory table (Table 5.1). The supply and consumption elements of the electricity balance are presented as 5-year time series in Table 5.2. Table 5.3 separates out the public distribution system for electricity from electricity generated and consumed by autogenerators and uses a commodity balance format. Fuels used to generate electricity in the United Kingdom in each of the last five years are covered in Table 5.4. Table 5.5 shows the relationship between the commodity balance definitions and traditional Digest definitions for electricity, so that the most recent data can be linked to the long term trends data, which can be found on the DTI energy statistics web site. Table 5.6 shows the relationship between fuels used, generation and supply in each of the latest five years. Tables on plant capacity (Tables 5.7, 5.8 and 5.9) and on plant loads and efficiency (Table 5.10) have been included. Two of these contain data at a sub-national level. Table 5.11 lists individual power stations in operation and it is supplemented by a table showing large scale CHP schemes in the United Kingdom (Table 5.12). The long term trends commentary and tables on fuel use, generation, supply and consumption back to 1970 are to be found on DTI's energy statistics web site and accessible from the Digest of UK Energy Statistics home page: www.dti.gov.uk/energy/statistics/publications/dukes/page29812.html .

Structure of the industry

5.3   For most of the period covered by this Digest the electricity industries of Scotland, Northern Ireland and England and Wales operated independently although interconnectors joined all three grid systems together. From April 2005 under the British Electricity Trading and Transmission Arrangements (BETTA), introduced in the Energy Act 2004, the electricity systems of England and Wales and Scotland have been integrated. The paragraphs below describe the position up to March 2005 but indicate the further changes that have been made under BETTA.

5.4   From the period immediately after privatisation of the industry in 1989, when there were 7 generating companies in England and Wales and 12 Regional Electricity companies distributing and supplying electricity to customers in their designated area, there were many structural and business changes. At the end of 2005 there were 30 major power producers operating in England and Wales[1]. Competition developed as follows:

(a)   From 1 April 1990, customers with peak loads of more than 1 MW (about 45 per cent of the non-domestic market) were able to choose their supplier.

(b)   From 1 April 1994, customers with peak loads of more than 100 kW were able to choose their supplier.

(c)   Between September 1998 and May 1999, the remaining part of the electricity market (ie below 100 kW peak load) was opened up to competition. Paragraph 5.9 and Table 5A give more details of the opening up of the domestic gas and electricity markets to competition.

5.5   Since the late 1990s, there have been commercial moves toward vertical re-integration between generators, electricity distribution and/or electricity supply businesses. Those mergers that have taken place were approved by the relevant competition authority. Since privatisation National Grid

---

[1] Some of these producers are joint ventures and so the number of generating companies involved is less than 30.

has operated the high voltage transmission system in England and Wales linking generators to distributors and some large customers. This transmission system is linked to the transmission system of continental Europe via an interconnector to France under the English Channel (see Table 5.11). Up to March 2005, the Scottish transmission system was regarded as being linked to that in England and Wales by two interconnectors but under BETTA National Grid has taken on responsibility for operating the transmission system in Scotland as well as England and Wales. Thus a single Great Britain market has been created and the transmission network is regarded as a single system.

5.6 In Scotland, until the end of March 2005, the two main companies, Scottish Power and Scottish and Southern Energy, covered the full range of electricity provision. They operated generation, transmission, distribution and supply businesses. In addition, there are about 25 small independent hydro stations and some independent generators operating fossil-fuelled stations, which sell their output to Scottish Power and Scottish and Southern Energy.

5.7 The electricity supply industry in Northern Ireland is also privately owned. Northern Ireland Electricity plc (NIE) (part of the Viridian Group) is responsible for power procurement, transmission, distribution and supply in the Province. Generation is in the hands of three private sector companies who own the four major power stations. There is a link (re-established in 1996) between the Northern Ireland grid and that of the Irish Republic, along which electricity is both imported and exported. In December 2001, the link between Northern Ireland's grid and that of Scotland was inaugurated.

5.8 In March 2001, the means of trading electricity changed with the introduction in England and Wales of the New Electricity Trading Arrangements (NETA). These arrangements were based on bi-lateral trading between generators, suppliers, traders and customers. They are designed to be more efficient and provide greater choice for market participants, whilst maintaining the operation of a secure and reliable electricity system. The system includes forwards and futures markets, a balancing

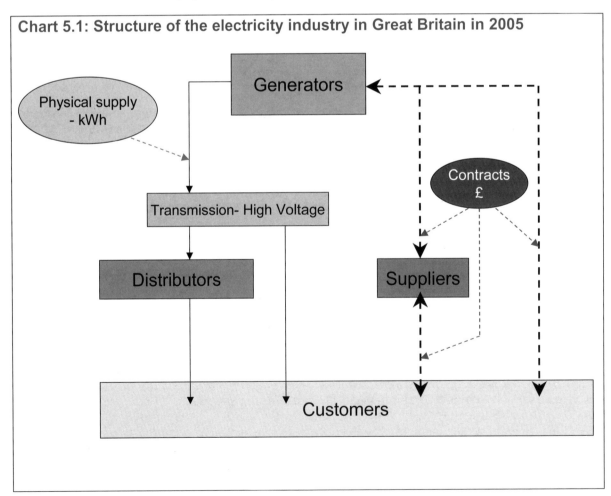

Chart 5.1: Structure of the electricity industry in Great Britain in 2005

mechanism to enable National Grid, as system operator, to balance the system, and a settlement process. This system has been extended to Scotland under BETTA. The system is shown in simplified form in Chart 5.1.

5.9   By December 2005, nearly 11.7 million electricity consumers (46 per cent) were no longer with their home supplier. Table 5A gives market penetration in the fourth quarter of 2005. By the end of 2005, the former regional electricity companies had lost around 40 per cent of the credit, over 50 per cent of the direct debit, and over 40 per cent of the prepayment market.

Table 5A: Domestic electricity market penetration (in terms of percentage of customers supplied) by Public Electricity Supply area and payment type, fourth quarter of 2005

Region	Home Supplier			Non-Home Supplier		
	Credit	Direct Debit	Prepayment	Credit	Direct Debit	Prepayment
North West	47	28	37	53	72	63
West Midlands	55	43	48	45	57	52
Merseyside and North Wales	60	47	55	40	53	45
Northern	54	39	45	46	61	55
Yorkshire	52	35	39	48	65	61
East Midlands	54	41	53	46	59	47
Eastern	55	40	45	45	60	55
South Wales	71	65	86	29	35	14
South East	65	46	52	34	54	48
London	64	47	61	36	53	39
South Scotland	64	59	64	36	41	36
South	72	59	73	28	41	27
South West	69	41	60	31	59	40
North Scotland	85	75	86	15	25	14
Great Britain	61	46	58	39	54	42

Commodity balances for electricity (Table 5.1)

5.10   The first page of this balance table shows that 98 per cent of UK electricity supply in 2005 was home produced and 2 per cent was from imports net of exports. Just ½ per cent of home produced electricity was exported. Of the 398,000 GWh produced (excluding pumped storage production), 90½ per cent was from major power producers and 9½ per cent from other generators, 22 per cent was from primary sources and 78 per cent from secondary sources.

5.11   Electricity generated by each type of fuel is shown on the second page of the commodity balance table. The link between electricity generated and electricity supplied is made in Table 5.6 and electricity supplied by each type of fuel is illustrated in Chart 5.3. Paragraph 5.27 examines further the ways of presenting each fuel's contribution to electricity production.

5.12   Demand for electricity is predominantly from final consumers, who accounted for 85 per cent in 2005. The remaining 15 per cent is split 7½ per cent to energy industries' use and 7½ per cent to losses. The electricity industry itself uses 57 per cent of the energy industries' total use of electricity, with a further 12 per cent used for pumping at pumped storage stations. Petroleum refineries are the next most significant consumer with 18 per cent of energy industry use. The losses item has three components. First, transmission losses from the high voltage transmission system represented about 19 per cent of the figure in 2005. Second, distribution losses, which occur between the gateways to the public supply system's network and the customers' meters, accounted for about 76 per cent of losses. Third, a small amount was lost through theft or meter fraud (less than 5 per cent) (see also paragraph 5.65).

5.13   Industrial consumption was 34 per cent of final consumption in 2005, marginally more than the consumption by households (also 34 per cent), with transport storage and communications and the services sector accounting for the remaining 32 per cent. Within the industrial sector the three largest consuming industries are chemicals, paper and food, which together account for 41 per cent of industrial consumption. The iron and steel sector is also a substantial user of electricity but part of its consumption is included against blast furnaces and coke ovens under energy industry uses. This is because electricity is used by coke ovens and blast furnaces in the transformation of solid fuels into coke, coke oven gas and blast furnace gas. Taken together, the engineering industries accounted for a further 18 per cent of final consumption of electricity. A note on the estimates included within these figures is to be found at paragraph 5.66. Chart 5.2 shows diagrammatically the demand for electricity in 2005.

5.14   The transport sector covers electricity consumed by companies involved in transport, storage and communications. Within the overall total of 8,609 GWh, it is known that national railways consume about 2,700 GWh each year for traction purposes, and this figure has been shown separately in the balances.

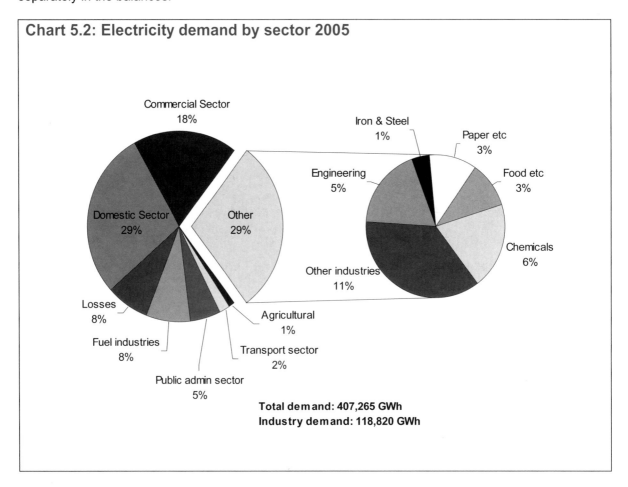

Chart 5.2: Electricity demand by sector 2005

Commercial Sector 18%
Iron & Steel 1%
Paper etc 3%
Engineering 5%
Food etc 3%
Domestic Sector 29%
Other 29%
Chemicals 6%
Other industries 11%
Losses 8%
Agricultural 1%
Fuel industries 8%
Transport sector 2%
Public admin sector 5%

Total demand: 407,265 GWh
Industry demand: 118,820 GWh

Supply and consumption of electricity (Table 5.2)

5.15   There was a 1½ per cent increase in the supply of electricity in 2005. Production (including pumped storage production) rose by 1¼ per cent, but imports of electricity net of exports were 11 per cent higher than in 2004. In 2003 high prices in continental Europe fostered a growth in electricity exports, which were nearly four times their level in 2002. Since then exports to continental Europe have returned to their 2002 level but exports have remained high because of the increase in exports from Northern Ireland to the Irish Republic. In 2005 Northern Ireland exports accounted for about three quarters of the total UK electricity exports.

5.16   Losses as a proportion of electricity demand in 2005 (7½ per cent) and energy industry use as a proportion of total demand, also at 7½ per cent, were both the same as in 2004. Industrial consumption of electricity was 2½ per cent up on 2004's level, and consumption in the services sector rose by 2 per cent. Consumption by transport, storage and communications also rose by 2 per cent and domestic sector consumption rose by 1 per cent. Temperatures influence the actual level of consumption in any one year in the winter months, as customers adjust heating levels in their homes. Temperatures in fourth quarter of 2003 were on average colder than in any of the 4 preceding years. In addition the hot summer of 2003 led to an increased use of electricity for air conditioning and cooling. 2004 did not have a hot summer, nor a cold fourth quarter but on average, temperatures were similar to those in 2003. 2005 had a mild first quarter, and a cold end to the year but on average during the year were similar to those of 2004 and 2003.

Regional electricity data

5.17 The restructuring of the electricity industry in 1990 and the privatisation of the electricity companies meant that it was no longer possible for this Digest to present regional data on the supply of electricity, as it would disclose information about individual businesses that were in competition with each other. Now that competition has been fully introduced, the Department of Trade and Industry has agreed with electricity suppliers and distributors the way in which electricity data can be collected at a regional (and sub-regional) level, in order to meet the requirements of users. The collection of data relating to regional and local consumption of electricity began in autumn 2004 and regional and local data on electricity consumption were published on an experimental basis in December of that year. The exercise was repeated in the autumn of 2005 building on lessons learned from the previous year's exercise and the results were published in December 2005 in *Energy Trends*. (See Annex C for more information about *Energy Trends*). Further information is available on the regional statistics pages of the DTI energy statistics web site www.dti.gov.uk/energy/statistics/regional/index.html . A summary of electricity consumption at regional level is given in Table 5B and relates to 2004.

5.18 The difference between total UK electricity sales, shown in Table 5B, and total UK electricity sales shown in Table 5.5 is a small statistical difference (4,008 GWh or just over 1 per cent) that mainly arises from the fact that the regional data are not based exactly on a calendar year.

Table 5B: Electricity consumed, 2004

	Domestic sector sales (GWh)	Number of domestic customers (thousand) (1)	Industrial and commercial sector sales (GWh)	Number of I & C customers (thousand) (1)	All consumers sales (GWh)
Wales	5,602	1,305	10,970	130	16,572
Scotland	12,317	2,571	17,982	218	30,299
North East	4,578	1,163	8,129	84	12,708
North West	13,316	3,031	20,913	253	34,230
Yorkshire and the Humber	9,760	2,253	15,842	185	25,602
East Midlands	8,775	1,890	15,686	162	24,461
West Midlands	10,761	2,298	16,632	205	27,393
East of England	12,267	2,410	15,884	221	28,150
Greater London	13,496	3,139	26,870	415	40,367
South East	17,354	3,520	23,704	347	41,057
South West	11,518	2,295	15,189	244	26,707
Unallocated Consumption	119	28	4,482	14	4,602
Sales direct from high voltage lines (2)					7,400
Great Britain	119,864	25,902	192,284	2,477	312,148
Northern Ireland (3)					7,558
Total (4)					319,706

(1) Figures are the number of Meter Point Administration Numbers (MPANs); every metering point has this unique reference number.
(2) Based on estimate provided by Ofgem.
(3) Northern Ireland data are based on data for electricity distributed provided by Northern Ireland Electricity.
(4) This is close to the figure for UK electricity sales in 2004 of 323,714 GWh shown in Table 5.5; see paragraph 5.18.

Commodity balances for the public distribution system and for other generators (Table 5.3)

5.19 Table 5.3 expands on the commodity balance format to show consumption divided between electricity distributed over the public distribution system and electricity provided by other generators (largely autogeneration). Autogeneration is the generation of electricity wholly or partly for a company's own use as an activity which supplements the primary activity. However, most generators of electricity from renewable sources (apart from large scale hydro and some biofuels) are included as other generators because of their comparatively small size, even though their main activity is electricity generation. For a full list of companies included as major power producers see paragraph 5.50.

5.20 Table 5.3 also expands the domestic sector to show consumption by payment type and the commercial sector is expanded to show detailed data beyond that presented in Tables 5.1 and 5.2.

5.21 The proportion of electricity supplied by generators other than major power producers rose slightly in 2005 to just under 9½ per cent. This is above the previous peak share it reached in 2000, and also a peak level in volume terms. The proportion of this electricity transferred to the public distribution system in 2005 was 28 per cent whereas in the previous 4 years this proportion has varied between 23 and 33 per cent according to market conditions. High gas prices and low electricity prices made it more difficult for electricity produced by other generators to compete in the electricity market in the most recent 4 years although the position eased in 2003. Over the last 5 years there has also been greater generation from renewables and wastes which are included in the "Other generators" category (see Chapter 7).

5.22 In 2005, 6 per cent of final consumption of electricity was by other generators and did not pass over the public distribution system. This proportion remains on a rising trend A substantial proportion of electricity used in the energy industries is self-generated with the proportion above 20 per cent in all three years shown in the table. At petroleum refineries the proportion is even higher and in 2005 nearly three quarters of electricity was self-generated.

5.23 In 2005, 15 per cent of the industrial demand for electricity was met by autogeneration. There was also a lesser proportion (about 3 per cent) from autogeneration within the commercial and transport sectors. Table 1.9 in Chapter 1 shows the fuels used by autogenerators to generate this electricity within each major sector and also the quantities of electricity generated and consumed.

5.24 Within the domestic sector, about a third of the electricity consumed was purchased under some form of off-peak pricing structure (the same as in the previous two years). Just over 16 per cent of consumption was through prepayment systems, a proportion that has varied little over the three years shown.

Fuel used in generation (Table 5.4)

5.25 In this table fuel used by electricity generators is measured in both original units and for comparative purposes, in the common unit of million tonnes of oil equivalent. In Table 5.6 figures are quoted in a third unit, namely GWh, in order to show the link between fuel use and electricity generated.

5.26 The energy supplied basis defines the primary input (in million tonnes of oil equivalent) needed to produce 1 TWh of hydro, wind, or imported electricity as:

$$\text{Electricity generated (TWh)} \times 0.085985$$

The primary input needed to produce 1 TWh of nuclear electricity is similarly

$$\frac{\text{Electricity generated (TWh)} \times 0.085985}{\text{Thermal efficiency of nuclear stations}}$$

In the United Kingdom the thermal efficiency of nuclear stations has risen in stages from 32 per cent in 1982 to just over 38 per cent in 2005 (see Table 5.10 and paragraph 5.57 for the definition)[2]. The factor of 0.085985 is the energy content of one TWh divided by the energy content of one million tonnes of oil equivalent (see page 203 and inside back cover flap).

5.27   Figures on fuel use for electricity generation can be compared in two ways. Table 5.4 illustrates one way by using the volumes of **fuel input** to power stations (after conversion of inputs to an oil equivalent basis), but this takes no account of how efficiently that fuel is converted into electricity. The fuel input basis is the most appropriate to use for analysis of the quantities of particular fuels used in electricity generation (eg to determine the additional amount of gas or other fuels required as coal use declines under tighter emissions restrictions). A second way uses the amount of electricity generated and supplied by each fuel. This **output** basis is appropriate for comparing how much, and what percentage, of electricity generation comes from a particular fuel. It is the most appropriate method to use to examine the dominance of any fuel and for diversity issues. Percentage shares based on fuel outputs reduce the contribution of coal and nuclear, and increase the contribution of gas (by about 6 percentage points in 2005) compared with the fuel input basis. This is because of the higher conversion efficiency of gas. This output basis is used in Chart 5.3, taking electricity supplied (gross) figures from Table 5.6. Trends in fuel used on this electricity supplied basis are described in the section on Table 5.6, in paragraphs 5.30 to 5.33, below.

5.28   A historical series of fuel used in generation on a consistent, energy supplied, fuel input basis is available at Table 5.1.1 on DTI's energy statistics web site and accessible from the Digest of UK Energy Statistics home page:
www.dti.gov.uk/energy/statistics/publications/dukes/page29812.html .

Relating measurements of supply, consumption and availability (Table 5.5)
5.29   The balance methodology uses terms that cannot be readily employed for years before [1998] because statistics were not available in sufficient detail. Table 5.5 shows the relationship between these terms for the latest five years. For the full definitions of the terms used in the commodity balances see the Annex A, paragraphs A.7 to A.42.

Electricity generated and supplied (Table 5.6)
5.30   The main data on generation and supply in Table 5.6 are presented by type of fuel. However, before 1996 data were presented by type of station and in order to maintain a link with this earlier data the final part of the table shows generation from conventional steam stations and from combined cycle gas turbine stations over the most recent five years.

5.31   Total electricity generated in the United Kingdom in 2005 was 1½ per cent higher than generation in 2004, just above the average rate of growth over the last 5 years. Major power producers (as defined in paragraph 5.49) accounted for 90½ per cent of electricity generation in 2005. Generation by other generators was 3½ per cent up on a year earlier mainly because most (66 per cent in 2005) of the generation from renewables is included in the "other generators" category.

5.32   Generation from coal-fired stations was ½ per cent higher in 2005 than in 2004. Generation from gas in 2005 was 2½ per cent lower than the record level in 2004 but still the second highest recorded level. In 2005 one new large station began generation and two completed their first full year of generation. Generation from nuclear sources rose by 2 per cent although the nuclear sector was again affected by a high level of outages for repairs and maintenance.

5.33   Table 5.6 also shows electricity supplied data. These data take into account the fact that some stations use relatively more electricity than others in the generation process itself. In total, electricity supplied (gross) was 4½ per cent less than the volume generated in 2005. For gas-fired stations it was only 2 per cent less, while for nuclear stations it was 8 per cent less. Chart 5.3 shows how shares of the generation market in terms of electricity output have changed over the last five years. Coal's share of electricity supplied (net) plus imports in 2005 at 33½ per cent was 2½ percentage

---

[2] *Note that the International Energy Agency uses 0.33 in its calculations, which is the European average thermal efficiency of nuclear stations in 1989, measured in net terms rather than the UK's gross terms.*

points higher than in 2000 but 1 percentage point lower than the high level in 2003. Gas' share at 39 per cent was lower than the 40 per cent record share in 2004 but equal to gas' average share over the most recent 7 years. Nuclear's 19½ per cent share was higher than the 19 per cent share of 2004, which was its lowest since 1987 having peaked at 26 per cent in 1998. Oil's share remained at the 1 per cent it has recorded in each of the last five years and imports' share has fallen from 4 per cent in 2000 to 2 per cent in 2005.

Chart 5.3: Fuel used in electricity generation, on an output basis[1]

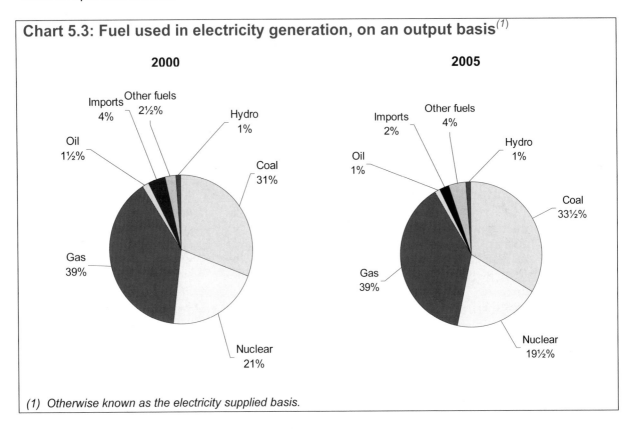

(1) Otherwise known as the electricity supplied basis.

Plant capacity (Tables 5.7, 5.8 and 5.9)

5.34   Table 5.7 shows capacity, ie the maximum power available at any one time, for major power producers and other generators by type of plant.

5.35   In 2005, there was an increase of just over 760 MW (+1 per cent) in the capacity of major power producers. This was due to 400 MW of new gas fired plant coming on stream (and replacing 180 MW of oil-fired plant) and 370 MW of oil-fired plant being re-instated. The balance was from other up-ratings net of down-ratings. In December 2005, major power producers accounted for 91 per cent of the total generating capacity, the same proportion as at the end of 2004. The capacity of other generators increased by 9½ per cent. Renewables capacity of other generators increased by 503 MW (35 per cent) (see Chapter 7).

5.36   A breakdown of the capacity of the major power producers' plants at the end of March each year from 1993 to 1996 and at the end of December for 1996 to 2005 is shown in Chart 5.4.

5.37   Table 5.8 separates the capacities of major power producers geographically to show England and Wales, Scotland and Northern Ireland. So as not to disclose data for individual stations that have been provided in confidence, the breakdowns by type of station cannot be given in as much detail as in Table 5.7. In 2005, 84 per cent of the generating capacity in the UK owned by major power producers was in England and Wales, 13 per cent was in Scotland and 3 per cent in Northern Ireland. Out of the net increase in UK capacity of 764 MW in 2005, 468 MW was in England and Wales, 97 MW was in Scotland and there was a 199 MW increase in Northern Ireland.

5.38   In Table 5.9, data for the generating capacity of industrial, commercial and transport undertakings are shown, according to the industrial classification of the generator. 17½ per cent of the capacity is in the chemicals sector. Petroleum refineries have 14 per cent of capacity, paper, printing and publishing has a 10 per cent share, and engineering and other metal trades has an 8½ per cent share. However, the major share (almost 40 per cent) and most of the growth in 2005 was outside the industrial sector.

Plant loads, demand and efficiency (Table 5.10)

5.39   Table 5.10 shows the maximum load met each year, load factors (by type of plant and for the system in total) and indicators of thermal efficiency. Maximum demand figures cover the winter period ending the following March. Up to 2004, maximum demand figures for England and Wales, Scotland, and Northern Ireland are shown separately as well as total UK maximum demand. With the advent of BETTA (see paragrpah 5.3), England, Wales and Scotland are covered by a single network and a single maximum load is shown for Great Britain in 2005.

5.40   Maximum demand in the UK during the winter of 2005/2006 occurred in November 2005. This was 1.1 per cent higher than the previous year's maximum in December 2004, but marginally below the record maximum demand that occurred in 2002/03. Maximum demand in 2005/2006 was 83.3 per cent of the UK capacity of major power producers (Table 5.7) as measured at the end of December 2005, the same as in 2004/05 and below the figure for each of the two previous winters. In Great Britain maximum demand at the end of November 2005 was 83.5 per cent of the England, Wales and Scotland capacity of major power producers (Table 5.8) compared with 83.1 per cent at the end of 2004. For Northern Ireland the proportion was 77.5 per cent (88.0 per cent in 2004) These percentages do not include the capacities available via the interconnectors with neighbouring grid systems nor demand for electricity via these interconnectors.

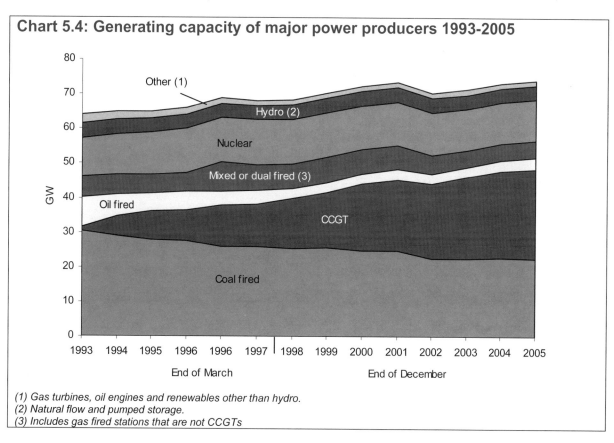

Chart 5.4: Generating capacity of major power producers 1993-2005

(1) Gas turbines, oil engines and renewables other than hydro.
(2) Natural flow and pumped storage.
(3) Includes gas fired stations that are not CCGTs

5.41   Plant load factors measure how intensively each type of plant has been used. The trend up to the end of the 1990s had been for conventional thermal plant to be used less intensively and CCGT stations more intensively. In 2000 increased maintenance and repair at nuclear stations and at CCGT stations, coupled with high gas prices at the end of the year, led to a departure from this trend. Nuclear stations recovered in 2001, suffered further outages in 2002, recovered again in 2003, but suffered further outages in 2004 and 2005. Continuing high gas prices since the end of 2000 have brought about a reduction in CCGT load factors, particularly since 2002. The use of coal in competition with gas is reflected in the increased load factor for conventional thermal stations and coal-fired stations, again since 2002.

5.42   2003 and 2001 were particularly dry years, especially in the areas where hydro electricity is produced. As a result the load factors for natural flow hydro show substantial falls in those years. Pumped storage use was less affected by the dry weather in 2003 than in 2001. The low availability of hydro was another contributory factor to the high load factor for conventional thermal in 2003.

5.43   Thermal efficiency measures the efficiency with which the heat energy in fuel is converted into electrical energy. The efficiency of coal-fired stations had been on a downward trend as coal became the marginal fuel for generation, but coal's increased role since 2000 has halted the decline in the thermal efficiency of coal-fired generation. CCGT efficiency has risen in 2005 because it has tended the be the older, less efficient CCGT stations that have not been used so intensively because of the high gas prices. The efficiency of nuclear stations has been on a rising trends in recent years as older, less efficient stations have closed, but the outages in 2004 reduced the efficiency slightly. The efficiencies presented in this table are calculated using **gross** calorific values to obtain the energy content of the fuel inputs. If **net** calorific values are used, efficiencies are higher, for example CCGT efficiencies rise by about 5 percentage points.

Power stations in the United Kingdom (Tables 5.11 and 5.12)

5.44   Table 5.11 lists the operational power stations in the United Kingdom as at the end of May 2006 along with their installed capacity and the year they began to generate electricity. Where a company operates several stations the stations are grouped together. In general the table aims to list all stations of 1 MW installed capacity or over. A new column has been added to this table to show the location of the pwer station in terms of Scotland, Wales, Northern Ireland and the regions of England. In the 2005 Digest Table 5.12 was included for the first time. It shows CHP of 1 MW and over stations for which the information is publicly available, but it is the total power output of these stations that is given, not just that which is classed as good quality CHP under CHPQA (see Chapter 6), since CHPQA information for individual sites is not publicly available. In Table 5.11 generating stations using renewable sources are also listed in aggregate form in the "Other power stations" section apart from hydro stations and wind farms operated by the major power producers, which appear in the main table. For completeness CHP stations not appearing in the main table are also listed in aggregate in this section. Details of the interconnectors between England and France, Scotland and Northern Ireland and Northern Ireland and the Irish Republic are also given in this table. The total installed capacity of all the power stations individually listed in Table 5.11 is 77,504 MW.

Carbon dioxide emissions from power stations.

5.45   It is estimated that carbon dioxide emissions from power stations accounted for 29½ per cent of the UK's total carbon dioxide emissions in 2005. Emissions vary by type of fuel used to generate the electricity and the latest figures are shown in Table 5C below:

Table 5C: Estimated carbon dioxide emissions from power stations in 2005

Fuel	Emissions (tonnes of carbon per GWh electricity supplied)
Coal	238
Oil	207
Gas	99
All fossil fuels	167
All fuels (including nuclear and renewables)	124

The Electricity Supply System in Great Britain in 2005

This map has been adapted from a map provided by Reed Business Publishing and National Grid; it is available in colour on the DTI energy website.

Technical notes and definitions

5.46 These notes and definitions are in addition to the technical notes and definitions covering all fuels and energy as a whole in Chapter 1, paragraphs 1.24 to 1.56. For notes on the commodity balances and definitions of the terms used in the row headings see Annex A, paragraphs A.7 to A.42. While the data in the printed and bound copy of this Digest cover only the most recent 5 years, these notes also cover data for earlier years that are available on the DTI web site.

Electricity generation from renewable sources
5.47 Figures on electricity generation from renewable energy sources are included in the tables in this section. Further detailed information on renewable energy sources is included in Chapter 7.

Combined heat and power
5.48 Electricity generated from combined heat and power (CHP) schemes, CHP generating capacities and fuel used for electricity generation are included in the tables in this chapter. However, more detailed analyses of CHP schemes are set out in Chapter 6.

Generating companies
5.49 Following the restructuring of the electricity supply industry in 1990, the term "Major generating companies" was introduced into the electricity tables to describe the activities of the former nationalised industries and distinguish them from those of autogenerators and new independent companies set up to generate electricity. The activities of the autogenerators and the independent companies were classified under the heading "Other generating companies". In the 1994 Digest, a new terminology was adopted to encompass the new independent producers, who were then beginning to make a significant contribution to electricity supply. Under this terminology, all companies whose prime purpose is the generation of electricity are included under the heading "Major power producers" (or MPPs). The term "Other generators" ("Autogenerators" in the balance tables) is restricted to companies who produce electricity as part of their manufacturing or other commercial activities, but whose main business is not electricity generation. "Other generators" also covers generation by energy services companies at power stations on an industrial or commercial site where the main purpose is the supply of electricity to that site, even if the energy service company is a subsidiary of a major power producer. Most generators of electricity from renewable sources (apart from large scale hydro and some biofuels) are also included as "Other generators" because of their comparatively small size, even though their main activity is electricity generation.

5.50 **Major power producers at the end of 2005 were:**
AES Electric Ltd., Baglan Generation Ltd., Barking Power Ltd., BNFL Magnox., British Energy plc., Centrica plc., Coolkeeragh ESB Ltd., Corby Power Ltd., Coryton Energy Company Ltd., Derwent Cogeneration Ltd., Drax Power Ltd., EDF Energy plc., E.On UK plc., Fellside Heat and Power Ltd., Fibrogen Ltd., Fibropower Ltd., Fibrothetford Ltd., First Hydro Company, Immingham CHP, International Power plc., Premier Power Ltd., Rocksavage Power Company Ltd., RWE Npower plc., Scottish Power plc., Scottish and Southern Energy plc., Seabank Power Ltd., SELCHP Ltd., Spalding Energy Company Ltd., Teesside Power Ltd., Western Power Generation Ltd.

Types of station
5.51 The various types of station identified in the tables of this chapter are as follows:

Conventional steam stations are stations that generate electricity by burning fossil fuels to convert water into steam, which then powers steam turbines.

Nuclear stations are also steam stations but the heat needed to produce the steam comes from nuclear fission.

Gas turbines use pressurised combustion gases from fuel burned in one or more combustion chambers to turn a series of bladed fan wheels and rotate the shaft on which they are mounted. This then drives the generator. The fuel burnt is usually natural gas or gas oil.

Combined cycle gas turbine (CCGT) stations combine in the same plant gas turbines and steam turbines connected to one or more electrical generators. This enables electricity to be produced at higher efficiencies than is otherwise possible when either gas or steam turbines are used in isolation. The gas turbine (usually fuelled by natural gas or oil) produces mechanical power (to drive the generator) and waste heat. The hot exhaust gases (waste heat) are fed to a boiler, where steam is raised at pressure to drive a conventional steam turbine that is also connected to an electrical generator.

Natural flow hydro-electric stations use natural water flows to turn turbines.

Pumped storage hydro-electric stations use electricity to pump water into a high level reservoir. This water is then released to generate electricity at peak times. Where the reservoir is open, the stations also generate some natural flow electricity; this is included with natural flow generation. As electricity is used in the pumping process, pumped storage stations are net consumers of electricity.

Other stations include wind turbines and stations burning fuels such as landfill gas, sewage sludge, biomass and waste.

Public distribution system
5.52 This comprises the grid systems in England and Wales, Scotland and Northern Ireland. From April 2005 the Scotland and England and Wales systems have been combined into a single grid.

Sectors used for sales/consumption
5.53 The various sectors used for sales and consumption analyses are standardised across all chapters of the 2005 Digest. For definitions of the sectors see Chapter 1 paragraphs 1.52 to 1.56 and Annex A paragraphs A.31 to A.42.

Declared net capability and declared net capacity
5.54 Declared net capability is the maximum power available for export from a power station on a continuous basis minus any power imported by the station from the network to run its own plant. It represents the nominal maximum capability of a generating set to supply electricity to consumers. The registered capacity of a generating set differs from declared net capability in that, for registered capacity, not all power consumed by the plant is subtracted from the normal full load capacity, only the MW consumed by the generating set through its transformer when generating at its normal full load capacity. For the nuclear industry, the World Association of Nuclear Operators (WANO) recommends that capacity of its reactors is measured in terms of Reference Unit Power (RUP) and it is the RUP figure that is given for both as equivalent to both the installed capacity and the declared net capability of nuclear stations.

5.55 Declared net capacity is used to measure the maximum power available from generating stations that use renewable resources. For wind and tidal power a factor is applied to declared net capability to take account of the intermittent nature of the energy source (eg 0.43 for wind).

Load factors
5.56 The following definitions are used in Table 5.10:

Maximum load – Twice the largest number of units supplied in any consecutive thirty minutes commencing or terminating at the hour.

Simultaneous maximum load met – The maximum load on the grid at any one time. From 2005 (following the introduction of BETTA – see paragraph 5.5) it is measured by the sum of the maximum load met in Great Britain and the load met at the same time in Northern Ireland. Prior to 2005 it was measured by the sum of the maximum load met in England and Wales and the loads met at the same time by companies in other parts of the United Kingdom. In 2005/06 the maximum load in Great Britain occurred on 29 November 2005 at 17.30 (60,100 MW). However, in Northern Ireland the maximum load occurred on 9 January 2006 at 17.30 (1,639 MW), which was 2.6 per cent below the province's record on 20 December 2004. In Great Britain the highest ever load met was 60,118 MW on 10 December 2002.

Plant load factor – The average hourly quantity of electricity supplied during the year, expressed as a percentage of the average output capability at the beginning and the end of year.

System load factor – The average hourly quantity of electricity available during the year expressed as a percentage of the maximum demand nearest the end of the year or early the following year.

Thermal efficiency

5.57   Thermal efficiency is the efficiency with which heat energy contained in fuel is converted into electrical energy. It is calculated for fossil fuel burning stations by expressing electricity generated as a percentage of the total energy content of the fuel consumed (based on average gross calorific values). For nuclear stations it is calculated using the quantity of heat released as a result of fission of the nuclear fuel inside the reactor. The efficiency of CHP systems is discussed separately in Chapter 6, paragraph 6.21and 6.22 and Table 6D. Efficiencies based on gross calorific value of the fuel (sometimes referred to as higher heating values or HHV) are lower than the efficiencies based on net calorific value (or lower heating value LHV). The difference between HHV and LHV is due to the energy associated with the latent heat of the evaporation of water products from the steam cycle which cannot be recovered and put to economic use.

Period covered

5.58   Until 2004 figures for the major power producers relate to periods of 52 weeks as listed below (although some data provided by electricity supply companies related to calendar months and were adjusted to the statistical calendar). In 2004 a change was made to a calendar year basis. This change was made in the middle of the year and the data are largely based on information collected monthly. The January to May 2004 data are therefore based on the 21 weeks ended 29 May 2004 and the calendar months June to December 2004, making a total of 361 days. In terms of days 2004 is therefore 1.1 per cent shorter than 2005:

Year	52 weeks ended
2000	31 December 2000
2001	30 December 2001
2002	29 December 2002
2003	28 December 2003
2004	21 weeks ended 29 May 2004 and 7 months ended 31 December 2004
2005	12 months ended 31 December 2005

5.59   Figures for industrial, commercial and transport undertakings relate to calendar years ending on 31 December, except for the iron and steel industry where figures relate to the following 52 or 53 week periods:

Year	52 weeks ended
2000	30 December 2000
2001	29 December 2001
2002	28 December 2002
	53 weeks ended
2003	3 January 2004
	52 weeks ended
2004	1 January 2005
2005	31 December 2005

Monthly and quarterly data

5.60   Monthly and quarterly data on fuel use, electricity generation and supply and electricity availability and consumption are available on DTI's Energy Statistics web site www.dti.gov.uk/energy/statistics/source/index.html .   Monthly data on fuel used in electricity generation by major power producers are given in Monthly Table 5.3 and monthly data on supplies by type of plant and type of fuel are given in Monthly Table 5.4. Monthly data on availability and consumption of electricity by the main sectors of the economy are given in Monthly Table 5.5. A quarterly commodity balance for electricity is published in DTI's quarterly statistical bulletin *Energy Trends* (Quarterly Table 5.2) along with a quarterly table of fuel use for generation by all generators and electricity supplied by major power producers (Quarterly Table 5.1). Both these quarterly tables are also available from DTI's Energy Statistics web site. See Annex C for more information about *Energy Trends*.

Data collection

5.61   For Major Power Producers, as defined in paragraph 5.49, the data for the tables in this Digest are obtained from the results of an annual DTI inquiry, sent to each company, covering generating capacity, fuel use, generation, sales and distribution of electricity.

5.62   Another annual inquiry is sent to electricity distributors to establish electricity distributed by these companies. Similarly an annual inquiry is sent to licensed suppliers of electricity to establish electricity sales by these companies. Electricity consumption for the iron and steel sector is based on data provided by the Iron and Steel Statistics Bureau (ISSB) rather than electricity suppliers since electricity suppliers were over estimating their sales to this sector. The difference between the ISSB and electricity suppliers' figures has been re-allocated to other sectors based on the results of the Office for National Statistics' Purchases Inquiry. A further means of checking electricity consumption data has been employed this year on the 2004 figures. Data obtained at meter point level for the purpose of construction regional and local level electricity consumption estimates has been cross-referenced to data obtained from the Inter Departmental Business Register (IDBR) held by the Office for National Statistics. These IDBR data give a standard industrial coding. Not all meter point data could be cross referenced but where a match was obtained the percentage shares of electricity consumption between the sectors given in the electricity tables of this chapter were generally within 2 percentage points of each other.

5.63   Companies that generate electricity mainly for their own use (known as autogenerators or autoproducers – see paragraph 5.49, above) are covered by an annual inquiry commissioned by DTI but carried out by the Office for National Statistics (ONS) from their Newport offices.   Where autogenerators operate a combined heat and power (CHP) plant, this survey is now supplemented by information from the CHP Quality Assessment scheme (for autogenerators who have registered under the scheme – see Chapter 6 on CHP). The ONS inquiry only covers generators with capacities greater than 100 kWe and DTI estimates fuel use and electricity generation for smaller companies or includes estimates made by FES for CHP electricity, described in Chapter 6. There are two areas of autogeneration that are covered by direct data collection by DTI, mainly because the return contains additional energy information needed by the Department. These are the Iron and Steel industry, and generation on behalf of London Underground.

Losses and statistical differences

5.64   Statistical differences are included in Tables 5.1, 5.2 and 5.3. These arise because data collected on production and supply do not match exactly with data collected on sales or consumption. One of the reasons for this is that some of the data are based on different calendars as described in paragraphs [5.58 and 5.59], above. Sales data based on calendar years will always have included more electricity consumption than the slightly shorter statistical year of exactly 52 weeks.

5.65   Of the losses shown in the commodity balance for electricity of just over 30,600 GWh in 2005, it is estimated that about 5,800 GWh (1½ per cent of electricity available) were lost from the high voltage transmission system of the National Grid and 23,500 GWh (6 per cent) between the grid supply points (the gateways to the public supply system's distribution network) and customers' meters. The balance (about ½ per cent of electricity available) is accounted for by theft and meter fraud, accounting differences and calendar differences (as described in paragraph 5.64, above).

5.66   Care should be exercised in interpreting the figures for individual industries in the commodity balance tables. As new suppliers have entered the market and companies have moved between suppliers, it has not been possible to ensure consistent classification between and within industry sectors and across years. The breakdown of final consumption includes some estimated data. In 2005, for about 2 per cent of consumption of electricity supplied by the public distribution system, the sector figures are partially estimated.

Contact: *Mike Janes (Statistician)*   *Joe Ewins*
            Energy Markets Information and Analysis   *Energy Information Systems*
            mike.janes@dti.gsi.gov.uk   *joe.ewins@dti.gsi.gov.uk*
            020-7215 5186   *020-7215 5190*

5.1 Commodity balances

Electricity

			GWh
	2003	2004	2005
Total electricity			
Supply			
Production	395,475r	392,657r	397,595
Other sources *(1)*	2,734	2,649	2,930
Imports	5,119	9,784	11,160
Exports	-2,959	-2,294	-2,839
Marine bunkers	-	-	-
Stock change *(2)*	-	-	-
Transfers	-	-	-
Total supply	**400,369r**	**402,795r**	**408,846**
Statistical difference *(3)*	**+2,208r**	**+3,355r**	**+1,581**
Total demand	**398,161r**	**399,440r**	**407,265**
Transformation	-	-	-
Electricity generation	-	-	-
Major power producers	-	-	-
Other generators	-	-	-
Heat generation	-	-	-
Petroleum refineries	-	-	-
Coke manufacture	-	-	-
Blast furnaces	-	-	-
Patent fuel manufacture	-	-	-
Other	-	-	-
Energy industry use	**32,081r**	**29,694r**	**31,384**
Electricity generation	18,136r	17,081r	17,832
Oil and gas extraction	551	558	505
Petroleum refineries	5,769r	4,944r	5,624
Coal extraction and coke manufacture	1,190	1,118	1,165
Blast furnaces	492	468	515
Patent fuel manufacture	-	-	-
Pumped storage	3,546	3,497	3,707
Other	2,398r	2,028r	2,036
Losses	**29,862**	**30,728**	**30,638**
Final consumption	**336,218r**	**339,018r**	**345,243**
Industry	**113,358r**	**115,906r**	**118,832**
Unclassified	-	-	-
Iron and steel	5,434	5,412	5,019
Non-ferrous metals	7,284r	7,352r	7,693
Mineral products	7,651	7,833r	7,965
Chemicals	20,941r	22,087r	23,162
Mechanical engineering, etc	8,839	8,509r	8,695
Electrical engineering, etc	6,019	6,821r	7,427
Vehicles	5,660	5,682r	5,859
Food, beverages, etc	11,949	12,361r	12,593
Textiles, leather, etc	3,443	3,407r	3,477
Paper, printing, etc	12,750r	12,921r	13,050
Other industries	21,686r	21,716r	21,962
Construction	1,701	1,804r	1,929
Transport	**8,212r**	**8,444r**	**8,609**
Air	-	-	-
Rail *(4)*	2,700	2,700	2,700
Road	-	-	-
National navigation	-	-	-
Pipelines	-	-	-
Other	**214,648r**	**214,667r**	**217,802**
Domestic	115,761	115,526	116,811
Public administration	20,623r	20,731r	21,545
Commercial	74,238	74,215	75,294
Agriculture	4,025	4,194	4,152
Miscellaneous	-	-	-
Non energy use	-	-	-

5.1 Commodity balances (continued)

Electricity

GWh

	2003	2004	2005
Electricity production			
Total production (5)	**395,475r**	**392,657r**	**397,595**
Primary electricity			
Major power producers	**91,254**	**83,999r**	**85,611**
Nuclear	88,686	79,999	81,618
Large scale hydro (5)	2,523r	3,908r	3,826
Small scale hydro (6)	44r	92r	167
Wind	-	-	-
Other generators	**1,948**	**2,869r**	**3,884**
Nuclear	-	-	-
Large scale hydro	561r	739r	668
Small scale hydro (6)	99r	190r	300
Wind	1,288	1,939	2,916
Secondary electricity			
Major power producers	**268,612**	**271,758**	**273,838**
Coal	134,023	127,827	132,233
Oil	2,197	1,883	2,716
Gas	131,238	140,577	137,483
Renewables	1,154	1,471	1,406
Other	-	-	-
Other generators	**33,660r**	**34,031r**	**34,261**
Coal	4,282	3,995r	4,024
Oil	2,397	2,990r	2,702
Gas	17,643r	16,761r	15,747
Renewables	5,537r	6,407	6,875
Other	3,800r	3,878r	4,914
Primary and secondary production (7)			
Nuclear	88,686	79,999	81,618
Hydro	3,228r	4,930r	4,961
Wind	1,288	1,939	2,916
Coal	138,305	131,822r	136,257
Oil	4,594r	4,873r	5,418
Gas	148,881r	157,338r	153,230
Other renewables	6,692r	7,878	8,281
Other	3,800r	3,878r	4,914
Total production	**395,475r**	**392,657r**	**397,595**

(1) Pumped storage production.
(2) Stock fall (+), stock rise (-).
(3) Total supply minus total demand.
(4) See paragraph 5.14.
(5) Excludes pumped storage production.
(6) A re-assessment in 2004 showed that some small scale hydro output previously classified to Other
     Generators should be classified to Major Power Producers. Work is continuing to see if the
     re-classification can be extended back to earlier years.
(7) These figures are the same as the electricity generated figures in Table 5.6 except that they exclude
     pumped storage production. Table 5.6 shows that electricity used on works is deducted to obtain
     electricity supplied. It is electricity supplied that is used to produce Chart 5.3 showing each fuel's share
     of electricity output (see paragraph 5.27).

5.2 Electricity supply and consumption

GWh

	2001	2002	2003	2004	2005
Supply					
Production	382,364	384,594	395,475r	392,657r	397,595
Other sources (1)	2,422	2,652	2,734	2,649	2,930
Imports	10,663	9,182	5,119	9,784	11,160
Exports	-264	-768	-2,959	-2,294	-2,839
Total supply	**395,185**	**395,661**	**400,369r**	**402,795r**	**408,846**
Statistical difference (2)	+1,175	+983	+2,208r	+3,355r	+1,581
Total demand	**394,010**	**394,678**	**398,161r**	**399,440r**	**407,265**
Transformation	-	-	-	-	-
Energy industry use	**30,387**	**31,297**	**32,081r**	**29,694r**	**31,384**
Electricity generation	17,394	17,126	18,136r	17,081r	17,832
Oil and gas extraction	675	540	551	558	505
Petroleum refineries	5,231	6,553	5,769r	4,944r	5,624
Coal and coke	1,223	1,163	1,190	1,118	1,165
Blast furnaces	885	502	492	468	515
Pumped storage	3,210	3,463	3,546	3,497	3,707
Other	1,769	1,950	2,398r	2,028r	2,036
Losses	**30,902**	**29,980**	**29,862**	**30,728**	**30,638**
Final consumption	**332,721**	**333,401**	**336,218r**	**339,018r**	**345,243**
Industry	**111,337**	**112,648**	**113,358r**	**115,906r**	**118,832**
Unclassified	-	-	-	-	-
Iron and steel	5,303	5,092	5,434	5,412	5,019
Non-ferrous metals	7,324	6,365	7,284r	7,352r	7,693
Mineral products	7,247	7,115	7,651	7,833r	7,965
Chemicals	21,079	22,861	20,941r	22,087r	23,162
Mechanical engineering. etc	8,569	8,794	8,839	8,509r	8,695
Electrical engineering, etc	5,697	5,880	6,019	6,821r	7,427
Vehicles	5,824	5,625	5,660	5,682r	5,859
Food, beverages, etc	11,570	12,166	11,949	12,361r	12,593
Textiles, leather, etc	3,303	3,463	3,443	3,407r	3,477
Paper, printing, etc	11,511	11,988	12,750r	12,921r	13,050
Other industries	22,213	21,599	21,686r	21,716r	21,962
Construction	1,698	1,700	1,701	1,804r	1,929
Transport	**8,828**	**8,454**	**8,212r**	**8,444r**	**8,609**
Other	**212,557**	**212,299**	**214,648r**	**214,667r**	**217,802**
Domestic	115,337	114,534	115,761	115,526	116,811
Public administration	21,105	20,657	20,623r	20,731r	21,545
Commercial	72,014	72,963	74,238	74,215	75,294
Agriculture	4,100	4,145	4,025	4,194	4,152
Miscellaneous	-	-	-	-	-
Non energy use	**-**	**-**	**-**	**-**	**-**

(1) Pumped storage production.
(2) Total supply minus total demand.

5.3 Commodity balances

Public distribution system and other generators

GWh

	2003			2004			2005		
	Public distribution system	Other generators	Total	Public distribution system	Other generators	Total	Public distribution system	Other generators	Total
Supply									
Major power producers	359,866	-	359,866	355,757r	-	355,757r	359,449	-	359,449
Other generators	-	35,609r	35,609r	-	36,900r	36,900r	-	38,146	38,146
Other sources (1)	2,734	-	2,734	2,649	-	2,649	2,930	-	2,930
Imports	5,119	-	5,119	9,784	-	9,784	11,160	-	11,160
Exports	-2,959	-	-2,959	-2,294	-	-2,294	-2,839	-	-2,839
Transfers	+11,917r	-11,917r	-	+10,954r	-10,954r	-	+10,533	-10,533	-
Total supply	**376,677r**	**23,692r**	**400,369r**	**376,849r**	**25,946r**	**402,795r**	**381,233**	**27,613**	**408,846**
Statistical difference (2)	**+2,208r**	**-r**	**+2,208r**	**+3,355r**	**-r**	**+3,355r**	**+1,581**	**-**	**+1,581**
Total demand	**374,469**	**23,692r**	**398,161r**	**373,494r**	**25,946r**	**399,440r**	**379,652**	**27,613**	**407,265**
Transformation	-	-	-	-	-	-	-	-	-
Energy industry use	**25,133**	**6,948r**	**32,081r**	**23,728r**	**5,967r**	**29,694r**	**24,816**	**6,568**	**31,384**
Electricity generation	16,747	1,389r	18,136r	15,582r	1,499r	17,081r	16,266	1,566	17,832
Oil and gas extraction	551	-	551	558	-	558	505	-	505
Petroleum refineries	1,550	4,219r	5,769r	1,478	3,466r	4,944r	1,593	4,031	5,624
Coal and coke	1,091	99	1,190	1,027	91	1,118	1,066	98	1,165
Blast furnaces	-	492	492	-	468	468	-	515	515
Pumped storage	3,546	-	3,546	3,497	-	3,497	3,707	-	3,707
Other fuel industries	1,649	749r	2,398r	1,585	443r	2,028r	1,679	358	2,036
Losses	**29,845**	**17**	**29,862**	**30,701**	**27**	**30,728**	**30,606**	**31**	**30,638**
Final consumption	**319,492**	**16,727r**	**336,218r**	**319,066r**	**19,952r**	**339,018r**	**324,230**	**21,013**	**345,243**
Industry	**98,507**	**14,852r**	**113,358r**	**98,594r**	**17,312r**	**115,906r**	**101,035**	**17,796**	**118,832**
Iron and steel	4,489	945	5,434	4,480	932	5,412	4,033	986	5,019
Non-ferrous metals	4,403	2,881r	7,284r	4,183	3,169r	7,352r	4,355	3,338	7,693
Mineral products	7,443	208	7,651	7,638r	195r	7,833r	7,772	193	7,965
Chemicals	15,481	5,460r	20,941r	14,611r	7,476r	22,087r	15,190	7,972	23,162
Mechanical engineering, etc	8,501	338	8,839	8,291r	217r	8,509r	8,531	164	8,695
Electrical engineering, etc	6,008	11	6,019	6,809r	11	6,821r	7,415	11	7,427
Vehicles	5,534	127	5,660	5,550r	132	5,682r	5,742	117	5,859
Food, beverages, etc	10,837	1,112	11,949	10,667r	1,694r	12,361r	10,887	1,706	12,593
Textiles, leather, etc	3,330	113	3,443	3,288r	119r	3,407r	3,387	90	3,477
Paper, printing, etc	9,590	3,159	12,750r	10,019r	2,902r	12,921r	10,235	2,815	13,050
Other industries	21,203	482r	21,686r	21,268	449r	21,716r	21,574	387	21,962
Construction	1,686	15	1,701	1,789r	15	1,804r	1,914	15	1,929
Transport	**7,534**	**678r**	**8,212r**	**7,320**	**1,125r**	**8,444r**	**7,464**	**1,145**	**8,609**
Of which National Rail (3)	2,700	-	2,700	2,700	-	2,700	2,700	-	2,700
Other	**213,451**	**1,197r**	**214,648r**	**213,152**	**1,516r**	**214,667r**	**215,730**	**2,072**	**217,802**
Domestic	115,761	-	115,761	115,526	-	115,526	116,811	-	116,811
Standard	64,381	-	64,381	64,441	-	64,441	64,676	-	64,676
Economy 7 and other off-peak	32,109	-	32,109	31,968	-	31,968	32,344	-	32,344
Prepayment (standard)	12,643	-	12,643	12,527	-	12,527	13,091	-	13,091
Prepayment (off-peak)	6,191	-	6,191	6,179	-	6,179	6,202	-	6,202
Sales under any other arrangement	437	-	437	411	-	411	498	-	498
Public administration	19,427	1,197r	20,623r	19,216	1,516r	20,731r	19,474	2,072	21,545
Public lighting (4)	2,050	-	2,050	1,991	-	1,991	2,095	-	2,095
Other public sector	17,377	1,197r	18,573r	17,225	1,516r	18,741r	17,379	2,072	19,451
Commercial	74,238	-	74,238	74,215	-	74,215	75,294	-	75,294
Shops	34,180	-	34,180	34,029	-	34,029	34,258	-	34,258
Offices	22,105	-	22,105	22,252	-	22,252	22,422	-	22,422
Hotels	8,611	-	8,611	8,645	-	8,645	8,705	-	8,705
Combined domestic/ commercial premises	1,896	-	1,896	1,831	-	1,831	2,230	-	2,230
Post and telecommunications	5,746	-	5,746	5,709	-	5,709	5,880	-	5,880
Unclassified	1,700	-	1,700	1,750	-	1,750	1,800	-	1,800
Agriculture	4,025	-	4,025	4,194	-	4,194	4,152	-	4,152

(1) Pumped storage production.
(2) Total supply minus total demand.
(3) See paragraph 5.14
(4) Sales for public lighting purposes are increasingly covered by wider contracts that cannot distinguish the public lighting element.

5.4 Fuel used in generation[1]

	Unit	2001	2002	2003	2004	2005
					Original units of measurement	
Major power producers (2)						
Coal	M tonnes	49.29	46.14	50.90	48.97	50.58
Oil (3)	"	0.79	0.67	0.63	0.55	0.79
Gas	GWh	276,764	291,264	284,662	304,495	295,643
Other generators (2)						
Transport undertakings:						
Gas	GWh	2,238	1,793	93	27	38
Undertakings in industrial and commercial sectors:						
Coal (4)	M tonnes	1.65	1.61	1.57	1.480r	1.50
Oil (5)	"	0.55	0.54	0.48	0.490r	0.46
Gas (6)	GWh	33,937	36,790	39,825r	36,590r	38,153
					Million tonnes of oil equivalent	
Major power producers (2)						
Coal		30.575	28.623	31.570	30.375	31.654
Oil (3)		0.818	0.689	0.654	0.577r	0.827
Gas		23.797	25.044	24.476	26.182	25.421
Nuclear		20.768	20.100	20.041	18.164	18.372
Hydro (natural flow) (7)		0.276	0.338	0.221	0.345r	0.343
Other renewables (7)		0.253	0.274	0.381	0.540	0.818
Net imports		0.894	0.724	0.186	0.644	0.715
Total major power producers (2)		**77.381**	**75.792**	**77.530r**	**76.827r**	**78.150**
Of which: conventional thermal and other stations (9)		32.629	30.574	33.289r	32.051r	32.096
combined cycle gas turbine stations		22.814	24.056	23.793	25.623	26.623
Other generators (2)						
Transport undertakings:						
Gas		0.192	0.154	0.008	0.002	0.003
Undertakings in industrial and commercial sectors:						
Coal (4)		1.031	1.003	0.972	0.925r	0.963
Oil (5)		0.605	0.599	0.539	0.541r	0.502
Gas (6)		2.918	3.163	3.424	3.146r	3.281
Hydro (natural flow) (7)		0.072	0.074	0.057	0.080r	0.083
Other renewables (7)		1.704	1.907	2.138r	2.394r	2.778
Other fuels (8)		1.036	1.061	1.522r	1.572r	2.073
Total other generators (2)		**7.559**	**7.962**	**8.659r**	**8.661r**	**9.684**
All generating companies						
Coal (4)		31.606	29.626	32.542	31.300r	32.617
Oil (3)(5)		1.423	1.288	1.192r	1.119r	1.329
Gas (6)		26.908	28.362	27.909	29.330r	28.705
Nuclear		20.768	20.100	20.041	18.164	18.372
Hydro (natural flow) (7)		0.348	0.412	0.278	0.424r	0.427
Other renewables (7)		1.957	2.181	2.519r	2.934r	3.596
Other fuels (8)		1.036	1.061	1.522r	1.572r	2.073
Net imports		0.894	0.724	0.186	0.644	0.715
Total all generating companies		**84.941**	**83.754**	**86.189r**	**85.487r**	**87.834**

(1) For details of where to find monthly updates of fuel used in electricity generation by major power producers and quarterly updates of fuel used in electricity generation by all generating companies see paragraph 5.60.

(2) See paragraphs 5.49 and 5.50 for information on companies covered

(3) Includes Orimulsion, oil used in gas turbine and diesel plants, and oil used for lighting up coal fired boilers

(4) Includes coke oven coke.

(5) Includes refinery gas.

(6) Includes colliery methane.

(7) Renewable sources, which are included under hydro and other renewables in this table, are shown separately in Table 7.7 o Chapter 7.

(8) Main fuels included are coke oven gas, blast furnace gas, and waste products from chemical processes

(9) Includes gas turbines, oil engines and plants producing electricity from renewable sources other than hydro

5.5 Electricity supply, electricity supplied (net), electricity available, electricity consumption and electricity sales

	2001	2002	2003	2004	GWh 2005
Total supply					
(as given in Tables 5.1 and 5.2)	395,185	395,661	400,369r	402,795r	408,846
less imports of electricity	-10,663	-9,182	-5,119	-9,784	-11,160
plus exports of electricity	+264	+768	+2,959	+2,294	+2,839
less electricity used in pumped storage	-3,210	-3,463	-3,546	-3,497	-3,707
less electricity used on works	-17,394	-17,126	-18,136r	-17,081r	-17,832
equals					
Electricity supplied (net)	364,182	366,657	376,527r	374,727r	378,986
(as given in Tables, 5.6, 5.1.2 and 5.1.3)					
Total supply					
(as given in Tables 5.1 and 5.2)	395,185	395,661	400,369r	402,795r	408,846
less electricity used in pumped storage	-3,210	-3,463	-3,546	-3,497	-3,707
less electricity used on works	-17,394	-17,126	-18,136r	-17,081r	-17,832
equals					
Electricity available	374,581	375,072	378,687r	382,217r	387,307
(as given in Table 5.1.2)					
Final consumption					
(as given in Tables 5.2 and 5.3)	332,721	333,401	336,218r	339,018r	345,243
plus Iron and steel consumption counted as energy industry use	+1,158	+648	+648	+625	+683
equals					
Final users	333,879	334,049	336,866r	339,643r	345,926
(as given in Table 5.1.2)					
Final consumption					
Public distribution system					
(as given in Table 5.3)	315,862	315,050	319,492	319,066r	324,230
plus Oil and gas extraction use	+675	+540	+551	+558	+505
plus Petroleum refineries use	+1,912	+1,598	+1,550	+1,478	+1,593
plus Coal and coke use	+1,047	+1,064	+1,091	+1,027	+1,066
plus Other fuel industries use	+1,571	+1,548	+1,649	+1,585	+1,679
equals					
UK Electricity sales (1)	321,067	319,800	324,333	323,714r	329,073

(1) The renewables obligation percentage is calculated using total renewables generation on an obligation basis from Table 7.4 (x 100) as the numerator, and this figure as the denominator. Separate electricity sales data for public electricity suppliers are given for England and Wales, Scotland and Northern Ireland in Table 5.5 of Energy Trends on the DTI web site at www.dti.gov.uk/energy/statistics/source/electricity/page18527.html (and scroll to the Monthly Tables section).

5.6 Electricity fuel use, generation and supply

GWh

	Coal	Oil	Gas	Nuclear	Renew-ables (1)	Other (3)	Total	Hydro-natural flow	Hydro-pumped storage	Other (4)	Total All sources
2001											
Major power producers (2)											
Fuel used	355,582	9,510	276,761	241,537	3,102	-	886,492	3,215	2,422	-	892,129
Generation	127,128	2,472	126,999	90,093	738	-	347,429	3,215	2,422	-	353,066
Used on works	5,830	281	2,709	7,108	46	-	15,973	11	82	-	16,066
Supplied (gross)	121,298	2,192	124,289	82,985	692	-	331,456	3,203	2,340	-	336,999
Used in pumping											3,210
Supplied (net)											333,789
Other generators (2)											
Fuel used	11,987	7,035	35,757	-	18,849	12,053	85,682	840	-	967	87,489
Generation	4,333	2,781	14,906	-	4,316	3,577	29,913	840	-	967	31,721
Used on works	230	196	480	-	246	165	1,316	12	-	-	1,328
Supplied	4,104	2,585	14,426	-	4,070	3,412	28,597	829	-	967	30,393
All generating companies											
Fuel used	367,569	16,545	312,518	241,537	21,951	12,053	972,174	4,055	2,422	967	979,618
Generation	131,461	5,253	141,905	90,093	5,054	3,577	377,342	4,055	2,422	967	384,786
Used on works	6,059	476	3,189	7,108	292	165	17,289	23	82	-	17,394
Supplied (gross)	125,402	4,777	138,716	82,985	4,762	3,412	360,053	4,032	2,340	967	367,392
Used in pumping											3,210
Supplied (net)											364,182
2002											
Major power producers (2)											
Fuel used	332,889	8,011	291,264	233,765	3,186	-	869,115	3,927	2,652	-	875,694
Generation	120,958	2,011	135,741	87,848	856	-	347,414	3,927	2,652	-	353,994
Used on works	5,574	378	2,877	6,758	55	-	15,643	14	90	-	15,746
Supplied (gross)	115,383	1,633	132,864	81,090	802	-	331,772	3,914	2,562	-	338,248
Used in pumping											3,463
Supplied (net)											334,785
Other generators (2)											
Fuel used	11,663	6,966	38,177	-	20,922	12,343	90,071	860	-	1,259	92,190
Generation	3,321	2,788	16,536	-	4,769	3,719	31,133	860	-	1,259	33,252
Used on works	230	204	530	-	264	141	1,369	11	-	-	1,380
Supplied	3,092	2,584	16,006	-	4,505	3,578	29,765	849	-	1,259	31,873
All generating companies											
Fuel used	344,552	14,977	329,442	233,765	24,107	12,343	959,186	4,788	2,652	1,259	967,884
Generation	124,279	4,799	152,277	87,848	5,625	3,719	378,548	4,788	2,652	1,259	387,246
Used on works	5,804	582	3,407	6,758	318	141	17,011	25	90	-	17,126
Supplied (gross)	118,475	4,217	148,870	81,090	5,307	3,578	361,537	4,763	2,562	1,259	370,120
Used in pumping											3,463
Supplied (net)											366,657
2003											
Major power producers (2)											
Fuel used	367,162	7,604	284,662	233,080	4,434	-	896,941	2,568r	2,734	-	902,243r
Generation	134,023	2,197	131,238	88,686	1,154	-	357,299	2,568r	2,734	-	362,600r
Used on works	6,325	249	3,201	6,775	95	-	16,645	9r	92	-	16,747r
Supplied (gross)	127,698	1,948	128,037	81,911	1,059	-	340,654	2,559	2,641	-	345,854
Used in pumping											3,546
Supplied (net)											342,308
Other generators (2)											
Fuel used	11,301	6,263	39,265r	-	23,574r	17,703r	98,106r	660	-	1,288	100,054r
Generation	4,282	2,397	17,643r	-	5,537r	3,800r	33,660r	660	-	1,288	35,609r
Used on works	220	174	547r	-	306r	135r	1,382r	7	-	-	1,389r
Supplied	4,062	2,223	17,097r	-	5,231r	3,665r	32,278r	653	-	1,288	34,220r
All generating companies											
Fuel used	378,463	13,867	323,926	233,080	28,008r	17,703r	995,047r	3,228r	2,734	1,288	1,002,297r
Generation	138,305	4,594r	148,881r	88,686	6,692r	3,800r	390,959r	3,228r	2,734	1,288	398,209r
Used on works	6,545	424	3,747	6,775	401r	135r	18,027r	16r	92	-	18,136r
Supplied (gross)	131,760	4,171	145,134r	81,911	6,290r	3,665r	372,932r	3,212	2,641	1,288	380,074r
Used in pumping											3,546
Supplied (net)											376,528r

5.6 Electricity fuel use, generation and supply (cont'd)

GWh

	Thermal sources							Non-thermal sources			
	Coal	Oil	Gas	Nuclear	Renew-ables (1)	Other (3)	Total	Hydro-natural flow	Hydro-pumped storage	Other (4)	Total All sources
2004											
Major power producers (2)											
Fuel used	353,256	6,743r	304,495r	211,248r	6,480	-	882,222r	4,000r	2,649	-	888,870r
Generation	127,827	1,883	140,577	79,999	1,471	-	351,757	4,000r	2,649	-	358,406r
Used on works	5,890	354	2,820	6,317	104	-	15,486	7r	90	-	15,582r
Supplied (gross)	121,937	1,528	137,758	73,682	1,367	-	336,271	3,993r	2,559	-	342,824r
Used in pumping											3,497
Supplied (net)											339,327r
Other generators (2)											
Fuel used	10,754r	6,297r	36,022r	-	25,903r	18,284r	97,260r	929r	-	1,939	100,129r
Generation	3,995r	2,990r	16,761r	-	6,407	3,878r	34,031r	929r	-	1,939	36,900r
Used on works	210r	213r	519r	-	406r	140r	1,488r	11r	-	-	1,499r
Supplied	3,785r	2,777r	16,242r	-	6,001r	3,738r	32,543r	919r	-	1,939	35,401r
All generating companies											
Fuel used	364,010r	13,041r	340,517r	211,248r	32,383r	18,284r	979,482r	4,930r	2,649	1,939	988,999r
Generation	131,822r	4,873r	157,338r	79,999	7,878	3,878r	385,788r	4,930r	2,649	1,939	395,306r
Used on works	6,100r	567r	3,339r	6,317	511r	140r	16,974r	17r	90	-	17,081r
Supplied (gross)	125,722r	4,306r	153,999r	73,682	7,368r	3,738r	368,814r	4,912r	2,559	1,939	378,224r
Used in pumping											3,497
Supplied (net)											374,727r
2005											
Major power producers (2)											
Fuel used	368,134	10,025	295,643	213,661	9,422	-	896,886	3,993	2,930	-	903,809
Generation	132,233	2,716	137,483	81,618	1,406	-	355,456	3,993	2,930	-	362,379
Used on works	6,094	511	2,958	6,445	97	-	16,106	7	154	-	16,266
Supplied (gross)	126,140	2,205	134,524	75,172	1,309	-	339,350	3,987	2,776	-	346,113
Used in pumping											3,707
Supplied (net)											342,406
Other generators (2)											
Fuel used	11,204	5,842	37,603	-	29,395	24,108	108,153	968	-	2,916	112,037
Generation	4,024	2,702	15,747	-	6,875	4,914	34,261	968	-	2,916	38,145
Used on works	214	183	488	-	473	192	1,550	16	-	-	1,566
Supplied	3,810	2,519	15,259	-	6,401	4,722	32,711	952	-	2,916	36,579
All generating companies											
Fuel used	379,339	15,867	333,246	213,661	38,818	24,108	1,005,039	4,961	2,930	2,916	1,015,846
Generation	132,447	2,899	153,230	81,618	8,281	4,914	389,718	4,961	2,930	2,916	400,525
Used on works	6,307	694	3,446	6,445	571	192	17,656	23	154	-	17,832
Supplied (gross)	129,950	4,724	149,783	75,173	7,710	4,722	372,062	4,938	2,776	2,916	382,692
Used in pumping											3,707
Supplied (net)											378,985

	2001		2002		2003		2004		2005	
	Conv-entional thermal (5)	CCGT	Conv-entional thermal (5)	CCGT	Conv-entional thermal (5)	CCGT	Conv-entional thermal (5)	CCGT	Conv-entional thermal (5)	CCGT
Major power producers (2)										
Generated	133,482	123,846	127,550	132,016	140,301r	128,311r	132,353r	139,405r	137,754	136,084
Supplied (gross)	127,126	121,344	121,297	129,384	133,112r	125,630r	125,419r	137,170r	130,465	133,713
Other generators										
Generated	20,937	8,979	20,557	10,577	22,781r	10,879r	22,105r	11,926r	22,425	11,836
Supplied (gross)	20,066	8,531	19,716	10,049	21,942r	10,336r	21,213r	11,330r	21,465	11,246
All generating companies										
Generated	154,418	132,825	148,107	142,593	163,083r	139,190r	154,458r	151,331r	160,180	147,920
Supplied (gross)	147,192	129,875	141,013	139,433	155,055r	135,966r	146,631r	148,500r	151,930	144,959

(1) Thermal renewable sources are those included under biofuels and non-biodegradable wastes in Chapter 7.
(2) See paragraphs 5.49 and 5.50 on companies covered.
(3) Other thermal sources include coke oven gas, blast furnace gas and waste products from chemical processes.
(4) Other non-thermal sources include wind, wave and solar photovoltaics.
(5) Includes gas turbines, oil engines and plants producing electricity from renewable sources other than hydro.

5.7 Plant capacity - United Kingdom

MW

	2001	2002	2003	2004	end December 2005
Major power producers (1)					
Total declared net capability	**73,382**	**70,369**	**71,465r**	**73,277r**	**74,041**
Of which:					
Conventional steam stations:	34,835	30,687	30,327	30,442r	30,768
Coal fired	24,810	22,427	22,524	22,639	22,627
Oil fired	2,933	2,708	2,930	2,930	3,262
Mixed or dual fired (2)	7,092	5,552	4,873	4,873r	4,879
Combined cycle gas turbine stations	20,517	21,800	23,577	25,323r	25,897
Nuclear stations	12,486	12,240	11,852	11,852	11,852
Gas turbines and oil engines	1,291	1,433	1,537	1,485r	1,346
Hydro-electric stations:					
Natural flow	1,348	1,304	1,267r	1,270r	1,273
Pumped storage	2,788	2,788	2,788	2,788	2,788
Renewables other than hydro	117	117	117	117	117
Other generators (1)					
Total capacity of own generating plant	**6,296**	**6,336**	**6,829**	**7,024r**	**7,697**
Of which:					
Conventional steam stations (3)	3,464	3,325	3,480r	3,416r	3,456
Combined cycle gas turbine stations	1,777	1,854	1,927r	2,019r	2,164
Hydro-electric stations (natural flow)	160	162	165r	135	120
Renewables other than hydro	895	995	1,257r	1,454r	1,957
All generating companies					
Total capacity	**79,678**	**76,705**	**78,294r**	**80,301r**	**81,738**
Of which:					
Conventional steam stations (3)	38,299	34,012	33,807r	33,858r	34,224
Combined cycle gas turbine stations	22,294	23,654	25,504r	27,342r	28,061
Nuclear stations	12,486	12,240	11,852	11,852	11,852
Gas turbines and oil engines	1,291	1,433	1,537	1,485r	1,346r
Hydro-electric stations:					
Natural flow	1,508	1,466	1,432r	1,405r	1,393
Pumped storage	2,788	2,788	2,788	2,788	2,788
Renewables other than hydro	1,012	1,112	1,374r	1,571r	2,074

(1) See paragraphs 5.49 and 5.50 for information on companies covered.
(2) Includes gas fired stations that are not Combined Cycle Gas Turbines.
(3) For other generators, conventional steam stations include combined heat and power plants (electrical capacity only) but
   exclude combined cycle gas turbine plants, hydro-electric stations and plants using renewable sources.

5.8 Plant capacity - England and Wales, Scotland, and Northern Ireland

MW

	2001	2002	2003	2004	2005
				end December	
Major power producers in England and Wales (1)					
Total declared net capability	**61,850**	**59,087**	**60,056r**	**61,865r**	**62,333**
Of which:					
Conventional steam stations:	28,128	25,634	26,171	26,286r	26,792
Coal fired	21,240	18,971	19,068	19,183	19,171
Oil fired	2,753	2,528	2,750	2,750	3,262
Mixed or dual fired (2)	4,135	4,135	4,353	4,353r	4,359
Combined cycle gas turbine stations	20,443	20,186	20,967	22,664r	22,765
Nuclear stations	10,046	9,800	9,412	9,412	9,412
Gas turbines and oil engines	897	1,131	1,168	1,167r	1,028
Hydro-electric stations:					
Natural flow	131	131	133r	131r	131
Pumped storage	2,088	2,088	2,088	2,088	2,088
Renewables other than hydro	117	117	117	117	117
Major power producers in Scotland (1)					
Total declared net capability	**9,601**	**9,465**	**9,494r**	**9,550r**	**9,647**
Of which:					
Conventional steam and	5,070	5,069	5,070	5,119	5,213
combined cycle gas turbine stations					
Nuclear stations	2,440	2,440	2,440	2,440	2,440
Gas turbines and oil engines	174	83	150	152	152
Hydro-electric stations:					
Natural flow	1,217	1,173	1,134r	1,139r	1,142
Pumped storage	700	700	700	700	700
Major power producers in Northern Ireland (1)					
Total declared net capability	**1,930**	**1,816**	**1,915**	**1,862**	**2,061**

(1) See paragraphs 5.49 and 5.50 for information on companies covered.
(2) Includes gas fired stations that are not Combined Cycle Gas Turbines.

5.9 Capacity of other generators

MW

	2001	2002	2003	2004	2005
				end December	
Capacity of own generating plant (1)					
Undertakings in industrial and commercial sector:					
Petroleum refineries	1,000	954	955	955	1,071
Iron and steel	379	309	312	313r	313
Chemicals	1,340	1,390	1,324	1,330r	1,354
Engineering and other metal trades	617	621	670r	660r	663
Food, drink and tobacco	394	404	379	378r	384
Paper, printing and publishing	548	598	804	795r	792
Other (2)	1,735	1,958	2,281r	2,490r	3,017
Total industrial and commercial sector	6,013	6,233	6,725r	6,921r	7,594
Undertakings in transport sector	283	103	103	103	103
Total other generators	**6,296**	**6,336**	**6,828r**	**7,024r**	**7,697**

(1) For combined heat and power plants the electrical capacity only is included. Further CHP capacity is included under major power producers in Table 5.7. A detailed analysis of CHP capacity is given in the tables of Chapter 6.
(2) Includes companies in the commercial sector.

5.10 Plant loads, demand and efficiency

Major power producers [1]

	Unit	2001	2002	2003	2004	2005
Simultaneous maximum load met [2][3]	MW	58,589	61,717	60,501	61,013	61,697
of which England and Wales	MW	51,548	54,430	52,965	53,795	..
Scotland	MW	5,504	5,688	5,909	5,579	..
Great Britain	MW	57,052	60,118	58,874	59,374	60,100
Northern Ireland	MW	1,537	1,599	1,627	1,639	1,597
Maximum demand as a percentage of UK capacity	Per cent	80.0	87.7	84.7r	83.3r	83.3
Plant load factor						
Combined cycle gas turbine stations	Per cent	69.7	70.0	63.4r	64.8r	59.6
Nuclear stations	"	76.1	75.1	77.8	71.8r	72.4
Hydro-electric stations:						
Natural flow	"	27.4	33.8	22.8r	36.3r	35.8
Pumped storage	"	9.6	10.5	10.8	10.6r	11.4
Conventional thermal and other stations (4)	"	40.2	40.6	47.5r	45.2r	46.3
of which coal-fired stations	"	56.0	55.9	65.0	62.3r	63.6
All plant	"	**53.0**	**53.9**	**55.8**	**54.7r**	**53.6**
System load factor	"	**68.7**	**64.8**	**67.2r**	**67.4r**	**66.6**
Thermal efficiency						
(gross calorific value basis)						
Combined cycle gas turbine stations	"	46.7	47.2	46.4	46.8	48.2
Coal fired stations	"	35.8	36.3	36.5	36.2	35.9
Nuclear stations	"	37.3	37.6	38.1	37.9	38.2

(1) See paragraphs 5.49 and 5.50 for information on companies covered.

(2) Data cover the 12 months ending March of the following year eg 2005 data are for the year ending March 2006

(3) Prior to 2005 the demands shown are those that occurred in Scotland and Northern Ireland at the same time as England and Wales had their maximum demand. In 2005 the Northern Ireland demand shown is that which occurred at the same time as in Great Britain. See paragraph 5.56 for further details.

(4) Conventional steam plants, gas turbines and oil engines and plants producing electricity from renewable sources other than hydro.

5.11 Power Stations in the United Kingdom
(operational at the end of May 2006)[1]

Company Name	Station Name	Fuel	Installed Capacity (MW)	Year of commission or year generation began	Location Scotland, Wales Northern Ireland, or English region
AES	Kilroot	coal/oil	520	1981	Northern Ireland
	Indian Queens	gas oil/kerosene	140	1996	South West
Airtricity	Ardrossan	wind	24	2004	Scotland
	Tappaghan	wind	20	2005	Northern Ireland
Alcan	Lynemouth	coal	420	1995	North East
	Fort William	hydro	62	1929	Scotland
	Kinlochleven	hydro	19.5	1907	Scotland
Baglan Generation Ltd	Baglan Bay	gas turbine	575	2002	Wales
Barking Power	Barking	CCGT	1,000	1994	London
Beaufort Wind Ltd	Bears Down	wind	10	2001	South West
	Bein Ghlas	wind	8	1999	Scotland
	Bryn Titli	wind	10	1994	Wales
	Carno	wind	34	1996	Wales
	Causeymire	wind	48	2004	Scotland
	Kirkby Moor	wind	5	1993	North West
	Lambrigg	wind	7	2000	North West
	Llyn Alaw	wind	20	1997	Wales
	Mynydd Gorddu	wind	10	1996	Wales
	Novar	wind	17	1997	Scotland
	Taff Ely	wind	9	1993	Wales
	Tow Law	wind	2	2001	North East
	Trysglwyn	wind	6	1996	Wales
	Windy Standard	wind	22	1996	Scotland
	North Hoyle	wind (offshore)	60	2003	Wales
Blyth Offshore Wind Ltd	Blyth Offshore	wind (offshore)	4	2000	Yorkshire and the Humber
British Energy	Dungeness B	nuclear	1,090	1983	South East
	Hartlepool	nuclear	1,190	1984	North East
	Heysham1	nuclear	1,160	1984	North West
	Heysham 2	nuclear	1,230	1988	North West
	Hinkley Point B	nuclear	1,220	1976	South West
	Sizewell B	nuclear	1,196	1995	East
	Hunterston B	nuclear	1,215	1976	Scotland
	Torness	nuclear	1,250	1988	Scotland
	Eggborough	coal	1,960	1967	Yorkshire and the Humber
	Aberdare District Energy	gas	10	2002	Wales
	Bridgwater District Energy	gas	10	2000	South West
	Sevington District Energy	gas	10	2000	South East
	Solutia District Energy	gas	10	2000	Wales
BNFL British Nuclear Group	Dungeness A	nuclear	450	1965	South East
	Oldbury	nuclear	434	1967	South West
	Sizewell A	nuclear	420	1966	East
	Wylfa	nuclear	980	1971	South East
	Maentwrog	hydro	28	1928	Wales
Cemmaes Windfarm Ltd	Cemmaes	wind	15	2002 (2)	Wales
Centrica	Barry	CCGT	250	1998	Wales
	Glanford Brigg	CCGT	268	1993	Yorkshire and the Humber
	Killingholme	CCGT	660	1994	the Humber
	Kings Lynn	CCGT	340	1996	East

For footnotes see page 143

5.11 Power Stations in the United Kingdom
(operational at the end of May 2006)[1] (continued)

Company Name	Station Name	Fuel	Installed Capacity (MW)	Year of commission or year generation began	Location Scotland, Wales Northern Ireland, or English region
Centrica (continued)	Peterborough	CCGT	380	1993	East
	Roosecote	CCGT	229	1991	North West
	South Humber Bank 1	CCGT	785	1996	Yorkshire and
	South Humber Bank 2	CCGT	527	1998	the Humber
Citigen (London) UK Ltd	Charterhouse St, London	gas/gas oil CHP	31	1995	London
Cold Northcott Windfarm Ltd	Cold Northcott	wind	7	1993	South West
Coolkeeragh ESB Ltd	Coolkeeragh	CCGT	420	2005	N. Ireland
Corby Power Ltd	Corby	CCGT	401	1993	East Midlands
Coryton Energy Company Ltd	Coryton	CCGT	753	2001	East
Crystal Rig Windfarm Ltd	Crystal Rig Windfarm	wind	50	2003	Scotland
Derwent Cogeneration	Derwent	gas CHP	236	1994	East Midlands
Drax Power Ltd	Drax	coal	3,870	1974	Yorkshire and
	Drax GT	gas oil	75	1971	the Humber
EDF Energy	Sutton Bridge	CCGT	800	1999	East
	Cottam	coal	2,008	1969	East Midlands
	West Burton	coal	1,972	1967	East Midlands
	West Burton GT	gas oil	40	1967	East Midlands
EPR Ely Limited	Elean	straw/gas	38	2001	Cambridgeshire
E.On UK	Kingsnorth	coal/oil	1,940	1970	South East
	Ironbridge	coal	970	1970	West Midlands
	Ratcliffe	coal	2,000	1968	East Midlands
	Grain (3)	oil	650	1979	South East
	Grain GT	gas oil	55	1978	South East
	Kingsnorth GT	gas oil	34	1967	South East
	Ratcliffe GT	gas oil	34	1966	East Midlands
	Taylor's Lane GT	gas oil	132	1979	London
	Connahs Quay	CCGT	1,380	1996	Wales
	Cottam Development Centre	CCGT	400	1999	East Midlands
	Enfield	CCGT	392	1999	London
	Killingholme	CCGT	900	1993	Yorkshire and the Humber
	Rheidol	hydro	49	1961	Wales
	Askam	wind	5	1999	North West
	Bessy Bell	wind	5	1995	Northern Ireland
	Blood Hill	wind	2	1992	East
	Bowbeat	wind	31	2002	Scotland
	Deucheran Hill	wind	16	2001	Scotland
	Great Eppleton	wind	3	1997	North East
	Hare Hill	wind	5	2004	North East
	High Volts	wind	8	2004	North East
	Holmside	wind	5	2004	North East
	Lowca	wind	5	2000	North West
	Oldside	wind	5	1996	North West
	Out Newton	wind	9	2002	Yorkshire and the Humber
	Rheidol	wind	50	1997	Wales
	Scroby Sands	wind (offshore)	60	2004	East
	Siddick	wind	4	1996	North West
	St Breock	wind	5	1994	South West

For footnotes see page 143

5.11 Power Stations in the United Kingdom

(operational at the end of May 2006)[1] (continued)

Company Name	Station Name	Fuel	Installed Capacity (MW)	Year of commission or year generation began	Location Scotland, Wales Northern Ireland, or English region
Fellside Heat and Power	Fellside	gas CHP	168	1993	North West
Fenland Windfarms Ltd	Deeping	wind	16	2006	East Midlands
	Glass Moor	wind	16	2006	East Midlands
	Red House	wind	12	2006	East Midlands
Fibrogen	Glanford	meat & bone meal	13	1993	East
Fibropower Ltd	Eye, Suffolk	poultry litter	13	1992	East
Fibrothetford	Thetford	poultry litter	39	1998	East
First Hydro Company	Dinorwig	pumped storage	1,728	1983	Wales
	Ffestiniog	pumped storage	360	1961	Wales
Gaz de France	Shotton	gas CHP	180	2001	Scotland
Great Orton Windfarm Ltd	Great Orton	wind	4	1999 (2)	North West
Haverigg III Ltd	Haverigg III	wind	3	2005	North West
HG Capital	Tyr Mostyn & Foel Goch	wind	21	2005	Wales
Immingham CHP LLP	Immingham CHP	gas CHP	741	2004	Yorkshire and the Humber
International Power	Rugeley	coal	1,006	1972	West Midlands
	Rugeley GT	gas oil	50	1972	West Midlands
	Deeside	CCGT	500	1994	Wales
	Saltend	CCGT	1,200	2000	Yorkshire and the Humber
K/S Winscales	Winscales 1	wind	2	1999	North West
	Winscales 2	wind	7	2005	North West
Llangwyryfon Windfarm Ltd	Llangwyryfon	wind	9	2003 (2)	Wales
Paul's Hill WindLtd	Paul's Hill	wind	55	2005	Scotland
Premier Power Ltd	Ballylumford B	Gas/oil	380	1968	Northern Ireland
	Ballylumford C	CCGT	616	2003	Northern Ireland
Rocksavage Power Co. Ltd	Rocksavage	CCGT	750	1997	North West
Rothes Wind Ltd	Rothes	wind	51	2004	Scotland
RWE Npower Plc	Aberthaw B	coal	1,455	1971	Wales
	Tilbury B (4)	coal/oil	1,029	1968	East
	Didcot A	coal/gas	1,940	1972	South East
	Aberthaw GT	gas oil	51	1971	Wales
	Cowes	gas oil	70	1982	South East
	Didcot GT	gas oil	100	1972	South East
	Fawley GT	gas oil	34	1969	South East
	Littlebrook GT	gas oil	105	1982	South East
	Tilbury GT	gas oil	34	1968	East
	Fawley (4)	oil	484	1969	South East
	Littlebrook D	oil	2,055	1982	South East
	Didcot B	CCGT	1,370	1998	South East
	Great Yarmouth	CCGT	420	2001	East
	Little Barford	CCGT	665	1995	East

For footnotes see page 143

5.11 Power Stations in the United Kingdom
(operational at the end of May 2006)[1] (continued)

Company Name	Station Name	Fuel	Installed Capacity (MW)	Year of commission or year generation began	Location Scotland, Wales Northern Ireland, or English region
RWE Npower Plc (continued)	Braevallich	hydro	2	2005	Scotland
	Cwm Dyli	hydro	10	2002 (2)	Wales
	Dolgarrog High Head	hydro	18	2002 (2)	Wales
	Dolgarrog Low Head	hydro	15	1926/2002	Wales
	Garrogie	hydro	2	2005	Scotland
	Inverbain	hydro	1	2006	Scotland
	Kielder	hydro	6	2006 (2)	Yorkshire and the Humber
Scottish & Southern Energy plc					
Hydro Schemes:					
Affric/Beauly	Mullardoch Tunnel	hydro	2.4	1955	Scotland
	Fasnakyle	hydro	69	1951	Scotland
	Fasnakyle Compensation Set	hydro	8	2006	Scotland
	Deanie	hydro	38	1963	Scotland
	Culligran	hydro	19	1962	Scotland
	Aigas	hydro	20	1962	Scotland
	Kilmorack	hydro	20	1962	Scotland
Breadalbane	Lubreoch	hydro	4	1958	Scotland
	Cashlie	hydro	11	1959	Scotland
	Lochay	hydro	47	1958	Scotland
	Finlarig	hydro	17	1955	Scotland
	Lednock	hydro	3	1961	Scotland
	St. Fillans	hydro	17	1957	Scotland
	Dalchonzie	hydro	4	1958	Scotland
Conon	Achanalt	hydro	3	1956	Scotland
	Grudie Bridge	hydro	19	1950	Scotland
	Mossford	hydro	19	1957	Scotland
	Luichart	hydro	34	1954	Scotland
	Orrin	hydro	18	1959	Scotland
	Torr Achilty	hydro	15	1954	Scotland
Foyers	Foyers	hydro/ pumped storage	300	1974	Scotland
Great Glen	Foyers Falls	hydro	5	1968	Scotland
	Mucomir	hydro	2	1962	Scotland
	Ceannacroc	hydro	20	1956	Scotland
	Livishie	hydro	15	1962	Scotland
	Glenmoriston	hydro	37	1957	Scotland
	Quoich	hydro	19	1955	Scotland
	Ivergarry	hydro	20	1956	Scotland
	Kingairloch	hydro	4	2005	Scotland
Shin	Cassley	hydro	10	1959	Scotland
	Lairg	hydro	4	1959	Scotland
	Shin	hydro	19	1958	Scotland
Sloy/Awe	Sloy	hydro	153	1950	Scotland
	Sron Mor	hydro	5	1957	Scotland
	Clachan	hydro	40	1955	Scotland
	Alt-na-Lairgie	hydro	6	1956	Scotland
	Nant	hydro	15	1963	Scotland
	Inverawe	hydro	25	1963	Scotland
	Kilmelfort	hydro	2	1956	Scotland
	Loch Gair	hydro	6	1961	Scotland
	Lussa	hydro	2	1952	Scotland
	Striven	hydro	8	1951	Scotland

For footnotes see page 143

5.11 Power Stations in the United Kingdom
(operational at the end of May 2006)[1] (continued)

Company Name	Station Name	Fuel	Installed Capacity (MW)	Year of commission or year generation began	Location Scotland, Wales Northern Ireland, or English region
Scottish & Southern Energy plc					
Hydro Schemes (continued)					
Tummel	Gaur	hydro	8	1953	Scotland
	Cuaich	hydro	3	1959	Scotland
	Loch Ericht	hydro	2	1962	Scotland
	Rannoch	hydro	44	1930	Scotland
	Tummel	hydro	34	1933	Scotland
	Errochty	hydro	75	1955	Scotland
	Clunie	hydro	61	1950	Scotland
	Pitlochry	hydro	15	1950	Scotland
Wind	Artfield Fell	wind	20	2005	Scotland
	Hadyard Hill	wind	120	2005	Scotland
	Spurness	wind	8	2004	Scotland
	Tangy	wind	13	2002	Scotland
Small Hydros:	Chliostair	hydro	1	1960	Scotland
	Cuileag	hydro	3	2002	Scotland
	Kerry Falls	hydro	1	1951	Scotland
	Loch Dubh	hydro	1	1954	Scotland
	Nostie Bridge	hydro	1	1950	Scotland
	Storr Lochs	hydro	2	1952	Scotland
Thermal:	Peterhead (4)	CCGT oil/gas	1,540	1980	Scotland
	Fife Power Station	CCGT	120	2000	Scotland
	Keadby	CCGT	745	1994	Yorkshire and the Humber
	Medway	CCGT	688	1995	South East
	Ferrybridge C	coal/biomass co-	1,955	1966	the Humber
	Fiddler's Ferry	coal/biomass co-	1,961	1971	North West
	Ferrybridge GT	gas oil	34	1966	Yorkshire and the Humber
	Fiddler's Ferry GT	gas oil	34	1969	North West
	Chickerell	gas	45	1998	South West
	Burghfield	gas	45	1998	South East
	Thatcham	diesel	9	1994	South East
	Five Oaks	diesel	9	1995	South East
	Chippenham	gas	10	2002	South West
	Wheldale	gas	10	2002	Yorkshire and the Humber
Island Generation	Arnish	diesel	3	2001	Scotland
	Barra	diesel	2	1990	Scotland
	Bowmore	diesel	6	1946	Scotland
	Kirkwall	diesel	16	1953	Scotland
	Lerwick	diesel	67	1953	Scotland
	Loch Carnan, South Uist	diesel	12	1971	Scotland
	Stornoway	diesel	24	1950	Scotland
	Tiree	diesel	3	1945	Scotland
Scottish Power					
Hydro schemes:					
Galloway	Carsfad	hydro	12	1936	Scotland
	Drumjohn	hydro	2	1985	Scotland
	Earlstoun	hydro	14	1936	Scotland
	Glenlee	hydro	24	1935	Scotland
	Kendoon	hydro	24	1936	Scotland
	Tongland	hydro	33	1935	Scotland
Lanark	Bonnington	hydro	11	1927	Scotland
	Stonebyres	hydro	6	1927	Scotland

For footnotes see page 143

5.11 Power Stations in the United Kingdom
(operational at the end of May 2006)[1] (continued)

Company Name	Station Name	Fuel	Installed Capacity (MW)	Year of commission or year generation began	Location Scotland, Wales Northern Ireland, or English region
Scottish Power					
Hydro schemes:					
(continued)					
Cruachan	Cruachan	pumped storage	440	1966	Scotland
Thermal:	Cockenzie	coal	1,152	1967	Scotland
	Longannet	coal	2,304	1970	Scotland
	Knapton	gas	40	1994	Yorkshire and the Humber
	Damhead Creek	CCGT	792	2000	South East
	Rye House	CCGT	715	1993	East
	Shoreham	CCGT	400	2000	South East
Wind	Beinn an Tuirc	wind	30	2002	Scotland
	Carland Cross	wind	6	1992	South West
	Coal Clough	wind	10	1992	Scotland
	Corkey	wind	5	1994	Northern Ireland
	Cruach Mhor	wind	30	2004	Scotland
	Dun Law	wind	17	2000	Scotland
	Elliots Hill	wind	5	1995	Northern Ireland
	Hagshaw Hill	wind	16	1995	Scotland
	Hare Hill	wind	13	2000	Scotland
	Penryddian & Llidiartywaun	wind	31	1992	Wales
	Rigged Hill	wind	5	1994	Northern Ireland
Seabank Power Limited	Seabank 1	CCGT	812	1998	South West
	Seabank 2	CCGT	410	2000	South West
Sita Tyre Recycling Ltd	Wolverhampton (5)	waste	20	1994	West Midlands
South East London Combined Heat & Power Ltd	Landmann Way, London	waste	32	1994	London
Spalding Energy Company Ltd	Spalding	CCGT	903	2004	East Midlands
Teesside Power Ltd	Teesside Power Station	CCGT	1,875	1992	North East
TPG Wind Ltd	Rhyd-y-Groes	wind	7	1992	Wales
Uskmouth Power Company Ltd	Uskmouth	coal	393	2000	Wales
Western Power Generation	Lynton	gas oil	2	1961	South West
	Princetown	kerosene	3	1959	South West
	Roseland	kerosene	5	1963	South West
	St Marys	gas oil	6	1958	South West
Yorkshire Windpower Ltd	Ovenden Moor	wind	9	1993	Yorkshire and the Humber
	Royd Moor	wind	7	1993	
Total			**77,504**		

For footnotes see page 143

5.11 Power Stations in the United Kingdom

(operational at the end of May 2006)[1] (continued)

Other power stations[6]

Station type	Fuel	Capacity (MW)
Renewable sources and combustible wastes	wind	411
	landfill gas	818
	sewage gas	128
	hydro	105
	waste	289
	other	95
CHP schemes listed in Table 5.12	various fuels	1,458
CHP schemes other than major power producers and renewables and those listed in Table 5.12	mainly gas	2,703
Other autogenerators	various fuels	1,008

Interconnectors

	Capacity (MW)
England - France	2,000
Scotland - Northern Ireland	500
Northern Ireland - Irish Republic	600

Footnotes
(1) This list covers stations of more than 1 MW capacity, but excludes some renewables stations of over 1 MW which are included in the sub table on page143.
(2) Recommissioning dates.
(3) Excludes mothballed capacity.
(4) Total capacity is 2,319 MW but because of transmission constraints only 1,540 MW can be used at any one time.
(5) There has been no generation from this site for several years.
(6) As at end December 2005.

5.12 Large scale CHP schemes in the United Kingdom
(operational at the end of December 2005)[1]

Company Name	Scheme Location	Installed Capacity (MWe) [2]
ABB CHP Ltd	Buckland Nurseries, Reigate, Surrey	1.9
ABB CHP Ltd	Royal Devon and Exeter NHS Trust Wonsford Hospital	1.0
Airbus UK	Broughton	6.2
Alta Estate Services Limited	The University of Birmingham	6.3
Archer Daniels Midland Ltd (ADM Ltd)	Erith	14.0
Arjo Wiggins Appleton plc	Dartford	10.0
Astra-Zeneca UK Ltd	Macclesfield	22.8
Bayer Cropscience	Norwich	4.4
BBC	Shepherds Bush, London	4.9
Boots Company plc	Beeston, Nottingham	14.1
BP CHP (UK) Ltd	Polimerieuropa, Hythe	53.1
BP PLC	BP Oil Grangemouth	294.9
BPB PLC	Aberdeen	8.4
British Nuclear Fuels Ltd	Preston	11.8
British Salt Ltd	Middlewich, Cheshire	10.0
British Sugar plc	Wissington, Norfolk	93.6
British Sugar plc	Bury St Edmunds, Suffolk	85.6
British Sugar plc	York	10.0
British Sugar plc	Allscott, Shropshire	9.0
Camden and Islington Community NHS Trust	Royal Free Hospital, London	4.7
Carlesberg Tetley Brewing Ltd	Leeds	1.0
CIBA Speciality Chemicals plc	Low Moor, Bradford	16.5
City Hospital NHS Trust	Dudley Road Hospital, Birmingham	1.6
City Hospitals Sunderland NHS Trust	Sunderland General Hospital, Tyne and Wear	1.1
Crisp Maltings Ltd	Fakenham, Norfolk	1.2
Dalkia Utility Services	Leeds General Infirmary	18.1
Dalkia Utility Services	Queen Elizabeth Hospital, Edgbaston, Warwickshire	3.6
Dalkia Utility Services	Royal Liverpool University Hospital	5.3
Dalkia Utility Services	Freeman Hospital, Newcastle-upon-Tyne	2.5
Dalkia Utility Services	North Tyne Hospital Tyne and Wear	1.5
De Mulder and Sons Ltd	Hartshill	2.9
DSM Nutritional Products UK Ltd	Dalry, Ayrshire	45.8
EE Realisation Ltd	Nottingham District Heating Scheme	14.4
Elvo Ltd	Nestle Rowntree, York	5.7
E.On UK (CHP) Ltd	Grovehurst Energy Ltd, Sittingbourne, Kent	80.6
E.On UK (CHP) Ltd	Queens Medical Centre, Nottingham	4.9
E.On UK (CHP) Ltd	A H Marks, Bradford	4.5
GlaxoSmithKline Ltd	Wellcome Foundation, Dartford	12.1
Humber Energy	Acordis, Grimsby, South Humberside	48.4
Hydro Polymers Ltd	Newton Aycliffe, Durham	9.8
Ineos Chlor	Runcorn, Cheshire	38.4
Innovia Films	Wigton, Cumbria	5.3
Imperial College of Science, Medicine and Technology	Kensington, London	8.4
Imperial Tobacco	Nottingham	4.0
International Paper UK Ltd	Federal Tait, Inverurie, Aberdeenshire	22.7
James Cropper Ltd	Kendal, Cumbria	6.9
Kappa SSK Ltd	Nechells, Birmingham	8.7
Kraft Jacobs Suchard Ltd	Banbury, Oxon	7.5
Laporte Industries	Fine Organics Ltd, Seal Sands	4.1
Manchester Airport plc	Manchester	10.4
Meterological Office	Exeter	1.5
Ministry of Defence	RAF Cranwell	3.4
NEL Power Ltd	Mill Nurseries, Keyingham, Hull	15.0
NORBORD Ltd	CSC Forest Products Ltd, Cowie	14.8
Northumbrian Water	All sites	16.8
Novartis	Grimsby, South Humberside	8.4
Pfizer Ltd	Sandwich, Kent	16.0
Poolbank Power CHP Ltd	Poolbank Salads, Brough	3.9
Rolls Royce Power Ventures Ltd	Derby Cogeneration Ltd, Derby	62.0

For footnotes see page 145

5.12 Large scale CHP schemes in the United Kingdom
(operational at the end of December 2005)[1] *(continued)*

Company Name	Scheme Location	Installed Capacity (MWe) [2]
Roquette UK Ltd	Corby	14.5
RWE Npower Cogen Ltd	Millenium Inorganic Chemicals, Stallingborough	15.8
Scottish and Southern Energy plc	Hedon Salads, Burstwick	10.0
Scottish and Southern Energy plc	Runcton Nursery, Chichester	4.0
Scottish and Southern Energy plc	Hedon Salads, Newport	3.9
Scottish and Southern Energy plc	Red Roofs, Cottingham, Yorks	3.4
Scottish and Southern Energy plc	Ninewells Hospital, Tayside	2.6
Scottish and Southern Energy plc	West End Nursery, Woking	2.0
Scottish and Southern Energy plc	Koopers UK Ltd, Port Clarence, Teesside	1.9
Scottish and Southern Energy plc	Hedon Salads, Slough	1.9
Scottish and Southern Energy plc	University of North Staffordshire NHS Trust	1.3
Scottish and Southern Energy plc	Western General Hospital, Edinburgh	1.0
Severn Trent Water Ltd	Minworth Water Reclamation Work, Sutton Coldfield	7.5
South Buckinghamshire NHS Trust	Wycombe General Hospital, Buckinghamshire	1.1
South West Water	All sites	1.5
Southampton Geothermal	Southampton	6.5
Southern Water	All sites	25.3
Stanlow Manufacturing Complex	Stanlow, Cheshire	108.4
St Georges's Healthcare NHS Trust	St George's Hospital, Tooting, London	4.3
St Regis Paper Company	Wansborough, Watchet, Somerset	6.0
St Regis Paper Company	Sudbrook Mill, Caldicot, Monmouthshire	5.0
St Regis Paper Company	Hollins Mill, Darwen, Lancashire	2.0
Syngenta Ltd	Huddersfield	16.3
Thames Valley Power Ltd	Heathrow Airport	15.0
Thameswey Energy	Woking, Surrey	1.4
Tullis Russell and Company Ltd	Glenrothes, Fife	25.0
University of Bath	Bath	1.4
University of Liverpool	Liverpool	3.7
Waste Recycling Group	Darrington Leys, Knottingley	5.0
W S Atkins Power	Arreton Valley Nursery, Isle of Wight	15.5
W S Atkins Power	Britannia Salads, Villa Nursery, Roydon, Essex	3.0
W S Atkins Power	Glen Avon Growers, Cottingham, North Humberside	3.0
W S Atkins Power	Anchor Nurseries Ltd, Beverley	3.0
W S Atkins Power	Abbey View Nurseries, Waltham Abbey, Essex	3.0
W S Atkins Power	UK Salads, Roydon, Essex	3.0
W S Atkins Power	Fen Drayton	1.6
Total [2]		1,536.2
Electrical capacity of good quality CHP for these sites in total		1,457.9

(1) These are sites of 1 MW installed electrical capacity or more that either have agreed to be listed in the Ofge of CHP plants or whose details are publicly available elsewhere, or who have provided the information directly to DTI. It excludes CHP sites that have been listed as major power producers in Table 5.11.

(2) This is the total power capacity from these sites and includes all the capacity at that site, not just that classed as good quality CHP under CHPQA.

Chapter 6
Combined heat and power

Introduction

6.1   This chapter sets out the contribution made by Combined Heat and Power (CHP) to the United Kingdom's energy requirements. The data presented in this Chapter have been derived from information submitted to the CHP Quality Assurance programme (CHPQA). This programme was introduced by Government to provide the methods and procedures to assess and certify the quality of the full range of CHP schemes. It is a rigorous system for the Government to ensure that the incentives on offer are targeted fairly and benefit schemes in relation to their environmental performance. The data presented in this chapter have been derived from information submitted to CHPQA or by following the same procedures where no information has been provided directly.

6.2   CHP is the simultaneous generation of usable heat and power (usually electricity) in a single process. The term CHP is synonymous with cogeneration and total energy, which are terms often used in other Member States of the European Community and the United States. CHP uses a variety of fuels and technologies across a wide range of sites and scheme sizes. The basic elements of a CHP plant comprise one or more prime movers (a reciprocating engine, gas turbine, or steam turbine) driving electrical generators, where the steam or hot water generated in the process is utilised via suitable heat recovery equipment for use either in industrial processes, or in community heating and space heating.

6.3   A CHP plant provides primary energy savings compared to separate generation of heat and power. In addition, CHP is typically sized to make use of the available heat, and connected to the lower voltage distribution system (ie embedded). This provides efficiency gains compared to electricity-only plant, which is larger, and connected at very high voltage to the grid transmission system, by avoiding significant transmission and distribution losses. CHP can also provide important network services such as black start, improvements to power quality, and the ability to operate in island mode if the grid goes down.

6.4   There are four principal types of CHP systems: steam turbine, gas turbine, combined cycle systems and reciprocating engines. Each of these is defined in paragraph 6.33 later in this Chapter.

Government policy towards CHP

6.5   To reduce carbon emissions and help deliver the UK's Climate Change Programme, the Government has a target of achieving at least 10,000 MWe of Good Quality CHP capacity by 2010. During 2005, there was an increase in the total number of CHP schemes from 1,527 at the beginning of the year to 1,534 at the end and the installed capacity increased from 5,684 MWe to 5,792 MWe. The 2004 revised capacity figure of 5,684 MWe is based on all final submissions to the CHPQA programme and is higher than the 5,606 MWe figure for the end of year 2004 reported in the 2005 Digest. Electricity from Good Quality CHP can also qualify for Climate Change Levy (CCL) exemption through Levy Exemption Certificates (LECs). This scheme allows CHP station operators to sell or transfer their LECs with the amount of electricity supplied indirectly from the station giving commercial freedom to maximise the benefit. It enables supplies of "Good Quality" electricity to be identified as such, as part of an auditable process. Since April 2003 56.5 million LECs have been issued by Ofgem (1 LEC per MWh) to 142 qualifying Good Quality CHP generators, 43.9 million of these were issued to 119 fully exempt CHP generators and 12.6 million to 23 partly exempt CHP operators.

International context

6.6   The EU Emissions Trading Scheme (EU ETS) commenced on 1st January 2005 and involves the trading of emissions allowances. The purpose of the EU ETS is to reduce emissions by a fixed amount across the EU at least cost to the regulated sources. Each year participants in the scheme are allocated a set number of allowances. At the end of each trading year allowances equal to the reported emissions must be surrendered. If participants reduce emissions below their allocations, they will have allowances to trade or keep for use in future years. If emissions rise above their allocations allowances must be purchased. In the UK's Phase I National Allocation Plan (NAP), CHP plants were treated in the same manner as other installations in the industrial sector they serve, which led to differential treatment of CHP plants across the EU ETS. For Phase II, the Government has consulted on a number of options for the treatment of CHP in the NAP to remove this distortion and provide further incentive to invest in CHP technologies. One of these options is the creation of a separate Good Quality CHP (GQ CHP) sector for all Good Quality CHP installations, which should ensure that the sector cap more closely reflects CHP emissions growth. Other specific proposals consulted on were to ring-fence a portion of the New Entrant Reserve for new plant generating GQ CHP electricity and for new entrant CHP to receive favourable allocation arrangements relative to non-CHP. The Government also consulted on proposals for incumbent CHP to receive an equitable allocation based on historic emissions within the GQ CHP sector.

UK Energy markets, and their effect on CHP

6.7   Two major factors affecting the economics of CHP are the relative cost of fuel (principally natural gas) and the value that can be realised for electricity. The difference between the price of electricity and the price of gas required to generate that electricity is known as the "spark spread". This represents the revenue available to finance annual fixed costs, capital costs, investment and profits and needs to be high enough to incentivise new CHP build. Energy price trends that are applicable to CHP schemes differ depending upon the size and sector of the scheme, but in general in recent years the CHP industry has faced adverse economic conditions due largely to the spark spread being insufficiently large to provide an adequate return on investment.

Use of CHPQA in producing CHP statistics

6.8   The CHPQA programme is now the major source for CHP statistics. The following factors need to be kept in mind when using the statistics produced:

- Scheme operators have previously determined the boundary of a CHP scheme (what is regarded as part of the CHP installation and what is not). Now, through CHPQA, scheme operators have been given guidance on how to determine scheme boundaries. A scheme can include multiple CHP prime movers, along with supplementary boilers and generating plant, subject to appropriate metering installed to support the CHP scheme boundaries proposed, and subject to appropriate metering and threshold criteria (see CHPQA Guidance Note 11 available at www.chpqa.com).

- The output of a scheme is based on gross power output, ignoring parasitic loads (ie ignoring power used in pumps, fans, etc within the scheme itself).

- The main purpose of a number of CHP schemes is the generation of electricity including export to others. Such schemes may not be sized to use all of the available heat. The total capacity and output of these schemes have been scaled back using the methodologies outlined in CHPQA. Only the portion of the capacity and output that qualifies as Good Quality is counted in this chapter and the remaining capacity and output are regarded as power only and reported in Chapter 5. The fuel allocated to the power-only portion of the output is calculated from the power efficiency of the prime mover.

- The load factor presented in Table 6A is based on the Good Quality Power Output and Good Quality Power Capacity reported in this Chapter. For schemes that are scaled back this load factor is likely to be smaller than the actual load factor (hours run) for the prime mover in these schemes. The low load factor experienced in 2004 (56.4 per cent), due to schemes coming on line part way through the year, has recovered in 2005 to 59.8 per cent which is just above that recorded in 2003 (59.5 per cent).

Progress towards the Government's targets

6.9   Chart 6.1 shows the change in installed CHP capacity over the last eight years. Installed capacity at the end of 2005 stood at 5,792 MWe. This represents an increase in installed capacity between 2004 and 2005 of 108 MWe and a net increase of 7 schemes.

Capacity in 2005

6.10   In 2005, 29 new schemes came into operation and 22 ceased to operate.

6.11   In the current market conditions, a number of operators have chosen to mothball their CHP schemes rather than continue to operate. As these schemes are still able to operate they have been included in the capacity figures. At the end of 2005, there were 67 mothballed schemes with a good Quality capacity of 69 MWe.

6.12   75 per cent of capacity is now gas turbine based, with about 85 per cent of this in combined cycle mode. Compared with the figures published in DUKES 2005 for the year 2004, there has been a significant increase in the installed CCGT capacity and a substantial decrease in the installed capacity for pass-out condensing steam turbine. This is due to a re-categorisation of 5 large schemes.

6.13   Allowing for re-categorisation, CCGT capacity increased by about 3 per cent between 2004 and 2005 and installed capacities in the other technologies have remained broadly unchanged when compared with the 2004 figures (see Tables 6A and 6.5). Heat generation fell slightly between 2000 and 2002 but has shown a recent up turn such that 2004 levels are back at those seen in 2000. In 2005 this increasing trend continued and heat generated in 2005 is 1.6 per cent higher than in 2004. There was a dip in electricity generation in 2001. This reflected the difficulties encountered by smaller generators faced with rising gas prices, and declining wholesale electricity prices in the early 2000s. As a result CHP plants were used less and the average load factor fell from 64 per cent in 2000 to 54 per cent in 2001. Since 2001 the average load factor has fluctuated between 55 and 60 per cent and stands at 59.8 per cent for 2005; the low load factor in 2004 was due to new schemes coming into operation part way through the year. Excluding these schemes the load factor for 2004 was 60 per cent. Between 2001 and 2005 electricity generation has slowly been increasing and in 2005 30,340 GWh of electricity were generated by Good Quality CHP schemes which is over 8 per cent higher than in 2004 (28,065 GWh).

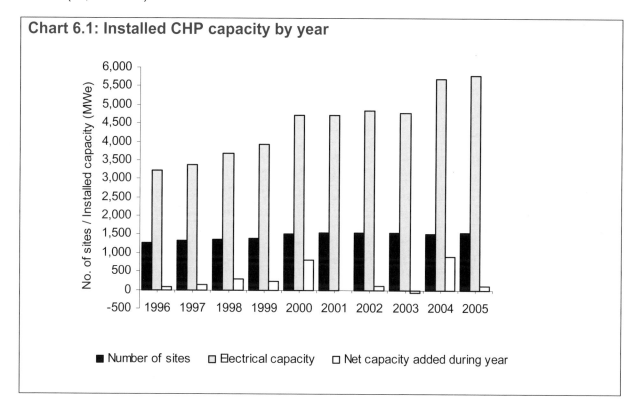

Chart 6.1: Installed CHP capacity by year

Installed capacity and output in 2005

6.14   Table 6A gives a summary of the overall CHP market. The electricity generated by CHP schemes in 2005 was 30,340 GWh. This represents 7½ per cent of the total electricity generated in the UK. Across the commercial and industrial sectors (including the fuel industries other than electricity generation) electrical output from CHP accounted for around 13 per cent of electricity consumption. CHP schemes in total supplied 63,124 GWh of heat in 2005.

6.15   In terms of electrical capacity by size of scheme, schemes larger than 10 MWe represent 83 per cent of the total electrical capacity of CHP schemes as shown in Table 6B. However, in terms of number of schemes, the largest share (>80 per cent) is in schemes less than 1 MWe. Schemes of 1

MWe or larger make up approximately 18 per cent of the total number of schemes. Table 6.5 provides data on electrical capacity for each type of CHP installation.

Table 6A: A summary of the recent development of CHP

	Unit	2001	2002	2003	2004	2005
Number of schemes		1,552	1,534	1,534	1,527	1,534
Net number of schemes added during year		*30*	*-18*	*-*	*-7*	*7*
Electrical capacity (CHP$_{QPC}$)	MWe	4,732	4,848	4,777	5,684	5,792
Net capacity added during year		*2*	*116*	*-71*	*907*	*108*
Capacity added in percentage terms	Per cent	*-*	*2.5*	*-1.4*	*19.0*	*1.9*
Heat capacity	MWth	11,898	11,559	11,221	12,096	12,396
Heat to power ratio *(1)*		2.69	2.45	2.41	2.21	2.08
Fuel input	GWh	119,735	123,064	122,199	130,322	136,878
Electricity generation (CHP$_{QPO}$)	GWh	22,444	24,420	24,916	28,065	30,340
Heat generation (CHP$_{QHO}$)	GWh	60,584	59,721	60,052	62,140	63,124
Overall efficiency *(2)*	Per cent	69.3	69.6	69.6	69.2	68.3
Load factor	Per cent	54.1	57.5	59.5	56.4	59.8

(1)   *Heat to power ratios are calculated from the qualifying heat output (QHO) and the qualifying power output (QPO).*
(2)   *These are calculated using gross calorific values; overall net efficiencies are some 5 percentage points higher.*
(3)   *The load factor reported in this table is based on the qualifying power generation and capacity and does not correspond exactly to the number of hours run by the prime movers in a year (see paragraph 6.21)*
A longer time series of these data (back to 1977) can be accessed on the DTI energy statistics web site from the Digest of UK Energy Statistics home page:
www.dti.gov.uk/energy/statistics/publications/dukes/page29812.html .

Table 6B: CHP schemes by capacity size ranges in 2005

Electrical capacity size range	Number of schemes	Share of total (per cent)	Total electricity capacity (MWe)	Share of total (per cent)
Less than 100 kWe	581	37.9	35	0.6
100 kWe - 999 kWe	682	44.4	171	3.0
1 MWe - 9.9 MWe	196	12.8	772	13.3
Greater than 10 MWe	75	4.9	4,814	83.1
Total	**1,534**	**100.0**	**5,792**	**100.0**

6.16   In terms of electrical and heat capacity by type of scheme, combined cycle gas turbines now make up the largest proportion for both capacities, (63 per cent and 49 per cent respectively), with steam turbines providing the next largest proportion, (14 per cent and 30 per cent respectively). Table 6.7 provides data on heat capacity for each type of CHP installation.

Fuel used by types of CHP installation

6.17   Table 6.2 shows the fuel used to generate electricity and heat in CHP schemes, (see paragraphs 6.34 to 6.36, below for an explanation of the convention for dividing fuel between electricity and heat production). Table 6.3 gives the overall fuel used by types of CHP installation (which are explained in paragraph 6.33). Total fuel use is summarised in Chart 6.2. In 2005, 67 per cent of the total fuel use was natural gas, up from 64 per cent in 2004. CHP schemes accounted for just over 9 per cent of UK gas consumption in 2005 (see Table 4.3).

6.18   Non-conventional fuels (liquids, solids or gases which are by-products or waste products from industrial processes, or are renewable fuels) account for 27 per cent of all fuel used in CHP in 2005. These are fuels that are not commonly used by the mainstream electricity generating industry, and some would otherwise be flared or disposed of by some means. These fuels, with the exception of some waste gases, will generally be utilised in steam turbines being fed by boilers. In almost all cases, the technical nature of the combustion process, and the lower fuel quality (lower calorific value of the fuel, high moisture content of the fuel, the need to maintain certain combustion conditions to ensure complete disposal etc) will generally result in a lower efficiency. However, given that the use of such fuels avoids the use of fossil fuels, and since they need to be disposed of in some way, the use of these fuels in CHP provides environmental benefits.

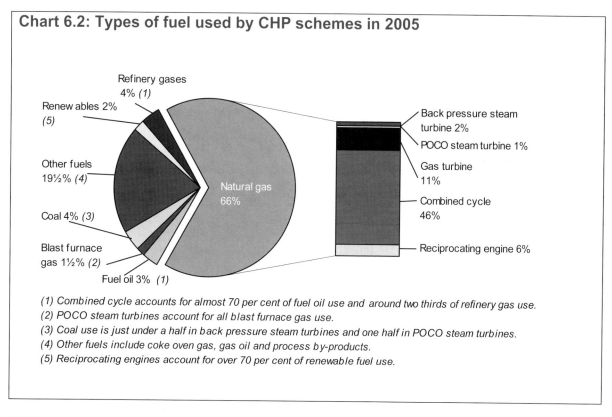

Chart 6.2: Types of fuel used by CHP schemes in 2005

Refinery gases 4% (1)

Renewables 2% (5)

Other fuels 19½% (4)

Coal 4% (3)

Blast furnace gas 1½% (2)

Fuel oil 3% (1)

Natural gas 66%

Back pressure steam turbine 2%

POCO steam turbine 1%

Gas turbine 11%

Combined cycle 46%

Reciprocating engine 6%

(1) Combined cycle accounts for almost 70 per cent of fuel oil use and around two thirds of refinery gas use.
(2) POCO steam turbines account for all blast furnace gas use.
(3) Coal use is just under a half in back pressure steam turbines and one half in POCO steam turbines.
(4) Other fuels include coke oven gas, gas oil and process by-products.
(5) Reciprocating engines account for over 70 per cent of renewable fuel use.

CHP capacity, output and fuel use by sector

6.19   Table 6.8 gives data on all operational schemes by economic sector. A definition of the sectors used in this table can be found in Chapter 1, paragraph 1.56 and Table 1G:

- 407 schemes (94 per cent of electrical capacity) are in the industrial sector and 1,127 schemes (6 per cent of capacity) are in the agricultural, commercial, public administration, residential and transport sectors.

- Four industrial sectors account for 77 per cent of the CHP electrical capacity - chemicals (27 per cent of capacity), oil refineries (32 per cent), paper, publishing and printing (11 per cent) and food, beverages and tobacco (7 per cent). Capacity by sector is shown in Chart 6.3.

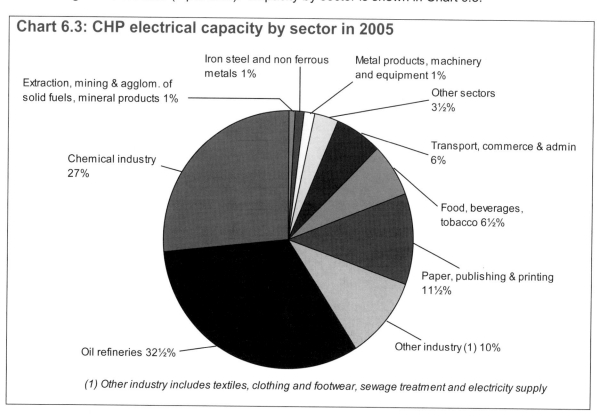

Chart 6.3: CHP electrical capacity by sector in 2005

Iron steel and non ferrous metals 1%

Metal products, machinery and equipment 1%

Extraction, mining & agglom. of solid fuels, mineral products 1%

Other sectors 3½%

Chemical industry 27%

Transport, commerce & admin 6%

Food, beverages, tobacco 6½%

Paper, publishing & printing 11½%

Oil refineries 32½%

Other industry (1) 10%

(1) Other industry includes textiles, clothing and footwear, sewage treatment and electricity supply

6.20   Table 6C gives a summary of the 1,092 schemes installed in the commercial, public sector and residential buildings. These schemes form a major part of the "Transport, commerce and administration" and "Other" sectors in Tables 6.8 and 6.9. The vast majority of these schemes (over 95 per cent) are based on spark ignition reciprocating engines fuelled with natural gas, though the larger schemes use compression ignition reciprocating engines or gas turbines. The largest proportion of the capacity is in the health sector, mainly hospitals. Leisure and hotels account for more than half the total number of schemes. Table 6.9 gives details of the quantities of fuels used in each sector.

Table 6C: Number and capacity of CHP schemes installed in buildings by sector in 2005

	Number of schemes	Electrical capacity (MWe)	Heat capacity (MWth)
Leisure	419	45.7	71.9
Hotels	302	38.9	62.6
Health	212	117.9	210.0
Residential Group Heating	45	42.9	97.5
Universities	36	42.7	85.7
Offices	26	20.0	22.7
Education	21	10.2	18.0
Government Estate	14	12.2	18.1
Retail	12	2.6	4.1
Other (1)	5	14.8	22.8
Total	**1,092**	**347.9**	**613.3**

(1) Other includes: agriculture, airports, and domestic buildings

CHP performance by main prime mover

6.21   Table 6D gives a summary of the performance of schemes in 2005 by main prime mover type. Combined cycle gas turbines have the highest average operating hours at 5,763 hours. The average for all schemes of 5,239 hours is higher than in 2004 (4,856 hours).

6.22   The average electrical efficiency is 22 per cent (gross CV basis) and heat efficiency 45 per cent (gross CV basis), giving an overall average of 66 per cent (gross CV basis).

Table 6D: A summary of scheme performance in 2005

	Typical operating hours per annum (Full load equivalent)	Average electrical efficiency (% GCV)	Average heat efficiency (% GCV)	Average overall efficiency (% GCV)	Average heat to power ratio
Main prime mover in CHP plant					
Back pressure steam turbine	4,093	10	66	76	6.4
Pass out condensing steam turbine	4,418	12	54	66	4.6
Gas turbine	4,911	22	48	70	2.2
Combined cycle	5,763	26	41	67	1.6
Reciprocating engine	3,789	26	43	69	1.7
All schemes	**5,239**	**22**	**46**	**68**	**2.1**

CHP schemes which export and schemes with mechanical power output

6.23   Table 6E shows the electrical exports from CHP schemes between 2003 and 2005. Where a scheme that exports is Good Quality for only a portion of its capacity and output, the exports have been scaled back in the same way as power output has been scaled back (see paragraph 6.8, above). Exports accounted for about 38 per cent of power generation from CHP in 2005.

6.24   Table 6E also shows revised figures for electrical exports for 2004 (2003 figures remain unchanged).

Table 6E: Electrical exports from CHP

	2003	2004	GWh 2005
To part of same qualifying group *(1)*	616	955	881
To a firm NOT part of same qualifying group	2,980	2,329	2,042
To an electricity supplier	6,938	6,151	8,505
Total	**10,534**	**9,435**	**11,428**

(1) A qualifying group is a group of two or more corporate consumers that are connected or related to each other, for example, as a subsidiary, or via a parent or holding company, or in terms of share capital.

6.25   37 large schemes also export heat, some larger schemes to more than one customer. Together they supplied 9,194 GWh of heat in 2005, an increase of around 25 per cent compared to 2004 (7,340 GWh (revised)).

6.26   There are an estimated 13 schemes with mechanical power output. For those schemes, mechanical power accounts for around 12 per cent of their capacity (Table 6F). These schemes are predominantly on petro-chemicals or steel sites, using by-product fuels in boilers to drive steam turbines. The steam turbine is used to provide mechanical rather than electrical power, driving compressors, blowers or fans, rather than an alternator.

Table 6F: CHP schemes with mechanical power output in 2005

	Unit	
Number of schemes		13
Total Power Capacity of these schemes (CHP_{TPC})	MWe	1,871
Mechanical power capacity of these schemes	MWe	219

Emissions savings

6.27   The calculation of carbon emissions savings from CHP is important, given the substantial contribution that CHP can make to the Climate Change Programme. However the derivation of the savings is complex because CHP displaces a variety of fuels, technologies and sizes of plant. The methodology and assumptions used for calculating carbon emission savings is outlined in Energy Trends June 2003 www.dti.gov.uk/files/file11869.pdf and the figures compare CHP with the UK fossil fuel basket carbon intensity and the UK total basket carbon intensity, which includes nuclear and renewable generation. The carbon emission savings from CHP in 2005 as compared to the fossil fuel basket was 4.9 MtC, which equates to 0.84 MtC per 1,000 MWe installed capacity. Against the total basket, in 2005 CHP saved 3.5 MtC, or 0.61 MtC per 1,000 MWe installed capacity. This is an increase in carbon savings from the 2004 (revised) figures of 0.79 MtC/MWe and 0.58 MtC/MWe respectively.

List of large scale CHP schemes in the United Kingdom

6.28   The table showing large scale CHP schemes in the United Kingdom which was produced for the first time last year again appears as Table 5.12 in Chapter 5 (Electricity) on page 144. This table supplements Table 5.11 which lists major power stations in operation in the UK. Table 5.12 lists only large scale (over 1 MWe) CHP stations for which the information is already in the public domain and it is the total power output of these stations that is given, not just that which is classed as Good Quality CHP under CHPQA. This is because CHPQA information for individual sites is not publicly available.

Technical notes and definitions

6.29 These notes and definitions are in addition to the technical notes and definitions covering all fuels and energy as a whole in Chapter 1, paragraphs 1.24 to 1.53.

Data for 2005

6.30 The data are summarised from the results of a long-term project being undertaken by Future Energy Solutions on behalf of the Department of Trade and Industry (DTI), the Department for Environment, Food and Rural Affairs (Defra), and the Statistical Office of the European Communities (Eurostat). Data are included for CHP schemes installed in all sectors of the UK economy.

6.31 The project continues to be overseen by a Steering Group that comprises officials from the DTI, Defra, the Office of Gas and Electricity Markets (OFGEM) and the Combined Heat and Power Association (CHPA), all of whom have an interest in either the collection of information on CHP schemes or the promotion of the wider use of CHP in the UK.

6.32 Data for 2005 were based largely on data supplied to the CHPQA programme, supplemented by a survey carried out by the Office for National Statistics (ONS) between December 2005 and March 2006 of companies (other than major power producers) who generate their own electricity, either in CHP schemes or in electricity-only schemes. Information on the CHP plant included in the major power producers category comes from surveys conducted by DTI as part of the electricity statistics system. Over half of CHP schemes and around 85 per cent of capacity are based on returns under CHPQA, while around 3 per cent of schemes and 5 per cent of CHP capacity are based on data from ONS. 2005 data for sewage treatment works that do not provide returns either to CHPQA or ONS in a format that can be used within these statistics, were based on Renewables Obligation Certificate information from Ofgem returns (see Chapter 7). That data source accounts for approximately 1 per cent, by electrical capacity, of the statistics and will continue to be used in future for these schemes. Data for other schemes not applying for CHPQA and not included in the ONS survey (eg because they were below the cut off capacity for the survey) were interpolated from historical data.

Definitions of schemes

6.33 There are four principal types of CHP systems:

- **Steam turbine,** where steam at high pressure is generated in a boiler. In **back pressure steam turbine systems**, the steam is wholly or partly used in a turbine before being exhausted from the turbine at the required pressure for the site. In **pass-out condensing steam turbine systems**, a proportion of the steam used by the turbine is extracted at an intermediate pressure from the turbine with the remainder being fully condensed before it is exhausted at the exit. (Condensing steam turbines without passout and which do not utilise steam are not included in these statistics as they are not CHP). The boilers used in such schemes can burn a wide variety of fuels including coal, gas, oil, and waste-derived fuels. With the exception of waste-fired schemes, steam turbine plant has often been in service for several decades. Steam turbine schemes capable of supplying useful steam have electrical efficiencies of between 10 and 20 per cent, depending on size, and thus between 70 per cent and 30 per cent of the fuel input is available as useful heat. Steam turbines used in CHP applications typically range in size from a few MWe to over 100 MWe.

- **Gas turbine systems**, often aero-engine derivatives, where fuel (gas, or gas-oil) is combusted in the gas turbine and the exhaust gases are normally used in a waste heat boiler to produce usable steam, though the exhaust gases may be used directly in some process applications. Gas turbines range from 30 kWe upwards, achieving electrical efficiency of 23 to 30 per cent (depending on size) and with the potential to recover up to 50 per cent of the fuel input as useful heat. They have been common in CHP since the mid 1980s. The waste heat boiler can include supplementary or auxiliary firing using a wide range of fuels, and thus the heat to power ratio of the scheme can vary.

- **Combined cycle systems**, where the plant comprises more than one prime mover. These are usually gas turbines where the exhaust gases are utilised in a steam generator, the steam from which is passed wholly or in part into one or more steam turbines. In rare cases reciprocating engines may be linked with steam turbines. Combined cycle is suited to larger installations of 7 MWe and over. They achieve higher electrical efficiency and a lower heat to power ratio than steam turbines or gas turbines. Recently installed combined cycle gas turbine (CCGT) schemes have achieved an electrical efficiency approaching 50 per cent, with 20 per cent heat recovery, and a heat to power ratio of less than 1:1.

- **Reciprocating engine systems** range from less than 100 kWe up to around 5 MWe, and are found in applications where production of hot water (rather than steam) is the main requirement, for example, on smaller industrial sites as well as in buildings. They are based on auto engine or marine engine derivatives converted to run on gas. Both compression ignition and spark ignition firing is used. Reciprocating engines operate at around 28 to 33 per cent electrical efficiency with around 33 per cent to 50 per cent of the fuel input available as useful heat. Reciprocating engines produce two grades of waste heat: high grade heat from the engine exhaust and low grade heat from the engine cooling circuits.

Determining fuel consumption for heat and electricity

6.34   In order to provide a comprehensive picture of electricity generation in the United Kingdom and the fuels used to generate that electricity, the energy input to CHP schemes has to be allocated between heat and electricity production. This allocation is notional and is not determinate.

6.35   The convention used to allocate the fuels to heat and electricity relates the split of fuels to the relative efficiency of heat and electricity supply. The efficiency of utility plant varies widely: electricity generation from as little as 25 per cent to more than 50 per cent and boilers from as little as 50 per cent to more than 90 per cent. Thus it is around twice as hard to generate a unit of electricity as it is to generate a unit of heat. Accordingly a simple convention can be implemented whereby twice as many units of fuel are allocated to each unit of electricity generated, as to each unit of heat supplied. This approach is consistent with the Defra Guidelines for Company Reporting on greenhouse gas emissions and for Negotiated Agreements on energy efficiency agreed between Government and industry as part of the Climate Change Levy (CCL) package. It recognises that in developing a CHP scheme, both the heat customer(s) and the electricity generator share in the savings, reflecting the fact that more than three-quarters of CHP build in the last few years has been supplied under an energy services arrangement.

6.36   The assumption in this convention that it is twice as hard to generate a unit of electricity as heat, is appropriate for the majority of CHP schemes. However, for some types of scheme (for example in the iron and steel sector) this allocation is less appropriate and can result in very high apparent heat efficiencies. These however are only notional efficiencies.

The effects on the statistics of using CHPQA

6.37   Paragraph 6.8 described how schemes were scaled back so that only CHP_{QPC} and CHP_{QPO} were included in the CHP statistics. This is illustrated in Table 6G. In 2005, 79 schemes have been scaled back; in 2004 61 schemes were scaled back. The power output from these schemes was scaled back from a total of 31,089 GWh to 7,452 GWh. The total fuel input to these schemes is 87,889 GWh of which 57,334 GWh is regarded as being for power only. The significant increase in the number of scaled back schemes in 2005 is due to changes in the CHPQA Programme; from April 2005 all schemes not fully qualifying as Good Quality are now scaled back. Prior to 2005 there was special dispensation for schemes below 2 MWe such that only schemes above 2 MWe were scaled back.

6.38   In 2004 the total power capacity of scaled back schemes was 7,122 MWe. The large reduction in total power for these schemes in 2005 is due to one large scheme, which previously supplied a small amount of heat and was very heavily scaled back, that is now no longer supplying heat.

Table 6G: CHP capacity, output and fuel use which has been scaled back in 2005

	Units	
Number of schemes requiring scaling back		79
Total Power Capacity of these schemes (CHP_{TPC})	MWe	4,903
Qualifying Power Capacity of these schemes (CHP_{QPC})	MWe	1,460
Total Power Output of these schemes (CHP_{TPO})	GWh	31,089*
Qualifying Power Output of these schemes (CHP_{QPO})	GWh	7,452
Electricity regarded as "Power only" not from CHP (CHP_{TPO} - CHP_{QPO})	GWh	23,636
Total Fuel Input of these schemes (CHP_{TFI})	GWh	87,889
Fuel input regarded as being for "Power only" use ie not for CHP	GWh	57,334

*This figure includes generation from major power producers

Contacts:
Adrian Crispin, Future Energy Solutions
adrian.crispin@aeat.co.uk
0870 190 6085

Mike Janes (Statistician), DTI
mike.janes@dti.gsi.gov.uk
0207 215 5186

6.1 CHP installations by capacity and size range

	2001	2002	2003	2004	2005
Number of schemes *(1)*	**1,552**	**1,534**	**1,534**	**1,527r**	**1,534**
Less than 100 kWe	664	641	622	592r	581
100 kWe to 999 kWe	631	637	648	667r	682
1 MWe to 9.9 MWe	185	184	190	195r	196
10.0 MWe and above	72	72	74	73r	75
					MWe
Total capacity	**4,732**	**4,848**	**4,777**	**5,684r**	**5,792**
Less than 100 kWe	40	39	38	36r	35
100 kWe to 999 kWe	155	154	158	166r	171
1 MWe to 9.9 MWe	747	750	756	779r	771
10.0 MWe and above	3,790	3,905	3,826	4,703r	4,814

(1) A site may contain more than one CHP scheme.

6.2 Fuel used to generate electricity and heat in CHP installations

					GWh
	2001	2002	2003	2004	2005
Fuel used to generate electricity *(1)*					
Coal *(2)*	2,412	2,303	2,372	1,924r	1,805
Fuel oil	2,817	2,237	2,053	1,921r	1,808
Natural gas	35,422	39,857	40,780	44,604r	48,709
Renewable fuels *(3)*	1,076	1,083	1,204	1,274r	1,374
Other fuels *(4)*	9,379	9,648	8,586	11,437r	12,632
Total all fuels	**51,106**	**55,128**	**54,995**	**61,161r**	**66,328**
Fuel used to generate heat					
Coal *(2)*	4,825	4,762	4,676	3,751r	3,506
Fuel oil	5,244	3,210	2,901	2,813r	2,485
Natural gas	38,501	41,273	40,155	41,338r	42,811
Renewable fuels *(3)*	1,090	1,183	1,419	1,431r	1,479
Other fuels *(4)*	18,968	17,508	18,052	19,828r	20,268
Total all fuels	**68,629**	**67,936**	**67,203**	**69,161r**	**70,550**
Overall fuel use					
Coal *(2)*	7,237	7,065	7,049	5,676r	5,311
Fuel oil	8,061	5,447	4,954	4,734r	4,293
Natural gas	73,923	81,129	80,935	85,942r	91,521
Renewable fuels *(3)*	2,166	2,267	2,623	2,705r	2,853
Other fuels *(4)*	28,348	27,156	26,638	31,265r	32,900
Total all fuels	**119,735**	**123,064**	**122,199**	**130,322r**	**136,878**

(1) See paragraphs 6.34 to 6.36 for an explanation of the method used to allocate fuel use between heat generation and electricity generation.
(2) Includes coke and semi-coke.
(3) Renewable fuels include: sewage gas; other biogases; municipal waste and refuse derived fuels.
(4) Other fuels include: process by-products, coke oven gas, blast furnace gas, gas oil and uranium.

6.3 Fuel used by types of CHP installation

GWh

	2001	2002	2003	2004	2005
Coal					
Back pressure steam turbine	2,103	1,923	1,853	2,106r	2,106
Gas turbine	34	46	42	50	50
Combined cycle	466	257	172	118	41
Reciprocating engine	-	-	-	-	-
Pass out condensing steam turbine	4,810	4,839	4,983	3,402r	3,115
Total coal	**7,414**	**7,065**	**7,049**	**5,676r**	**5,311**
Fuel oil					
Back pressure steam turbine	551	452	487	479r	479
Gas turbine	403	288	506	30r	56
Combined cycle	5,995	4,077	3,607	3,805r	3,408
Reciprocating engine	175	221	197	189r	168
Pass out condensing steam turbine	937	409	156	232	182
Total fuel oil	**8,061**	**5,447**	**4,954**	**4,683r**	**4,293**
Natural gas					
Back pressure steam turbine	5,267	5,212	4,617	3,396r	3,396
Gas turbine	13,025	12,998	14,370	13,613r	13,107
Combined cycle	43,878	51,147	52,606	59,110r	65,701
Reciprocating engine	7,436	8,539	7,938	8,416r	8,213
Pass out condensing steam turbine	4,317	3,233	1,405	1,407r	1,104
Total natural gas	**73,923**	**81,129**	**80,935**	**85,942r**	**91,521**
Renewable fuels (1)					
Back pressure steam turbine	10	14	13	422r	422
Gas turbine	19	21	21	21	30
Combined cycle	40	28	263	411	634
Reciprocating engine	1,573	1,564	1,434	1,398r	1,367
Pass out condensing steam turbine	524	640	892	453r	400
Total renewable fuels	**2,166**	**2,267**	**2,623**	**2,705r**	**2,853**
Other fuels (2)					
Back pressure steam turbine	5,811	5,310	5,343	5,356r	5,356
Gas turbine	1,481	1,577	1,435	1,783r	1,974
Combined cycle	7,409	8,062	6,842	10,511r	12,024
Reciprocating engine	89	58	59	85	87
Pass out condensing steam turbine	13,381	12,149	12,959	13,530r	13,459
Total other fuels	**28,171**	**27,156**	**26,638**	**31,265r**	**32,900**
Total - all fuels					
Back pressure steam turbine	13,743	12,911	12,313	11,758r	11,758
Gas turbine	14,961	14,929	16,373	15,497r	15,217
Combined cycle	57,787	63,571	63,490	73,955r	81,808
Reciprocating engine	9,274	10,382	9,627	10,087r	9,835
Pass out condensing steam turbine	23,970	21,271	20,395	19,024r	18,259
Total all fuels	**119,735**	**123,064**	**122,199**	**130,322r**	**136,878**

(1) Renewable fuels include: sewage gas; other biogases; municipal waste and refuse derived fuels.
(2) Other fuels include: process by-products, coke oven gas, blast furnace gas, gas oil and uranium.

6.4 CHP - electricity generated by fuel and type of installation

GWh

	2001	2002	2003	2004	2005
Coal					
Back pressure steam turbine	151	151	140	173r	173
Gas turbine	6	7	7	8	8
Combined cycle	56	29	25	15	3
Reciprocating engine	-	-	-	-	-
Pass out condensing steam turbine	771	732	795	570r	543
Total coal	**984**	**920**	**967**	**767r**	**728**
Fuel oil					
Back pressure steam turbine	51	51	54	53	53
Gas turbine	84	60	89	6r	10
Combined cycle	902	765	732	794r	710
Reciprocating engine	54	67	60	59r	53
Pass out condensing steam turbine	145	46	23	34r	29
Total fuel oil	**1,236**	**989**	**957**	**947r**	**854**
Natural gas					
Back pressure steam turbine	437	508	540	262r	262
Gas turbine	2,936	2,817	3,262	2,980r	2,910
Combined cycle	10,134	12,330	13,018	15,360r	17,347
Reciprocating engine	1,991	2,129	1,948	2,084r	2,062
Pass out condensing steam turbine	432	264	112	170r	156
Total natural gas	**15,930**	**18,049**	**18,881**	**20,857r**	**22,737**
Renewable fuels *(1)*					
Back pressure steam turbine	1	1	1	52r	52
Gas turbine	3	4	4	4	5
Combined cycle	6	2	16	25	43
Reciprocating engine	365	368	333	381r	374
Pass out condensing steam turbine	57	60	89	37r	32
Total renewable fuels	**432**	**435**	**443**	**499r**	**506**
Other fuels *(2)*					
Back pressure steam turbine	661	678	640	657r	657
Gas turbine	293	314	267	378r	365
Combined cycle	1,174	1,526	1,403	2,516r	3,050
Reciprocating engine	28	17	15	22	21
Pass out condensing steam turbine	1,705	1,492	1,342	1,423r	1,422
Total other fuels	**3,862**	**4,026**	**3,668**	**4,996r**	**5,515**
Total - all fuels					
Back pressure steam turbine	1,301	1,389	1,375	1,198r	1,198
Gas turbine	3,323	3,202	3,630	3,377r	3,298
Combined cycle	12,272	14,653	15,194	18,711r	21,152
Reciprocating engine	2,437	2,581	2,356	2,546r	2,511
Pass out condensing steam turbine	3,110	2,595	2,361	2,234r	2,181
Total all fuels	**22,444**	**24,420**	**24,916**	**28,065r**	**30,340**

(1) Renewable fuels include: sewage gas; other biogases; municipal waste and refuse derived fuels.
(2) Other fuels include: process by-products, coke oven gas, blast furnace gas, gas oil and uranium.

6.5 CHP - electrical capacity by fuel and type of installation

MWe

	2001	2002	2003	2004	2005
Coal					
Back pressure steam turbine	55	48	40	51r	51
Gas turbine	1	1	1	1	1
Combined cycle	11	5	6	3	-
Reciprocating engine	-	-	-	-	-
Pass out condensing steam turbine	195	208	227	161r	158
Total coal	**261**	**262**	**274**	**216r**	**210**
Fuel oil					
Back pressure steam turbine	17	14	14	15	15
Gas turbine	27	23	39	2	4
Combined cycle	251	144	130	143r	134
Reciprocating engine	16	20	21	21	17
Pass out condensing steam turbine	33	13	6	9r	8
Total fuel oil	**344**	**213**	**211**	**191r**	**178**
Natural gas					
Back pressure steam turbine	143	177	159	77r	77
Gas turbine	521	533	601	539r	544
Combined cycle	1,834	2,040	2,151	2,813r	2,999
Reciprocating engine	473	513	537	541	546
Pass out condensing steam turbine	97	79	40	55r	51
Total natural gas	**3,068**	**3,341**	**3,488**	**4,025r**	**4,216**
Renewable fuels *(1)*					
Back pressure steam turbine	-	-	-	13r	13
Gas turbine	-	-	1	1	1
Combined cycle	1	-	3	6	6
Reciprocating engine	85	84	81	93r	94
Pass out condensing steam turbine	16	18	23	10r	10
Total renewable fuels	**103**	**104**	**107**	**122r**	**124**
Other fuels *(2)*					
Back pressure steam turbine	109	109	109	136r	136
Gas turbine	97	99	89	127r	122
Combined cycle	292	275	263	596r	530
Reciprocating engine	9	4	5	6	6
Pass out condensing steam turbine	448	441	232	266r	268
Total other fuels	**955**	**928**	**697**	**1,131r**	**1,062**
Total - all fuels					
Back pressure steam turbine	323	348	322	293r	293
Gas turbine	646	656	731	670r	672
Combined cycle	2,389	2,464	2,552	3,562r	3,670
Reciprocating engine	584	621	643	660r	662
Pass out condensing steam turbine	790	759	529	500r	494
Total all fuels	**4,732**	**4,848**	**4,777**	**5,684r**	**5,791**

(1) Renewable fuels include: sewage gas; other biogases; municipal waste and refuse derived fuels.
(2) Other fuels include: process by-products and uranium.

6.6 CHP - heat generated by fuel and type of installation

GWh

	2001	2002	2003	2004	2005
Coal					
Back pressure steam turbine	1,342	1,226	1,180	1,359r	1,359
Gas turbine	18	27	31	28	28
Combined cycle	219	109	89	58	7
Reciprocating engine	-	-	-	-	-
Pass out condensing steam turbine	2,370	2,451	2,543	1,593r	1,487
Total coal	**3,949**	**3,813**	**3,843**	**3,038r**	**2,880**
Fuel oil					
Back pressure steam turbine	394	329	352	351r	351
Gas turbine	231	168	245	16r	26
Combined cycle	3,419	2,110	1,954	2,214r	1,821
Reciprocating engine	60	71	61	61	55
Pass out condensing steam turbine	518	180	83	114r	85
Total fuel oil	**4,622**	**2,858**	**2,695**	**2,755r**	**2,338**
Natural gas					
Back pressure steam turbine	3,867	3,637	3,263	2,569r	2,569
Gas turbine	6,389	6,076	6,874	6,694r	6,381
Combined cycle	18,904	22,442	22,772	24,920r	26,740
Reciprocating engine	3,314	3,601	3,642	3,736r	3,627
Pass out condensing steam turbine	3,032	1,770	1,060	860r	685
Total natural gas	**35,507**	**37,526**	**37,611**	**38,780r**	**40,003**
Renewable fuels *(1)*					
Back pressure steam turbine	5	6	5	160r	160
Gas turbine	9	11	11	11	16
Combined cycle	16	7	61	83	108
Reciprocating engine	577	580	531	561r	547
Pass out condensing steam turbine	223	267	324	174r	147
Total renewable fuels	**830**	**870**	**931**	**989r**	**978**
Other fuels *(2)*					
Back pressure steam turbine	3,145	2,943	3,361	3,285r	3,285
Gas turbine	838	871	690	896r	864
Combined cycle	3,877	3,888	3,669	4,938r	5,215
Reciprocating engine	35	27	29	37	38
Pass out condensing steam turbine	7,781	6,924	7,223	7,423r	7,524
Total other fuels	**15,676**	**14,653**	**14,971**	**16,579r**	**16,926**
Total - all fuels					
Back pressure steam turbine	8,753	8,142	8,162	7,723r	7,723
Gas turbine	7,487	7,153	7,851	7,645r	7,315
Combined cycle	26,435	28,556	28,545	32,212r	33,891
Reciprocating engine	3,986	4,278	4,262	4,395r	4,267
Pass out condensing steam turbine	13,924	11,592	11,232	10,165r	9,929
Total all fuels	**60,584**	**59,721**	**60,052**	**62,140r**	**63,124**

(1) Renewable fuels include: sewage gas; other biogases; municipal waste and refuse derived fuels.
(2) Other fuels include: process by-products and uranium.

6.7 CHP - heat capacity by fuel and type of installation

MWth

	2001	2002	2003	2004	2005
Coal					
Back pressure steam turbine	405	305	246	326r	326
Gas turbine	3	4	3	4	4
Combined cycle	34	18	19	10	1
Reciprocating engine	-	-	-	-	-
Pass out condensing steam turbine	573	606	646	445r	435
Total coal	**1,014**	**934**	**915**	**785r**	**766**
Fuel oil					
Back pressure steam turbine	128	90	94	96	96
Gas turbine	95	87	162	10r	17
Combined cycle	572	357	337	396r	363
Reciprocating engine	20	21	25	25	23
Pass out condensing steam turbine	104	51	19	29r	23
Total fuel oil	**920**	**605**	**637**	**556r**	**521**
Natural gas					
Back pressure steam turbine	761	685	588	506r	506
Gas turbine	1,146	1,121	1,130	1,367r	1,362
Combined cycle	3,417	3,774	3,911	4,389r	4,828
Reciprocating engine	918	930	840	876r	864
Pass out condensing steam turbine	573	400	208	226r	194
Total natural gas	**6,815**	**6,910**	**6,678**	**7,364r**	**7,754**
Renewable fuels *(1)*					
Back pressure steam turbine	1	5	5	46r	46
Gas turbine	2	2	2	2	3
Combined cycle	2	1	9	13	16
Reciprocating engine	139	136	131	124r	124
Pass out condensing steam turbine	46	62	86	43r	43
Total renewable fuels	**190**	**206**	**233**	**228r**	**233**
Other fuels *(2)*					
Back pressure steam turbine	357	357	381	435r	435
Gas turbine	384	388	314	472r	469
Combined cycle	787	803	786	900r	853
Reciprocating engine	9	6	6	8	8
Pass out condensing steam turbine	1,421	1,350	1,271	1,348r	1,357
Total other fuels	**2,959**	**2,904**	**2,757**	**3,162r**	**3,122**
Total - all fuels					
Back pressure steam turbine	1,652	1,442	1,315	1,409r	1,409
Gas turbine	1,630	1,602	1,612	1,854r	1,854
Combined cycle	4,812	4,953	5,062	5,708r	6,062
Reciprocating engine	1,087	1,094	1,003	1,033r	1,019
Pass out condensing steam turbine	2,717	2,469	2,230	2,092r	2,052
Total all fuels	**11,898**	**11,559**	**11,221**	**12,096r**	**12,396**

(1) Renewable fuels include: sewage gas; other biogases; municipal waste and refuse derived fuels.
(2) Other fuels include: process by-products and uranium.

6.8 CHP capacity, output and total fuel use[1] by sector

	Unit	2001	2002	2003	2004	2005
Iron and steel and non ferrous metals						
Number of sites		7	5	6	7	7
Electrical capacity	MWe	80	63	66	67r	67
Heat capacity	MWth	497	285	285	285	285
Electrical output	GWh	493	365	253	243r	238
Heat output	GWh	2,197	1,321	1,707	1,708r	1,765
Fuel use	GWh	3,251	1,914	3,085	3,244r	3,045
of which : for electricity	GWh	984	693	654	662r	609
for heat	GWh	2,267	1,221	2,431	2,582r	2,436
Chemicals						
Number of sites		49	50	50	49r	49
Electrical capacity	MWe	1,517	1,475	1,517	1,549r	1,551
Heat capacity	MWth	3,940	3,763	3,605	3,836r	3,836
Electrical output	GWh	8,344	8,016	8,402	8,906r	8,509
Heat output	GWh	21,645	21,087	20,580	20,644r	20,225
Fuel use	GWh	43,839	43,786	42,407	42,893r	41,962
of which : for electricity	GWh	19,048	18,601	18,884	19,484r	18,782
for heat	GWh	24,792	25,185	23,523	23,409r	23,181
Oil refineries						
Number of sites		10	9	9	10	12
Electrical capacity	MWe	984	954	955	1,767	1,883
Heat capacity	MWth	3,098	3,066	3,088	3,688r	3,830
Electrical output	GWh	4,214	5,198	5,181	7,194r	10,174
Heat output	GWh	14,823	14,630	15,216	16,864r	18,524
Fuel use	GWh	27,472	28,396	27,479	33,076r	41,738
of which : for electricity	GWh	10,119	11,993	11,069	15,264r	21,716
for heat	GWh	17,352	16,403	16,410	17,813r	20,022
Paper, publishing and printing						
Number of sites		35	37	36	34r	33
Electrical capacity	MWe	529	596	691	675r	661
Heat capacity	MWth	1,316	1,390	1,453	1,397r	1,367
Electrical output	GWh	3,413	3,660	3,943	4,255r	4,001
Heat output	GWh	8,852	8,508	8,394	8,428r	8,332
Fuel use	GWh	16,611	16,710	16,844	17,441r	16,835
of which : for electricity	GWh	7,145	7,603	8,075	8,634r	8,154
for heat	GWh	9,466	9,107	8,770	8,807r	8,681
Food, beverages and tobacco						
Number of sites		45	45	42	43r	43
Electrical capacity	MWe	393	404	379	377r	380
Heat capacity	MWth	1,121	1,108	982	991r	1,204
Electrical output	GWh	1,674	1,953	1,957	1,901r	1,923
Heat output	GWh	5,101	5,767	5,620	5,173r	5,191
Fuel use	GWh	8,706	9,990	9,734	9,215r	9,263
of which : for electricity	GWh	3,402	3,984	3,937	3,860r	3,909
for heat	GWh	5,304	6,005	5,797	5,355r	5,354
Metal products, machinery and equipment						
Number of sites		16	14	15	15	13
Electrical capacity	MWe	82	78	101	71r	70
Heat capacity	MWth	91	66	79	79	73
Electrical output	GWh	182	202	317	193r	164
Heat output	GWh	388	344	403	290r	268
Fuel use	GWh	821	800	1,105	739r	660
of which : for electricity	GWh	391	430	674	412r	356
for heat	GWh	430	370	431	327r	304

For footnotes see page 164

6.8 CHP capacity, output and total fuel use[1] by sector (continued)

	Unit	2001	2002	2003	2004	2005
Mineral products, extraction, mining and agglomeration of solid fuels						
Number of sites		10	10	10	9r	9
Electrical capacity	MWe	56	54	53	50r	50
Heat capacity	MWth	180	180	180	170r	170
Electrical output	GWh	242	225	227	195r	186
Heat output	GWh	848	819	800	729r	743
Fuel use	GWh	1,474	1,443	1,321	1,189r	1,179
of which : for electricity	GWh	536	514	490	423r	401
for heat	GWh	938	929	831	766r	778
Sewage treatment						
Number of sites		113	113	112	119r	123
Electrical capacity	MWe	102	101	101	112r	114
Heat capacity	MWth	162	159	158	151r	151
Electrical output	GWh	424	429	395	440r	430
Heat output	GWh	654	659	611	639r	618
Fuel use	GWh	1,782	1,776	1,652	1,607r	1,561
of which : for electricity	GWh	997	991	921	932r	909
for heat	GWh	786	784	731	675r	653
Electricity supply						
Number of sites		6	8	7	7	6
Electrical capacity	MWe	470	584	369	425r	422
Heat capacity	MWth	370	530	455	455	445
Electrical output	GWh	1,157	2,049	2,184	2,353r	2,306
Heat output	GWh	1,837	2,449	2,721	3,111r	3,012
Fuel use	GWh	6,173	8,066	9,332	10,241r	9,940
of which : for electricity	GWh	3,577	5,046	5,763	6,180r	6,054
for heat	GWh	2,596	3,020	3,569	4,061r	3,886
Other industrial branches (2)						
Number of sites		16	14	14	14r	16
Electrical capacity	MWe	57	55	51	51r	53
Heat capacity	MWth	181	161	96	96	96
Electrical output	GWh	333	333	306	338r	286
Heat output	GWh	699	648	529	573r	483
Fuel use	GWh	1,419	1,303	1,135	1,248r	1,059
of which : for electricity	GWh	680	653	609	676r	575
for heat	GWh	739	651	526	571r	484
Total industry						
Number of sites		307	305	301	307r	311
Electrical capacity	MWe	4,269	4,364	4,283	5,145r	5,251
Heat capacity	MWth	10,954	10,708	10,381	11,148r	11,458
Electrical output	GWh	20,474	22,428	23,166	26,019r	28,215
Heat output	GWh	57,042	56,233	56,580	58,159r	59,160
Fuel use	GWh	111,548	114,183	114,094	120,894r	127,243
of which : for electricity	GWh	46,877	50,508	51,075	56,528r	61,464
for heat	GWh	64,671	63,675	63,019	64,366r	65,779

6.8 CHP capacity, output and total fuel use[1] by sector (continued)

	Unit	2001	2002	2003	2004	2005
Transport, commerce and administration						
Number of sites		1,148	1,134	1,138	1,124r	1,127
Electrical capacity	MWe	293	294	308	349r	353
Heat capacity	MWth	657	555	526	669r	664
Electrical output	GWh	1,337	1,271	1,256	1,491r	1,565
Heat output	GWh	2,388	2,310	2,377	2,810r	2,871
Fuel use	GWh	5,289	5,279	5,074	6,131r	6,328
of which : for electricity	GWh	2,798	2,765	2,603	3,137r	3,293
for heat	GWh	2,491	2,514	2,472	2,994r	3,035
Other (3)						
Number of sites		97	94	95	96r	96
Electrical capacity	MWe	170	190	186	190r	187
Heat capacity	MWth	287	296	314	278r	277
Electrical output	GWh	633	720	495	555r	561
Heat output	GWh	1,156	1,178	1,095	1,171r	1,094
Fuel use	GWh	2,898	3,601	3,030	3,297r	3,307
of which : for electricity	GWh	1,431	1,854	1,317	1,496r	1,571
for heat	GWh	1,467	1,746	1,713	1,801r	1,736
Total CHP usage by all sectors						
Number of sites		1,552	1,533	1,534	1,527r	1,534
Electrical capacity	MWe	4,732	4,848	4,777	5,684r	5,792
Heat capacity	MWth	11,898	11,558	11,221	12,096r	12,398
Electrical output	GWh	22,445	24,419	24,916	28,065r	30,341
Heat output	GWh	60,586	59,721	60,052	62,140r	63,126
Fuel use	GWh	119,735	123,064	122,199	130,322r	136,878
of which : for electricity	GWh	51,106	55,128	54,995	61,161r	66,328
for heat	GWh	68,629	67,936	67,203	69,161r	70,550

(1) The allocation of fuel use between electricity and heat is largely notional and the methodology is outlined in paragraphs 6.34 to 6.36.

(2) Other industry includes Textiles, clothing and footwear sector.

(3) Sectors included under Other are agriculture, community heating, leisure, landfill and incineration.

6.9 CHP - use of fuels by sector

GWh

	2001	2002	2003	2004	2005
Iron and steel and non ferrous metals					
Coal	97	-	-	-	-
Fuel oil	179	49	45	102r	55
Natural gas	513	247	217	282r	202
Blast furnace gas	1,971	1,256	2,401	2,523r	2,313
Coke oven gas	445	363	422	337r	475
Other fuels *(2)*	46	-	-	-	-
Total iron and steel and non ferrous metals	**3,251**	**1,914**	**3,085**	**3,244r**	**3,045**
Chemicals					
Coal	4,479	4,473	4,818	3,337r	3,258
Fuel oil	1,182	526	148	197r	193
Gas oil	98	74	32	406r	516
Natural gas	27,584	28,213	26,823	27,276r	26,293
Refinery gas	66	28	-	-	-
Renewable fuels *(1)*	19	21	21	21	30
Other fuels *(2)*	10,412	10,451	10,565	11,657r	11,673
Total chemical industry	**43,839**	**43,786**	**42,407**	**42,893r**	**41,962**
Oil refineries					
Fuel oil	5,946	4,136	4,079	3,787	3,378
Gas oil	134	134	134	44	44
Natural gas	7,794	10,248	10,884	14,460r	21,394
Refinery gas	7,526	8,152	5,612	5,472r	5,631
Other fuels *(2)*	6,072	5,727	6,771	9,314r	11,289
Total oil refineries	**27,472**	**28,396**	**27,479**	**33,076r**	**41,738**
Paper, publishing and printing					
Coal	797	713	450	635	635
Fuel oil	361	313	268	266	306
Gas oil	43	43	22	30r	73
Natural gas	15,217	15,450	15,958	16,378r	15,673
Renewable fuels *(1)*	4	3	2	1	1
Other fuels *(2)*	188	188	145	130	147
Total paper, publishing and printing	**16,611**	**16,710**	**16,844**	**17,441r**	**16,835**
Food, beverages and tobacco					
Coal	1,292	1,241	1,179	1,067r	1,067
Fuel oil	184	188	214	191	190
Gas oil	66	11	20	767r	76
Natural gas	7,164	8,550	8,313	7,168r	7,887
Renewable fuels *(1)*	-	-	-	-	-
Other fuels *(2)*	-	-	8	23	42
Total food, beverages and tobacco	**8,706**	**9,990**	**9,734**	**9,215r**	**9,263**
Metal products, machinery and equipment					
Coal	32	-	-	-	-
Fuel oil	51	92	91	92r	92
Gas oil	-	-	-	-	-
Natural gas	737	708	1,014	646r	568
Total metal products, machinery and equipment	**821**	**800**	**1,105**	**739r**	**660**
Mineral products, extraction, mining and agglomeration of solid fuels					
Coal	176	-	-	-	-
Fuel oil	-	-	2	-	-
Natural gas	1,148	1,048	1,091	967r	956
Coke oven gas	150	395	228	223r	223
Total mineral products, extraction, mining and agglomeration of solid fuels	**1,474**	**1,443**	**1,321**	**1,189r**	**1,179**

For footnotes see page 166

6.9 CHP - use of fuels by sector (cont'd)

GWh

	2001	2002	2003	2004	2005
Sewage treatment					
Fuel oil	71	71	61	61	55
Gas oil	30	30	30	30	22
Natural gas	114	114	129	120r	120
Renewable fuels *(1)*	1,567	1,561	1,432	1,396r	1,365
Total sewage treatment	**1,782**	**1,776**	**1,652**	**1,607r**	**1,561**
Electricity supply					
Coal	178	216	288	288	-
Fuel oil	3	3	3	4	3
Gas oil	-	-	-	2	2
Natural gas	5,213	7,669	8,828r	9,705r	9,692
Refinery gas	-	-	-	1r	1
Other fuels *(2)*	780	178	212r	241r	241
Total electricity supply	**6,173**	**8,066**	**9,332**	**10,241r**	**9,940**
Other industrial branches *(3)*					
Fuel oil	2	-	-	-	-
Gas oil	1	-	-	-	9
Natural gas	1,411	1,298	1,130	1,242r	1,045
Renewable fuels *(1)*	5	5	5	5	5
Total other industrial branches	**1,419**	**1,304**	**1,135**	**1,248r**	**1,059**
Transport, commerce and administration					
Coal	34	46	42	50	50
Fuel oil	67	64	42	35r	21
Gas oil	65	18	17	19r	64
Natural gas	5,116	5,148	4,971	6,024r	6,191
Refinery gas	1	1	-	-	-
Renewable fuels *(1)*	5	2	2	2r	2
Other fuels *(2)*	1	1	1	1	1
Total transport, commerce and administration	**5,289**	**5,279**	**5,074**	**6,131r**	**6,328**
Other *(4)*					
Coal	329	377	272	299	301
Fuel oil	14	6	-	-	-
Gas oil	22	17	15	42	52
Natural gas	1,913	2,438	1,579	1,673r	1,502
Renewable fuels *(1)*	566	675	1,161	1,280r	1,450
Other fuels *(2)*	54	88	3	3	3
Total other	**2,898**	**3,601**	**3,030**	**3,297r**	**3,307**
Total - all sectors					
Coal	7,414	7,065	7,049	5,676r	5,311
Fuel oil	8,061	5,447	4,954	4,734r	4,293
Gas oil	458	327	271	1,341r	860
Natural gas	73,923	81,129	80,935	85,942r	91,521
Blast furnace gas	1,971	1,256	2,401	2,523r	2,313
Coke oven gas	595	758	650	559r	698
Refinery gas	7,594	8,182	5,612	5,473r	5,632
Renewable fuels *(1)*	2,166	2,267	2,623	2,705r	2,853
Other fuels *(2)*	17,553	16,633	17,704	21,369r	23,397
Total CHP fuel use	**119,735**	**123,064**	**122,199**	**130,322r**	**136,878**

(1) Renewable fuels include: sewage gas; other biogases; clinical waste; municipal waste.
(2) Other fuels include: process by-products and uranium.
(3) Other industry now includes textiles, clothing and footwear which was shown as a separate sector in previous Digests.
(4) Sectors included under Other are agriculture, community heating, leisure, landfill and incineration.

Chapter 7
Renewable sources of energy

Introduction

7.1   This chapter provides information on the contribution of renewable energy sources to the United Kingdom's energy requirements. It includes sources that under international definitions are not counted as renewable sources or are counted only in part. This is to ensure that this Digest covers all sources of energy available in the United Kingdom. However, within this chapter the international definition of total renewables is used and this excludes non-biodegradable wastes. The energy uses of wastes are still shown in the tables of this chapter but as "below the line" items. This chapter covers both the use of renewables to generate electricity and the burning of renewable fuels to produce heat either in boilers (or cookers) or in combined heat and power plants.

7.2   The data summarise the results of an ongoing study undertaken by the Future Energy Solutions (FES - part of AEA Technology (AEAT) Environment), on behalf of the Department of Trade and Industry, to update a database containing information on all relevant renewable energy sources in the United Kingdom. This database is called RESTATS, the Renewable Energy STATisticS database.

7.3   The study started in 1989, when all relevant renewable energy sources were identified and, where possible, information was collected on the amounts of energy derived from each source. The renewable energy sources identified were the following: active solar heating; photovoltaics; onshore and offshore wind power; wave power; large and small scale hydro; biofuels; geothermal aquifers. The technical notes at the end of this chapter define each of these renewable energy sources. The database now contains 17 years of data from 1989 to 2005.

7.4   The information contained in the database is collected by a number of methods. For larger projects, an annual survey is carried out in which questionnaires are sent to project managers. For technologies in which there are large numbers of small projects, the values given in this chapter are estimates based on information collected from a sub-sample of the projects. Further details about the data collection methodologies used in RESTATS, including the quality and completeness of the information, are given in the technical notes at the end of this chapter.

7.5   Commodity balances for renewable energy sources covering each of the last three years form the first three tables (Tables 7.1 to 7.3). These are followed by 5-year tables showing capacity of, and electricity generation from, renewable sources (Table 7.4), and generation from sources eligible for the Renewables Obligation and sources qualifying under the Renewables Directive (Table 7.5). Table 7.6 summarises all the renewable orders and Table 7.7 shows renewable sources used to generate electricity and heat in each of the last five years. A long-term trends commentary and table (Table 7.1.1) covering the use of renewables to generate electricity and heat is available on DTI's energy statistics web site and accessible from the Digest of UK Energy Statistics home page: www.dti.gov.uk/energy/statistics/publications/dukes/page29812.html .

7.6   Unlike in the commodity balance tables in other chapters of the Digest, Tables 7.1 to 7.3 have zero statistical differences. This is because the data for each category of fuel are, in the main, taken from a single source where there is less likelihood of differences due to timing or measurement. These commodity balances do not include biofuels used for transport which are currently part of Chapter 3 of this Digest because they are blended with conventional road transport fuels. However, DTI has a project in hand that will investigate obtaining further statistics about these fuels.

Renewables Obligation and Renewables Directive

7.7   In April 2002 the Renewables Obligation (RO) (and the analogous Renewables Obligation (Scotland)) came into effect[1]. It is an obligation on all electricity suppliers to supply a specific proportion of electricity from eligible renewable sources. Eligible sources include all those covered by this chapter but with specific exclusions. These are: existing hydro plant of over 20 MW; all plant

---

[1] *Parliamentary approval of the Renewables Obligation Orders under The Utilities Act 2000 was given in March 2002.*

using renewable sources built before 1990 (unless re-furbished and less than 20 MW); and energy from mixed waste combustion unless the waste is first converted to fuel using advanced conversion technology. Only the biodegradable fraction of any waste is eligible (in line with the EU Directive, see paragraph 7.8, below). All stations outside the United Kingdom (the UK includes its territorial waters and the continental shelf) are also excluded. The upper part of table 7.5 shows all the components of total electricity generation on an RO basis. Strictly speaking until 2005, the RO covers only Great Britain, but in these UK based statistics Northern Ireland renewable sources have been treated as if they were also part of the RO.

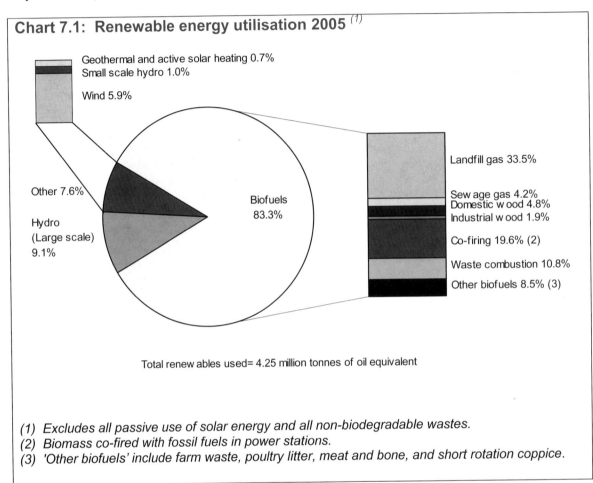

Chart 7.1: Renewable energy utilisation 2005 [1]

Geothermal and active solar heating 0.7%
Small scale hydro 1.0%
Wind 5.9%
Other 7.6%
Hydro (Large scale) 9.1%
Biofuels 83.3%
Landfill gas 33.5%
Sewage gas 4.2%
Domestic wood 4.8%
Industrial wood 1.9%
Co-firing 19.6% (2)
Waste combustion 10.8%
Other biofuels 8.5% (3)

Total renewables used= 4.25 million tonnes of oil equivalent

(1) *Excludes all passive use of solar energy and all non-biodegradable wastes.*
(2) *Biomass co-fired with fossil fuels in power stations.*
(3) *'Other biofuels' include farm waste, poultry litter, meat and bone, and short rotation coppice.*

7.8   The European Union's Renewables Directive (RD) (which came into force in October 2001) has a different definition of eligible renewables. The Directive's definition is the same as the international definition used in this chapter (in that it excludes non-biodegradable wastes). In 2006 the European Commission clarified its definition and as a result imports of electricity generated from renewable sources cannot be included, although such imports will be part of the overall consumption of electricity in the UK which forms the denominator in the calculation of the Renewables Directive percentage (see paragraph 7.12, below). FES has estimated the percentage of municipal solid waste (MSW) that was non-biodegradable for all the years in the RESTATS database. For 2005 the estimate is that 37½ per cent of MSW was non-biodegradable and all of waste tyres (but see paragraph 7.68) and hospital waste. The lower part of Table 7.5 shows the components of total electricity generation on an RD basis.

7.9   In the past the main instruments for pursuing the development of renewables capacity were the Non Fossil Fuel Obligation (NFFO) Orders for England and Wales and for Northern Ireland, and the Scottish Renewable Orders (SRO). In this chapter the term "NFFO Orders" is used to refer to these instruments collectively. For projects contracted under NFFO Orders in England and Wales, the Non Fossil Purchasing Agency (NFPA) provided details of capacity and generation. The Scottish Executive and Northern Ireland Electricity provided information on the Scottish and Northern Ireland NFFO Orders, respectively.

Renewables Targets

7.10   Since February 2000, the United Kingdom's renewables policy has consisted of four key strands:

- a new Renewables Obligation on all electricity suppliers in Great Britain to supply a specific proportion of electricity from eligible renewables;
- exemption of electricity from renewables[2] from the Climate Change Levy;
- an expanded support programme for new and renewable energy including capital grants and an expanded research and development programme;
- development of a regional strategic approach to planning and targets for renewables.

The aim of the Renewables Obligation (RO) is to increase the contribution of electricity from renewables in the UK so that by 2010, 10 per cent of licensed UK electricity sales should be from renewable sources eligible for the RO, and by 2015 15 per cent should be eligible.

7.11   The EU Directive proposes that Member States adopt national targets for renewables that are consistent with reaching the overall EU target of 12 per cent of energy (22.1 per cent of electricity) from renewables by 2010. The proposed UK "share" of this target is that renewables sources eligible under the RD should account for 10 per cent of UK electricity **consumption** by 2010.

7.12   Chart 7.2 shows the growth in all sources of renewables generation since 1990 and Table 7A gives renewables shares on three different bases for the three most recent years. They show progress towards the RO and RD 10 per cent targets. Generation from all renewables in the UK (on the international definition basis) accounted for 4.22 per cent of UK electricity generation in 2005 (see paragraph 7.16, below). In 2005 the RO percentage showed its largest ever growth in a single year rising by 0.91 percentage points to 4.00 per cent of electricity sales by licensed suppliers. On the basis favoured by the Renewables Directive, the percentage of UK electricity consumption accounted for by RD eligible renewable sources rose from 3.52 per cent in 2004 to 4.14 per cent in 2005. All three percentages are affected by the rate of growth in the respective denominators as well as the numerators. For the overall percentage electricity generation in 2005 rose by just under 1½ per cent, while for the RO percentage there was also an increase of just over 1½ per cent in electricity sales by licensed suppliers. For the RD basis electricity consumption also grew by 1½ per cent in 2005.

Table 7A: Percentages of electricity derived from renewable sources

	2003	2004	2005
Overall renewables percentage (revised to the international basis)	2.67	3.58	4.22
Percentage on a Renewables Obligation basis	2.21	3.09r	4.00
Percentage on a Renewables Directive basis	2.66r	3.52r	4.14

Commodity balances for renewables in 2005 (Table 7.1), 2004 (Table 7.2) and 2003 (Table 7.3)

7.13   Nine different categories of renewable fuels are identified in the commodity balances. Some of these categories are themselves groups of renewables because a more detailed disaggregation could disclose data for individual companies. In the commodity balance tables the distinction between biodegradable and non-biodegradable wastes cannot be maintained for this reason. The largest contribution to renewables in **input** terms (over 83 per cent) is from biofuels, with large-scale hydro electricity production contributing the majority of the remainder as Chart 7.1 shows. Only 7½ per cent of renewable energy comes from renewable sources other than biofuels and large-scale hydro, but this proportion is growing. These include solar, wind, small-scale hydro and geothermal aquifers.

7.14   87 per cent of the renewable energy produced in 2005 was transformed into electricity. This is an increase from 82 per cent in 2004 and 80 per cent in 2003. While biofuels appear to dominate the picture when fuel inputs are being measured, hydro electricity is a larger contributor when the output of electricity is being measured as Table 7.4 shows. This is because on an energy supplied basis (see Chapter 5, paragraph 5.26) hydro (and also wind, wave and solar) inputs are assumed to be equal to the electricity produced. For landfill gas, sewage sludge, municipal solid waste and other

---

[2] Electricity generated by hydro stations with a declared net capacity of more than 10 MW is not exempt from the Climate Change Levy.

renewables a substantial proportion of the energy content of the input is lost in the process of conversion to electricity.

7.15   Overall, renewable sources, excluding passive uses of solar energy, provided 1.9 per cent of the United Kingdom's total primary energy requirements in 2005. This was 0.2 of a percentage point higher than in 2004, which in turn was 0.3 of a percentage point higher than in 2003.

Capacity of, and electricity generated from renewable sources (Table 7.4)

7.16   Table 7.4 shows the capacity of, and the amounts of electricity generated from, each renewable source. Total electricity generation from renewables in 2005 amounted to 16,919 GWh, an increase of 2,748 GWh (+19.4 per cent) on 2004. The main contributors to this substantial increase were 1,511 GWh from co-firing of biomass with fossil fuels (+147.9 per cent), 769 GWh from onshore wind (+44.3 per cent), 287 GWh from landfill gas (+7.2 per cent), 204 GWh from offshore wind (+102.3 per cent), and 185 GWh (+65.7 per cent) from small scale hydro schemes. There was a small decrease (-3.3 per cent) in large scale hydro generation which can be attributed to drier weather. Only 26½ per cent of generation from renewables was from large scale hydro in 2005 compared with 33 per cent in 2004. Hydro (taking both large and small scale together) remains the most important renewables technology in output terms followed by landfill gas, wind (both onshore and offshore) and the co-firing of biomass.

7.17   As a result all renewable sources provided 4.22 per cent of the electricity generated in the United Kingdom in 2005, 0.64 percentage points higher than in 2004. Chart 7.2 shows the growth in the proportion of electricity produced from renewable sources. It includes the progress towards the renewables targets set under the Renewables Obligation and Renewables Directive (see paragraphs 7.10 to 7.12 above and 7.23 below).

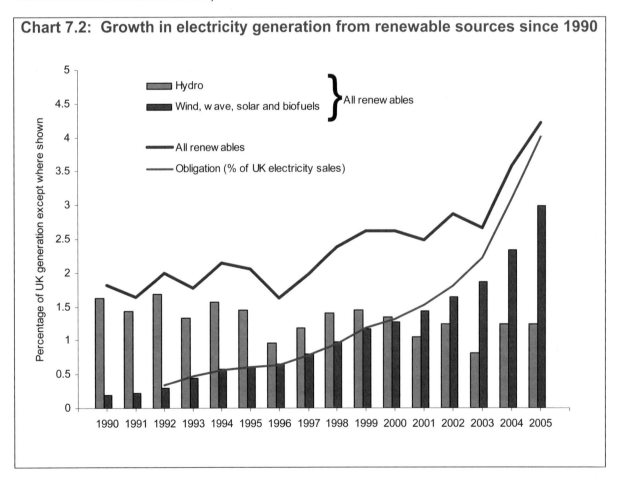

Chart 7.2: Growth in electricity generation from renewable sources since 1990

7.18   There was a 21 per cent increase (+772 MWe) in the installed generating capacity of renewable sources in 2005, mainly as a result of a 67 per cent increase (+542 MWe) in onshore wind capacity and a 75 per cent increase (+90 MWe) in offshore wind capacity. There was also a 13 per increase (+96 MWe) in the capacity fuelled by landfill gas and a 7½ per cent increase (+9 MWe) in sewage gas capacity. Large-scale hydro capacity is 6 per cent lower than it was in 2001 as some stations have been adapted to fall within the capacity limits specified by the renewables obligation. The capacity to generate from solar photovoltaics showed a 33 per cent increase and has thus quadrupled in 4 years.

7.19   Chart 7.3 (which covers all renewables capacity except large scale hydro) illustrates the continuing increase in the electricity generation capacity from all significant renewable sources. This upward trend in the capacity of renewable sources will continue as recently consented onshore and offshore windfarms and other projects come on stream.

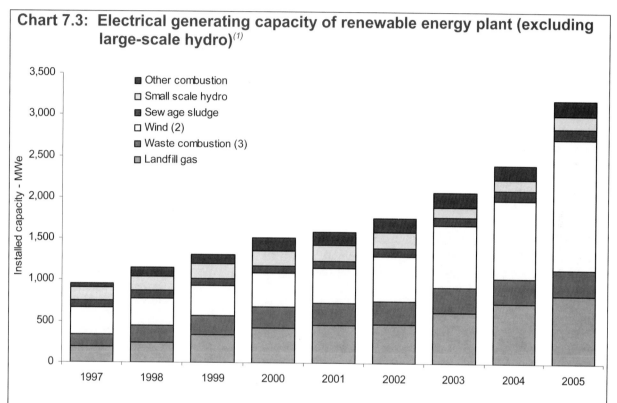

Chart 7.3: Electrical generating capacity of renewable energy plant (excluding large-scale hydro)[(1)]

(1) Large scale hydro capacity was 1,355 MWe in 2005.

(2) Wind includes both onshore and offshore and also includes solar photovoltaics (10.9 MWe in 2005) and shoreline wave (0.5 MWe in 2005).

(3) All waste combustion plant is included because both biodegradable and non-biodegradable wastes are burned together in the same plant.

7.20   In 2005, (excluding large-scale hydro) 45 per cent of electricity from renewables was generated under NFFO contracts. If ex-NFFO sites (NFFO 1 and 2 in England and Wales – see paragraphs 7.24 to 7.36, below) are included the proportion increases to 58 per cent. Table 7.4, however, includes both electricity generated outside of these contracts and electricity from large-scale hydro schemes and thus reports on total electricity generation from renewables. All electricity generated from renewables is also reported within the tables of Chapter 5 of this Digest (eg Table 5.6).

7.21   Plant load factors in Table 7.4 have been calculated in terms of installed capacity and express the average hourly quantity of electricity generated as a percentage of the average capacity at the beginning and end of the year. In the past the overall figure has been heavily influenced by the availability of hydro capacity during the year, which in turn has been influenced by the amount of rainfall during the preceding period. Low rainfall in the winter of 2002/2003 led to 2003 having lower hydro load factors than in the previous very dry year of 1996. Two factors contributed to the lower load factor for wind in 2003. Firstly 110 MWe was installed late in the year and had little opportunity to contribute to generation. Secondly the long hot summer of 2003 was not as windy as previous years. While both hydro and onshore wind load factors were slightly lower in 2005 than in 2004, the load factor for biofuels fell more substantially, probably because new landfill gas capacity did not begin to operate until late in the year. As a result the overall load factor for renewables and wastes was below the record level seen on 2004. Plant load factors for all generating plant in the UK are shown in Chapter 5, Table 5.10.

7.22   To overcome the biasing of load factors for wind caused by new turbines coming on stream either early or late in a calendar year, DTI asked FES to calculate a new statistic which appears for the first time in Table 7.4. This statistic is calculated in the same way as the load factor but includes only those wind farms that have operated throughout the calendar year with an unchanged configuration. See paragraphs 7.80 and 7.81 for the full definitions. Originally this new statistic was termed the "capacity factor" to distinguish it from the traditionally calculated load factor, but "capacity factor" is already used as an alternative term for load factor in some countries and its use could lead to confusion. The unchanged configuration load factor for offshore wind is between 1.7 and 2.6 percentage points higher than the conventionally calculated load factor in each of the 3 most recent years.

Electricity generated from renewable sources; Renewables Obligation and Renewables Directive bases (Table 7.5)

7.23   Electricity generated in the UK from renewable sources eligible under the Renewables Obligation in 2005 was 32 per cent greater than in 2004. This compares with growth of 39 per cent in 2004, 25 per cent in 2003 and 18 per cent in 2002. Electricity generated in the UK from renewable sources eligible under the Renewables Directive in 2005 was 19 per cent greater than in 2004. This compares with growth of 33 per cent in 2004, a 4 per cent fall in 2003 and growth of 17 per cent in 2002. Chart 7.2 shows the growth in the proportion of electricity produced from renewable sources under the Renewables Obligation and international definitions.

Renewable orders and operational capacity (Table 7.6)

7.24   In 1990, the first year of NFFO, projects contracted within NFFO accounted for about 32 per cent of the total capacity (excluding large-scale hydro). This percentage rose to a peak in 2001 of 91 per cent. Following the introduction of the Renewables Obligation it fell back as new capacity eligible for the RO outweighed the growth in NFFO 3, 4 and 5 and SRO and NI-NFFO projects, so that the NFFO capacity proportion (excluding large scale hydro) had decreased to 70 per cent in 2004 and fell further to 60 per cent in 2005. Fifteen new NFFO schemes totalling 70 MW (DNC) came on line during 2005. These trends are shown in Chart 7.4.

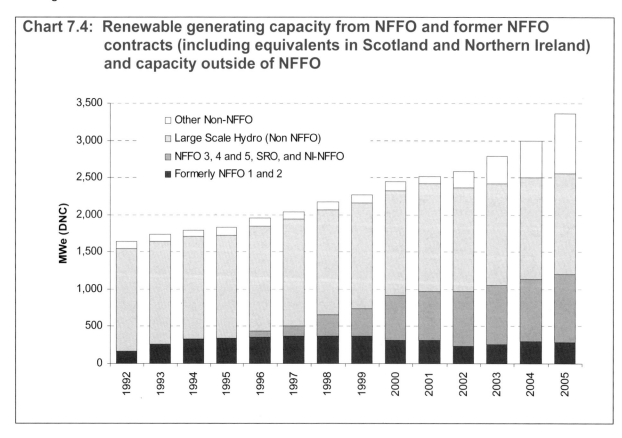

Chart 7.4: Renewable generating capacity from NFFO and former NFFO contracts (including equivalents in Scotland and Northern Ireland) and capacity outside of NFFO

(a)   Non Fossil Fuel Obligation (NFFO)

7.25   The 1989 Electricity Act empowered the Secretary of State to make orders requiring the Regional Electricity Companies in England and Wales (the RECs) to secure specified amounts of electricity from renewable energy sources.

7.26   Five NFFO Orders were made, of which the first in 1990 was set for a total of 102 MW DNC. This first order resulted in contracts for 75 projects for 152 MW DNC and provided a premium price for the electricity produced which was funded from a levy on electricity sales in England and Wales. (The bulk of this levy was used to support electricity from nuclear stations).

7.27   The second Order, made in late 1991, was set for 457 MW DNC. This resulted in 122 separate contracts (for a total of 472 MW DNC) between the generators and the Non-Fossil Purchasing Agency (NFPA), which acted on behalf of the RECs. For landfill gas, sewage gas and waste-derived generation contracts were awarded at around 6p/kWh, while for wind-based generation a price of 11p/kWh was established. These prices reflected the limited period for the recovery of capital costs.

7.28   The third Order covers the period 1995 to 2014; this was for 627 MW DNC of contracted capacity at an average price of 4.35 p/kWh. The lower bid prices reflect the longer-term contracts, which are now available together with further developments that have led to improvements in the technologies. Taking into account factors such as the failure to gain planning permission it is estimated that about 300-400 MW DNC are likely to go forward for commissioning.

7.29   The fourth Order was announced in February 1997. Contracts have been let to 195 projects with a total DNC of 843 MW, at an average price of 3.46 p/kWh. In the fifth and largest Order, which was announced in September 1998, contracts have been let to 261 projects with a total DNC of 1,177.1 MW, at an average price of 2.71 p/kWh.

7.30   Since the expiry of the NFFO 1 and 2 contracts on 31 December 1998, these projects are no longer included in the monitoring of NFFO Orders and DTI no longer receives any status/output data on them from the NFPA. For some of these projects operational data have been obtained from other sources, while for the others estimates have been made based on output in 1998. From 2002 another source of information became available in the form of the Renewables Obligation data. This enabled Future Energy Solutions to identify which former NFFO 1 and 2 schemes were applying for ROCs and therefore were still running. Of the 114 NFFO 1 and 2 projects identified in this way as still live, 42 were contracted under the first order and 72 under the second order. It is appreciated that there may be some ex NFFO 1 and 2 schemes that are continuing to operate but whose output is too small to qualify for ROCs or which may need to re-furbish in order to qualify for ROCs. To that extent the estimates of NFFO capacity may be an underestimate.

7.31   As at the end of December 2005, 87 projects in the third Order were operational, with total capacities of 340 MW DNC. There were also 88 schemes with a capacity of 242 MW DNC commissioned from the fourth Order projects and 89 schemes totalling 178 MW DNC from the fifth Order. Table 7.6 sets out the technologies and capacities of schemes in all five Orders.

(b)   Scottish Renewable Order (SRO)

7.32   In Scotland, the first Renewables Order was made in 1994 for approximately 76 MW DNC of new capacity and comprising 30 schemes. Four generation technology bands were covered; 12 wind, 15 hydro, two waste-to-energy and one biomass. At the end of December 2005, 20 schemes were commissioned with a capacity of 49 MW DNC.

7.33   A second SRO was launched in 1995 and was made in March 1997 for 114 MW DNC of new capacity comprising 26 schemes, 9 of which were waste to energy projects, 9 were hydro projects, 7 were wind projects and one was a biomass project. Under this Order, at the end of 2005 there were 13 commissioned schemes with a capacity of 50 MW DNC.

7.34   A third SRO was laid before Parliament in February 1999 for 145 MW DNC of new capacity comprising 53 schemes. Sixteen of these were waste to energy projects, 5 were hydro projects, 28 were wind projects, one was a biomass project and 3 were wave energy projects. Under this Order, at the end of 2005 there were 17 commissioned schemes with a capacity of 35 MW DNC. Table 7.6 sets out the technologies and capacities of schemes in all three Scottish Orders.

(c)   Northern Ireland Non Fossil Fuel Obligation (NI NFFO)
7.35   In Northern Ireland, a first Order was made in March 1994 for approximately 16 MW DNC comprising 20 schemes. The contracted schemes were spread throughout Northern Ireland and were divided into three technology bands. There were 6 wind schemes of around 2 MW DNC each, totalling 12.7 MW DNC; 5 sewage gas projects totalling 0.56 MW DNC; and 9 small-scale hydro schemes totalling 2.4 MW DNC. At the end of 2005, 15 schemes were commissioned with a capacity of 15 MW DNC.

7.36   A second NI Order was made in 1996 for 10 schemes, totalling 16 MW DNC. These comprised two wind schemes, two hydro schemes, two biomass, one biogas, two landfill gas and one municipal and industrial waste scheme, as shown in Table 7.6. At the end of 2005, 5 schemes were commissioned with a capacity of 3 MW DNC.

Renewable sources used to generate electricity and heat (Table 7.7)
7.37   Between 2004 and 2005 there was an increase of 21½ per cent in the **input** of renewable sources into electricity generation. Biofuels grew by 23 per cent, and wind by 52 per cent, but hydro grew by only ½ per cent.

7.38   Compared with 5 years earlier in 2000 total inputs to electricity generation have doubled aided by 123 per cent growth in the use of biofuels and a tripling of the use of wind.

7.39   Table 7.7 also shows the contribution from renewables to heat generation. Renewables used to generate heat are now only just over half the level they were 9 years earlier in 1996. The decline is mainly due to tighter emissions controls discouraging on-site burning of biofuels, especially wood waste, although domestic and industrial use of wood and wood waste still provide the main contribution. However the use of active solar heating has increased by 165 per cent in the last 5 years and the use of heating from biodegradable wastes has increased by 36 per cent over the same period.

Technical notes and definitions

7.40   Energy derived from renewable sources is included in the aggregate energy tables in Chapter 1 of this Digest. The main commodity balance tables (Tables 7.1 to 7.3) present figures in the common unit of energy, the tonne of oil equivalent, which is defined in Chapter 1 paragraph 1.24. The gross calorific values and conversion factors used to convert the data from original units are given on page 206 of Annex A and inside the back cover flap. The statistical methodologies and conversion factors are in line with those used by the International Energy Agency and the Statistical Office of the European Communities. Primary electricity contributions from hydro and wind are expressed in terms of an electricity supplied model (see Chapter 5, paragraph 5.26). Electrical capacities in this chapter are quoted as Installed capacities.   However, in Chapter 5 Declared Net Capacity (DNC) of renewables is used when calculating the overall UK generating capacity. DNC takes into account the intermittent nature of the power output from some renewable sources (see paragraph 7.78, below).

7.41   The various renewable energy sources are described in the following paragraphs. This section also provides details of the quality of information provided within each renewables area, and the progress made to improve the quality of this information. While the data in the printed and bound copy of this Digest cover only the most recent 5 years, these notes also cover data for earlier years that are available on the DTI web site.

Use of existing solar energy
7.42   Nearly all buildings make use of some passive solar energy because they have windows or roof lights, which allow in natural light and provide a view of the surroundings. This existing use of passive solar energy is making a substantial contribution to the energy demand in the UK building stock. Passive solar design (PSD), in which buildings are designed to enhance solar energy use, results in additional savings in energy. The installed capacity of PSD in the UK and other countries can only be estimated and is dependent on how the resource is defined. The unplanned benefit of solar energy for heating and lighting in UK buildings is estimated to be 145 TWh/year. The figure is very approximate and, as in previous years, has therefore not been included in the tables in this chapter. Only a few thousand buildings have been deliberately designed to exploit solar energy – a very small proportion of the total UK building stock. It has been estimated that the benefit of deploying PSD in these buildings is equivalent to a saving of about 10 GWh/year.

Active solar heating
7.43 Active solar heating employs solar collectors to heat water mainly for domestic hot water systems but also for swimming pools and other applications. Updated figures have been obtained by FES (on behalf of the Department of Trade and Industry). For 2005 an estimated 77.1 GWh for domestic hot water generation replaces gas heating; for swimming pools, an estimated 172.4 GWh generation for 2005 replaces gas (45 per cent), oil (45 per cent) or electricity (10 per cent).

Photovoltaics
7.44   Photovoltaics (PV) is the direct conversion of solar radiation into direct current electricity by the interaction of light with the electrons in a semiconductor device or cell. There has been a significant increase in capacity and generation of PV over the last year due to increased support from the Government. There is a Major Photovoltaic Demonstration Programme offering grants for small, medium and large-scale installations, which is encouraging a significant number of new projects. This programme supported 80 per cent of the new PV capacity. The installed capacity increased from 8.2 MW in 2004 to 10.9 MW in 2005.

Onshore wind power
7.45   A wind turbine extracts energy from the wind by means of a rotor fitted with aerodynamic-section blades using the lifting forces on the blades to turn the rotor primary shaft. This mechanical power is used to drive an electrical generator. The figures included for generation from wind turbines are based on actual metered exports from the turbines and, where these data are unavailable, are based on estimates using regional load factors (see paragraphs 7.80 and 7.81 regarding load factors) and the wind farm installed capacity.

7.46   There are 277 wind farms or separately registered wind projects in the RESTATS database. Of these projects, 73 are under a current NFFO contract totalling 504.8 MW. There are an additional

27 ex-NFFO schemes accounting for a further 145.2 MW, of which 25 (144.6 MW) are now claiming ROCs. NFFO and ex-NFFO schemes account for 48.1 per cent of the UK installed capacity. A further 683.8 MW of wind power (63 schemes) claim ROCs with the remainder not receiving any form of subsidy. Wind power installations in the UK continue at pace with 577MW of onshore turbines being constructed in 2005.

Offshore wind power

7.47   The UK's offshore wind resource is vast, with the potential to provide more than the UK's current demand for electricity. Offshore wind speeds are higher than those onshore (typically up to 0.5m/s higher 10 km offshore) and also less turbulent. However, elevated inland sites can have higher wind speeds.

7.48   Due to the higher costs of installing each turbine offshore it is expected that, in general, the machines will be larger than their onshore counterparts (2 MW and above). This is driven by economics, with larger machine more cost effective per unit of electricity generated. The larger turbines also experience higher wind speeds, because taller towers put the rotors into the stronger winds. In addition, onshore constraints such as planning, noise effects and visual impact are likely to be reduced offshore. As of December 2005 there were 4 operational offshore wind farms totalling 213.8 MW. These were Blyth, North Hoyle, Scroby Sands and Kentish Flats. The last named is 90 MW and was commissioned in September 2005.

Wave and Tidal Stream Power

7.49   Waves in the oceans are created by the interaction of winds with the surface of the sea. Because of the direction of the prevailing winds and the size of the Atlantic Ocean, the United Kingdom has wave power levels, which are amongst the highest in the world. Under the DTI's shoreline programme a 75kW experimental prototype an oscillating water column device came on line in late 1991 on the Hebridean island of Islay but was decommissioned in 1999. Currently in the UK there is one grid connected wave device, the Limpet oscillating water column, also on the isle of Islay, which is a successor to the 75kW device. Limpet has a nameplate capacity of 500kW and was expected to produce an annual average output of approximately 200kW. In fact it has only produced approximately one tenth of this because the seabed profile in front of the machine was shallower than expected. A number of other wave devices are currently under development, most notably the Pelamis - an articulated tube with sections linked by hinged joints - being developed since 1998 by Edinburgh-based Ocean Power Delivery Ltd. A full-scale prototype has undergone a number of sea trials including 200 hours of grid-connected operation in 2004. The DTI has recently launched the Wave and Tidal-stream Energy Demonstration Scheme that provides a 25 per cent capital grant and £100 per MWh additional revenue support for multi-device farms. This is expected to lead to the deployment of a number of wave farms in the next few years.

7.50   Tidal currents are created by the movement of the tides, often magnified by local topographical features such as headlands, inlets to inland lakes, and straits. Tidal current energy is the extraction of energy from this flow, analogous to the way a wind turbine operates in air. A recent study estimated that the available UK resource is up to 22 TWh per year. Since 2000 the DTI's Technology Programme has supported the development of a number of concepts. A number of tidal current devices are currently emerging from their R&D phases and some of these may lead to pre-commercial farms under the DTI's new Wave and Tidal-stream Energy Demonstration Scheme. To-date, two device concepts have had full-scale prototypes deployed at sea. The first is the Seaflow machine that was installed by Bristol-based Marine Current Turbines Ltd near Lynmouth in June 2003. This has not yet been decommissioned but is not grid-connected and only operates during specific tests. The other device was the Stingray, which uses an oscillating hydrofoil instead of a rotating turbine, developed by Northumberland-based The Engineering Business Ltd (EB). The 180 tonne device was installed in Yell Sound, Shetland, in September 2002 and again in 2003. After analysing the results of these tests and the costs of building the machine, EB decided to put its development on indefinite hold.

7.51   The only commercial facilities operating by 2010 are likely to be those constructed under the DTI's Wave and Tidal-stream Energy Demonstration Scheme. These are not expected to amount to more than around 20 MW of capacity in total, the majority of which will come on stream after 2010. The costs of wave and tidal-current technologies are still much too high to enable profitable operation under current or foreseeable future market conditions. Although all new technologies generally reduce in cost with cumulative production, it is not clear that these technologies, particularly wave, will be able to achieve sufficiently low costs without a large step change. Their long term prospects will become much clearer after the first deployments under the DTI's new Wave and Tidal-stream Energy Demonstration scheme have begun to deliver results.

Large scale hydro

7.52   In hydro schemes the turbines that drive the electricity generators are powered by the direct action of water either from a reservoir or from the run of the river. Large-scale hydro covers plants belonging to companies with capacity of 5 MWe and over. Most of the plants are located in Scotland and Wales and mainly draw their water from high-level reservoirs with their own natural catchment areas. Major Power Producers (MPPs) report their output to the Department of Trade and Industry in DTI's regular electricity surveys. Prior to 2004 these data were submitted in aggregate form and not split down by size of scheme. This meant that some small-scale schemes were hidden within the generation data for the large-scale schemes. For 2004 and 2005 MPPs have provided a more detailed breakdown of their data and some smaller sites previously included under "large scale" are for 2004 and 2005 under "small scale". There is some 1,355 MW of installed capacity for large-scale hydroelectric schemes in the UK. The coverage of these large-scale hydro figures is the same as that used in the tables in the Chapter 5 of this Digest. The data in this Chapter exclude pumped storage stations (see paragraph 5.49).

Small scale hydro

7.53   Electricity generation schemes with a hydro capacity below 5 MWe are classified as small scale. These are schemes being used for either domestic/farm purposes or for local sale to electricity supply companies. A new survey of small-scale hydro sites was carried out in 2004 giving a more detailed picture of the current situation. The survey concentrated on the non-NFFO and non-RO funded small-scale hydroelectric sites. Small-scale hydro capacity has decreased compared with previous years despite some re-allocation to small scale of schemes belonging to major power producers (see paragraph 7.52, above). This is through a combination of some scheme closures coupled with others re-powering and being elevated into the large-scale hydro band. In addition, extra work has been put in to improve confidence in the data, which has resulted in the identification and removal of incorrect and duplicated entries. Despite this reconciliation and drop in capacity, the number of small-scale sites identified in 2005 shows an 8 per cent growth compared to 2004. Data given for generation are actual figures where available, but otherwise are estimated using a typical load factor (based on NFFO schemes actual data). The variation in the time-series generation figures primarily reflects the variation in precipitation.

Geothermal aquifers

7.54   Aquifers containing water at elevated temperatures occur in some parts of the United Kingdom at between 1,500 and 3,000 metres below the surface. This water can be pumped to the surface and used, for example, in community heating schemes. There is currently only one scheme operating in the UK at Southampton.

Biofuels

(a)   Landfill gas

7.55   Landfill gas is a methane-rich biogas formed from the decomposition of organic material in landfill. The gas can be used to fuel reciprocating engines or turbines to generate electricity or used directly in kilns and boilers. In other countries, the gas is cleaned to pipeline quality or used as a vehicle fuel. Landfill gas exploitation has benefited considerably from the NFFO and this can be seen from the large rise in the amount of electricity generated since 1992. Further commissioning of landfill gas projects under NFFO will continue to increase the amount of electricity generated from this technology. Ofgem's ROCs database also provides details of landfill gas sites claiming ROCs. Information on landfill gas was supplemented by a RESTATS survey carried out by FES in 2004 on behalf of the DTI, and covered the period up to the end of 2004. In 2005, 29 new schemes came on line under NFFO.

(b)   Sewage sludge digestion

7.56   In all sewage sludge digestion projects, some of the gas produced is used to maintain the optimum temperature for digestion. In addition, many use combined heat and power (CHP) systems. The electricity generated is either used on site or sold under the NFFO. Information from these projects was provided from the CHAPSTATS Database, which is compiled and maintained by FES on behalf of the Department of Trade and Industry (see Chapter 6). Within the CHAPSTATS database the majority of the data are gathered through the CHPQA Programme and the DTI's Electricity Generated Inquiry (EGI). However, many sewage treatment works are not part of the CHPQA Programme and data provided to the EGI is often in a consolidated form where data on multiple sites are amalgamated. For these reasons, a large proportion (>90%) of the sewage treatment data in CHAPSTATS was based upon historical records. To improve the quality of this data set, from 2005 onwards data on sewage treatment plant are based upon electricity generation figures provided to Ofgem via the NFFO and ROC registers.

(c)   Domestic wood combustion

7.57   Domestic wood use includes the use of logs in open fires, "AGA"-type cooker boilers and other wood burning stoves. The figure given is an approximate estimate based on a survey carried out in 1989. The Forestry Commission carried out a survey of domestic wood fuel use in 1997 but the results from this were inconclusive. As an upper limit, about 600,000 oven-dried tonnes (ODTs) were estimated to be available for domestic heating. In 2001, FES undertook a study of UK domestic wood use on behalf of DTI. A methodology was devised for surveying the three major sectors involved in wood use – the stove or boiler supplier, the wood supplier and the end user. Questionnaires were devised for all these parties and then attempts were made to contact representative samples in the various regions of the UK. From the evidence obtained via the questionnaires and telephone interviews we believe that the domestic wood burning market is growing but not in the area of wood as the primary heat source. This still remains a relatively small market and a small percentage of the wood burnt. Unfortunately, the survey was unable to provide statistically sound evidence as to the amount of wood used in the domestic sector and although it was felt that there has been a small increase in the domestic use of wood as a fuel, on the basis of the results of the approach, FES could not justify modifying the current estimate for the UK. In view of the importance attached to finding out about domestic wood use, the Forestry Commission has therefore decided to undertake another study guided by the lessons learnt from the previous work. In particular they would approach the newly emerging wood cooperatives, as they are likely to be a good source if information now that they should be more well established, the National House-Building Council (NHBC) to examine new build and treating equipment suppliers, fuel suppliers and users under separate surveys. In 2005, as part of an omnibus survey, a pilot study was undertaken in Scotland by the Forestry Commission to assist in developing the correct methodology prior to a National survey but unfortunately the response rate was poor. Preliminary results suggest that current usage may be slightly less than in 1997; estimates based on population data imply 588,000 ODTs per year, whereas an estimate based on numbers of households suggests 550,000 ODTs per year.

(d)   Industrial wood combustion

7.58   In 1997, the industrial wood figure (which includes sawmill residues, furniture manufacturing waste etc.) was included as a separate category for the first time. This was due to the availability of better data as a result of a survey carried out in 1996 on wood fired combustion plants above 400 kW thermal input. A follow-up survey was subsequently carried out for 2000. This survey highlighted that there were fewer sites (174) operating than in 1996 due to the imposition of more stringent emissions control. A survey of industrial wood use carried out in 2006, for schemes above 400 kW thermal input, concluded that in-house use of wood waste continued to be in decline. There is, however, increased interest in off-site use of untreated wood for space heating in schools, hospitals, nursing homes, government buildings, etc. The Port Talbot Bioenergy Plant, a 13.7 MW electric scheme involving untreated wood, is due to be commissioned in 2008. Untreated wood will increasingly form a major fuel input to schemes involving energy crops; this is further discussed in the next section.

(e)   Energy crops

7.59   Short rotation willow coppice plantations have become well established but the rate of uptake of the technology has been fairly slow. Interest has also been shown in Miscanthus. Under Northern Ireland's second Non-Fossil Fuel Renewable Energy order for electricity, two projects were live at the end of 2005.

7.60   In England, Project ARBRE in South Yorkshire was contracted under NFFO 3 to generate 10 MW of electricity of which 8 MW were to be exported to the local grid. This project ran into difficulties and was sold to new owners who are still evaluating their options on taking the project forward. However, SembCorp Utilities UK has almost completed a 30 MW wood-burning power station, burning 55,000 tonnes a year of short rotation coppice (SRC) at Wilton. It should be commercially operating in

2007. Construction has also begun on a 44MW plant at Steven's Croft near Lockerbie fuelled with wood and SRC (25 per cent). A 2.6MW plant in Eccleshall, burning wood and Miscanthus, is currently being built by Eccleshall Biomass Ltd and due to be commercially operating in 2007. Work has also begun on a CHP plant (7 MW electricity plus 7 MW heat) at Charlton Energy, Somerset fuelled with Miscanthus and sawmill residues; this too is due to come on stream in 2007. In future, it is most likely that all such projects will be fuelled with a mixture of untreated wood plus energy crop as this approach represents a less risky strategy for developers.

(f)   Straw combustion

7.61   Straw can be burnt in high temperature boilers, designed for the efficient and controlled combustion of solid fuels and biomass to supply heat, hot water and hot air systems. There are large numbers of these small-scale batch-fed whole bale boilers. The figures given are estimates based partly on 1990 information and partly on a survey of straw-fired boilers carried out in 1993-94. A 37 MW straw fired power station near Ely, Cambridgeshire is currently the only electricity generation scheme in operation.

(g)   Waste combustion

7.62   Domestic, industrial and commercial wastes represent a significant resource for materials and energy recovery. Wastes may be combusted, as received, in purpose built incinerators or processed into a range of refuse derived fuels for both on-site and off-site utilisation. Only the non-biodegradable portion of waste is counted in renewables statistics although non-biodegradable wastes are included in this chapter as "below the line" items. The paragraphs below describe various categories of waste combustion in greater detail.

7.63   Twenty four waste-to-energy plants were in operation in 2005 burning municipal solid waste (MSW), refuse derived fuel (RDF) and general industrial waste (GIW).

7.64   **Municipal solid waste combustion:** Information was provided from the refuse incinerator operators in the United Kingdom that practice energy recovery using the RESTATS questionnaire. This included both direct combustion of unprocessed MSW and the combustion of RDF. In the latter, process waste can be partially processed to produce coarse RDF that can then be burnt in a variety of ways. By further processing the refuse, including separating off the fuel fraction, compacting, drying and densifying, it is possible to produce an RDF pellet. This pellet has around 60 per cent of the gross calorific value of British coal. The generation from MSW has been split between biodegradable sources and non-biodegradable sources using information outlined in paragraph 7.65 below. Approximately 62½ per cent of generation from MSW was estimated to be from biodegradable sources. Non-biodegradable municipal solid waste is not included in the overall renewables percentage under the international definition of renewables (see paragraph 7.1). However, such wastes are still shown in the tables accompanying this chapter as 'below the line' items.

7.65   There has been an ongoing programme of waste analysis in the UK for many years; such analyses may be carried out to an accuracy of ± 1 per cent. Such studies are guided by the use of ACORN (A Classification of Residential Neighbourhoods) socio-economic profiles which are used to select sample areas for the analysis of household collected waste and is based on the premise that households of similar socio-economic characteristics are likely to have similar behavioural, purchasing and lifestyle characteristics; this will be reflected in the quantity and composition of waste that those households produce. The large scale study in Wales showed that the only category in domestic waste to show a statistically significant seasonal variation was garden waste; as garden waste is a small percentage (certainly when compared to food and kitchen waste), the effect on the operation of biomass-to-energy plants should be almost unnoticed. As there is now virtually no regional variation to be seen within the UK; these data will probably become the UK standard. UK domestic waste has a biodegradable content of 67½ per cent ± 1 per cent and this accounts for about 62½ per cent of the energy generated from its combustion. Municipal Solid Waste (MSW) comprises of domestic waste plus other feedstocks, such as, general industrial waste, building demolition waste and tree clippings from civil amenities. This has the net effect of reducing the percentage composition of the biodegradable content to 61 per cent ± 1 per cent. Because the combustion properties of some of the other biodegradable materials added is similar to that of domestic waste, this has virtually no effect on the percentage of the energy generated from the biodegradables component, which remains at about 62½ per cent.

7.66 **General industrial waste combustion:** Certain wastes produced by industry and commerce can be used as a source of energy for industrial processes or space heating. These wastes include general waste from factories such as paper, cardboard, wood and plastics.

7.67 A survey conducted in 2001 noted that GIW is now burnt in MSW waste-to-energy facilities. As no sites are solely burning GIW for heat or electricity generation, this feedstock is being handled under the MSW category.

7.68 **Specialised waste combustion:** Specialised wastes arise as a result of a particular activity or process. Materials in this category include scrap tyres, hospital wastes, poultry litter, meal and bone and farm waste digestion. Although the large tyre incineration plant with energy recovery has not generated since 2000 the cement industry has burned some waste tyres in its cement and lime kilns. Although part of waste tyre combustion is of biodegradable waste, because there is no agreed method of calculating the small biodegradable content, all of the generation from waste tyres has been included under non-biodegradable wastes in this chapter (see paragraph 7.65, above).

7.69 In 2005 information on hospital waste incineration was supplemented by a RESTATS survey, carried out by FES in 2004 on behalf of DTI, and covered a period up to the end of 2003. The survey confirmed whether the older sites were still operating, and identified any new operating facilities. Information on both their thermal and electrical outputs between 2000 and 2003 were gathered where data were available. There were no major changes, as the sector appeared to have stabilised since the introduction of the new emission legislation. There may, however, be future changes due to the appearance of new technologies, such as microwave treatment, and increased segregation of clinical waste.

7.70 One poultry litter combustion project started generating electricity in 1992; a second began in 1993. Both of these are NFFO projects. In addition, a small-scale CHP scheme began generating towards the end of 1990 however this has now closed due to new emissions regulations. A further NFFO scheme started generating in 1998, and during 2000 an SRO scheme began to generate. Over the most recent 5 years one of the earlier poultry litter projects was fuelled mainly by meat and bone. A further poultry litter scheme became fully operational in 2001.

7.71 Information on farm waste digestion in the United Kingdom is based on a survey carried out during 1991-1992 with follow-up studies in 1996 and 2005. There was a farm digestion project generating electricity under the NFFO; its output was included in the commodity balances but ceased to operate in 1998. In 2003, however, a large centralised anaerobic digestion scheme (Holsworthy) generating electricity under NFFO 5 came on-line. With the exception of this scheme, data collected from the surveys were used to derive estimates for 1997 through to 2004. The 2005 survey has shown that number of sites using farm waste digestion fell significantly since 1996, which was mainly attributed to tightening waste regulations and lack of maintenance. However, this has not prevented new digesters being built and commissioned in 2005.

(h)   Co-firing of biomass with fossil fuels
7.72 Co-firing of biomass fuel in fossil fuel power stations is not a new idea. Technically it has been proven in power stations worldwide, although, until 2002, it was not practised in the UK. The biomass fuel is usually fed by means of the existing stoking mechanism as a partial substitute for the fossil fuel. The combustion system may cope with up to a 25 per cent substitution without any major changes to the boiler design and airflows, but fuel preparation and transport systems may be the limiting feature at percentages much lower than this.

7.73 Since 2002, co-firing of biomass with fossil fuels has been eligible under the RO, the first time that any renewable energy initiative has included co-firing. As the purpose of this was to enable markets and supply chains for biomass to develop, and not to support coal fired power stations, the following limits were placed on co-firing:
- only electricity generated before 1 April 2011 would be eligible;
- from 1 April 2006 at least 75 per cent of the biomass must consist of energy crops.

7.74 However, the scheme has now been extended to allow longer for an energy crop market to develop, through establishing biomass operations at co-fired stations. The key changes are as follows:

- fossil fuel stations are allowed to convert to biomass without refurbishment;
- any biomass can be co-fired until 31 March 2009 with no minimum percentage of energy crops;
- 25 per cent of co-fired biomass must be energy crops from 1 April 2009 until 31 March 2010;
- 50 per cent of co-fired biomass must be energy crops from 1 April 2010 until 31 March 2011;
- 75 per cent of co-fired biomass must be energy crops from 1 April 2011 until 31 March 2016. Co-firing ceases to be eligible for ROCs after this date.

To balance the above changes and reduce the risk of flooding the ROC market with co-firing ROCs, thereby affecting ROC prices and investor confidence adversely, it is proposed that the 25 per cent cap from 1 April 2006 on an individual supplier should be changed to:

- 10 per cent from 1 April 2006 until 31 March 2011;
- 5 per cent from 1 April 2011 until 31 March 2016.

(i) Biodiesel and bioblend

7.75 In the UK biodiesel is defined for taxation purposes as diesel quality liquid fuel produced from biomass or waste cooking oil, the ester content of which is not less than 96.5 per cent by weight and the sulphur content of which does not exceed 0.005 per cent by weight or is nil. Diesel fuel currently sold at a number of outlets is a blend with 5 per cent biodiesel. The use of biofuels in the UK, an estimated 445,000 tonnes in 2005, continues to grow. A plant in Motherwell, Scotland is currently producing 40-50,000 tonnes of biodiesel a year and a 250,000 tonnes per year plant on Teesside was still under construction in 2005. A 100,000 tonnes per year plant is under construction at Immingham, near Hull and is due to come on line at the end of 2006. The most usual way for biodiesel to be sold is for it to be blended with ultra-low sulphur diesel fuel and thus it would be reported as part of the road transport use of diesel in Chapter 3. The duty payable on biodiesel is just over half the duty payable on road diesel and in blended fuels the duty payable is proportionate to the duty payable on the constituent fuels. There are currently plans under consideration in the UK for the construction of a bio-ethanol plant.

Combined Heat and Power

7.76 A Combined Heat and Power (CHP) plant is an installation where there is a simultaneous generation of usable heat and power (usually electricity) in a single process. Some CHP installations are fuelled either wholly or partially by renewable sources of energy. The main renewable sources that are used for CHP are biofuels particularly sewage gas.

7.77 Chapter 6 of this Digest summarises information on the contribution made by CHP to the United Kingdom's energy requirements in 2001 to 2005 using the results of annual studies undertaken to identify all CHP schemes. Included in Tables 6.1 to 6.9 of that chapter is information on the contribution of renewable sources to CHP generation in each year from 2001 to 2005. Corresponding data for 1996 to 2000 are available on the DTI energy web site. The information contained in those tables is therefore a subset of the data contained within the tables presented in this chapter.

Generating capacity and load factor

7.78 The electrical capacities are given in Table 7.4 as installed capacities ie the maximum continuous rating of the generating sets in the stations. In Chapter 5 DNC (Declared Net Capacity) is used, ie the maximum continuous rating of the generating sets in the stations, less the power consumed by the plant itself, and reduced by a specified factor to take into account the intermittent nature of the energy source e.g. 0.43 for wind and 0.33 for shoreline wave. DNC represents the nominal maximum capability of a generating set to supply electricity to consumers. For electrical capacities of generation using renewables in DNC terms see Table 7.1.1 on the DTI energy web site.

7.79 Plant load factors in this chapter have been calculated in terms of installed capacity (ie the maximum continuous rating of the generating sets in the stations) and express the average hourly quantity of electricity generated as a percentage of the average of the capacities at the beginning and end of the year.

7.80 In this year's Digest a new term has been introduced to describe the amount of electricity generated from wind farms compared with the amount that such turbines would have generated had they been available for the whole of the calendar year and running continually and at maximum output throughout the calendar year. This term is "load factor on an unchanged configuration basis". A full account of the exercise to derive these factors can be found in *Energy Trends*, March 2006 pages 28 to 32. *Energy Trends* is available on the DTI energy web site at www.dti.gov.uk/energy/statistics/publications/trends/index.html, although here the term "capacity factor" was used. Load factors on an unchanged configuration basis for offshore windfarms cannot be given at this time because the small number of sites would lead to the disclosure of statistical information provided in confidence for the purpose of calculating overall wind generation statistics.

7.81 To compare the two calculations, the **load factor** for a calendar year (as historically reported in this Digest) is:

$$\frac{\text{Electricity generated during the year (kWh)}}{(\text{Installed capacity at the beginning of the year} + \text{Installed capacity at the end of the year (kW)}) \times 0.5 \times 8760 \text{ hours}}$$

whilst the **load factor on an unchanged configuration basis** for a calendar year is:

$$\frac{\text{Electricity generated during the year (kWh)}}{(\text{Installed capacity of wind farms operating throughout the year with an unchanged configuration (kW)}) \times 8760 \text{ hours}}$$

In addition, because load factors on an unchanged configuration basis are mainly of interest for commercial scale wind power rather than small/micro generation, turbines under 100 kW are excluded and any single turbine of 100 kW or above is considered to be a wind farm.

Contact :   *Steve Dagnall, Future Energy Solutions*   *Mike Janes, DTI, Statistician*
            steve.dagnall@aeat.co.uk   mike.janes@dti.gsi.gov.uk
            0870 190 6092   *020-7215 5186*

7.1 Commodity balances 2005
Renewables and waste

	Wood waste	Wood	Poultry litter, meat and bone, biomass, straw, farm waste and SRC(3)	Sewage gas	Landfill gas
Supply					
Production	81	204	434	179	1,421
Other sources	-	-	-	-	-
Imports	-	-	755	-	-
Exports	-	-	-	-	-
Marine bunkers	-	-	-	-	-
Stock change (1)	-	-	-	-	-
Transfers	-	-	-	-	-
Total supply	81	204	1,188	179	1,421
Statistical difference (2)	-	-	-	-	-
Total demand	81	204	1,188	179	1,421
Transformation	-	-	1,116	131	1,407
Electricity generation	-	-	1,116	131	1,407
Major power producers	-	-	721	-	-
Autogenerators	-	-	396	131	1,407
Heat generation	-	-	-	-	-
Petroleum refineries	-	-	-	-	-
Coke manufacture	-	-	-	-	-
Blast furnaces	-	-	-	-	-
Patent fuel manufacture	-	-	-	-	-
Other	-	-	-	-	-
Energy industry use	-	-	-	-	-
Electricity generation	-	-	-	-	-
Oil and gas extraction	-	-	-	-	-
Petroleum refineries	-	-	-	-	-
Coal extraction	-	-	-	-	-
Coke manufacture	-	-	-	-	-
Blast furnaces	-	-	-	-	-
Patent fuel manufacture	-	-	-	-	-
Pumped storage	-	-	-	-	-
Other	-	-	-	-	-
Losses	-	-	-	-	-
Final consumption	81	204	72	48	14
Industry	81	-	-	-	14
Unclassified	81	-	-	-	14
Iron and steel	-	-	-	-	-
Non-ferrous metals	-	-	-	-	-
Mineral products	-	-	-	-	-
Chemicals	-	-	-	-	-
Mechanical engineering, etc	-	-	-	-	-
Electrical engineering, etc	-	-	-	-	-
Vehicles	-	-	-	-	-
Food, beverages, etc	-	-	-	-	-
Textiles, leather, etc	-	-	-	-	-
Paper, printing, etc	-	-	-	-	-
Other industries	-	-	-	-	-
Construction	-	-	-	-	-
Transport	-	-	-	-	-
Air	-	-	-	-	-
Rail	-	-	-	-	-
Road	-	-	-	-	-
National navigation	-	-	-	-	-
Pipelines	-	-	-	-	-
Other	-	204	72	48	-
Domestic	-	204	-	-	-
Public administration	-	-	-	48	-
Commercial	-	-	-	-	-
Agriculture	-	-	72	-	-
Miscellaneous	-	-	-	-	-
Non energy use	-	-	-	-	-

(1) Stock fall (+), stock rise (-).
(2) Total supply minus total demand.
(3) SRC is short rotation coppice and other energy crops.

(4) Municipal solid waste, general industrial waste and hospital waste.
(5) The amount of shoreline wave included is less than 0.1 ktoe.

7.1 Commodity balances 2005 (continued)

Renewables and waste

Waste(4) and tyres	Geothermal and active solar heat	Hydro	Wind and wave (5)	Total renewables	
					Supply
842	31	427	250	3,868	Production
-	-	-	-	-	Other sources
-	-	-	-	755	Imports
-	-	-	-	-	Exports
-	-	-	-	-	Marine bunkers
-	-	-	-	-	Stock change (1)
-	-	-	-	-	Transfers
842	31	427	250	4,623	**Total supply**
-	-	-	-	-	**Statistical difference (2)**
842	31	427	250	4,623	**Total demand**
691	1	427	250	4,022	**Transformation**
691	1	427	250	4,022	Electricity generation
89	-	343	-	1,153	Major power producers
602	1	83	250	2,870	Autogenerators
-	-	-	-	-	Heat generation
-	-	-	-	-	Petroleum refineries
-	-	-	-	-	Coke manufacture
-	-	-	-	-	Blast furnaces
-	-	-	-	-	Patent fuel manufacture
-	-	-	-	-	Other
-	-	-	-	-	**Energy industry use**
-	-	-	-	-	Electricity generation
-	-	-	-	-	Oil and gas extraction
-	-	-	-	-	Petroleum refineries
-	-	-	-	-	Coal extraction
-	-	-	-	-	Coke manufacture
-	-	-	-	-	Blast furnaces
-	-	-	-	-	Patent fuel manufacture
-	-	-	-	-	Pumped storage
-	-	-	-	-	Other
-	-	-	-	-	**Losses**
151	30	-	-	600	**Final consumption**
56	-	-	-	151	**Industry**
56	-	-	-	151	Unclassified
-	-	-	-	-	Iron and steel
-	-	-	-	-	Non-ferrous metals
-	-	-	-	-	Mineral products
-	-	-	-	-	Chemicals
-	-	-	-	-	Mechanical engineering, etc
-	-	-	-	-	Electrical engineering, etc
-	-	-	-	-	Vehicles
-	-	-	-	-	Food, beverages, etc
-	-	-	-	-	Textiles, leather, etc
-	-	-	-	-	Paper, printing, etc
-	-	-	-	-	Other industries
-	-	-	-	-	Construction
-	-	-	-	-	**Transport**
-	-	-	-	-	Air
-	-	-	-	-	Rail
-	-	-	-	-	Road
-	-	-	-	-	National navigation
-	-	-	-	-	Pipelines
95	30	-	-	450	**Other**
23	30	-	-	256	Domestic
51	-	-	-	100	Public administration
10	-	-	-	10	Commercial
2	-	-	-	74	Agriculture
9	-	-	-	9	Miscellaneous
-	-	-	-	-	**Non energy use**

7.2 Commodity balances 2004
Renewables and waste

Thousand tonnes of oil equivalent

	Wood waste	Wood	Poultry litter, meat and bone, biomass, straw, farm waste and SRC(3)	Sewage gas	Landfill gas
Supply					
Production	196r	204	304r	177	1,327
Other sources	-	-	-	-	-
Imports	-	-	402r	-	-
Exports	-	-	-	-	-
Marine bunkers	-	-	-	-	-
Stock change (1)	-	-	-	-	-
Transfers	-	-	-	-	-
Total supply	196r	204	705r	177	1,327
Statistical difference (2)	-	-	-	-	-
Total demand	196r	204	705r	177	1,327
Transformation	-	-	633r	124	1,313
Electricity generation	-	-	633r	124	1,313
Major power producers	-	-	449	-	-
Autogenerators	-	-	184r	124	1,313
Heat generation	-	-	-	-	-
Petroleum refineries	-	-	-	-	-
Coke manufacture	-	-	-	-	-
Blast furnaces	-	-	-	-	-
Patent fuel manufacture	-	-	-	-	-
Other	-	-	-	-	-
Energy industry use	-	-	-	-	-
Electricity generation	-	-	-	-	-
Oil and gas extraction	-	-	-	-	-
Petroleum refineries	-	-	-	-	-
Coal extraction	-	-	-	-	-
Coke manufacture	-	-	-	-	-
Blast furnaces	-	-	-	-	-
Patent fuel manufacture	-	-	-	-	-
Pumped storage	-	-	-	-	-
Other	-	-	-	-	-
Losses	-	-	-	-	-
Final consumption	196r	204	72r	53	14
Industry	196r	-	-	-	14
Unclassified	196r	-	-	-	14
Iron and steel	-	-	-	-	-
Non-ferrous metals	-	-	-	-	-
Mineral products	-	-	-	-	-
Chemicals	-	-	-	-	-
Mechanical engineering, etc	-	-	-	-	-
Electrical engineering, etc	-	-	-	-	-
Vehicles	-	-	-	-	-
Food, beverages, etc	-	-	-	-	-
Textiles, leather, etc	-	-	-	-	-
Paper, printing, etc	-	-	-	-	-
Other industries	-	-	-	-	-
Construction	-	-	-	-	-
Transport	-	-	-	-	-
Air	-	-	-	-	-
Rail	-	-	-	-	-
Road	-	-	-	-	-
National navigation	-	-	-	-	-
Pipelines	-	-	-	-	-
Other	-	204	72r	53	-
Domestic	-	204	-	-	-
Public administration	-	-	-	53	-
Commercial	-	-	-	-	-
Agriculture	-	-	72r	-	-
Miscellaneous	-	-	-	-	-
Non energy use	-	-	-	-	-

(1) Stock fall (+), stock rise (-).
(2) Total supply minus total demand.
(3) SRC is short rotation coppice and other energy crops.
(4) Municipal solid waste, general industrial waste and hospital waste.
(5) The amount of shoreline wave included is less than 0.1 ktoe.

7.2 Commodity balances 2004 (continued)

Renewables and waste

Waste(4) and tyres	Geothermal and active solar heat	Hydro	Wind and wave (5)	Total renewables	
					Supply
848r	26r	424	166r	3,670r	Production
-	-	-	-	-	Other sources
-	-	-	-	402r	Imports
-	-	-	-	-	Exports
-	-	-	-	-	Marine bunkers
-	-	-	-	-	Stock change (1)
-	-	-	-	-	Transfers
848r	**26r**	**424**	**166r**	**4,072r**	**Total supply**
-	-	-	-	-	**Statistical difference (2)**
848r	**26r**	**424**	**166r**	**4,072r**	**Total demand**
696r	**-**	**424**	**166r**	**3,357r**	**Transformation**
696r	-	424	166r	3,357r	Electricity generation
90	-	366r	-	905r	Major power producers
606r	-	58r	166r	2,453r	Autogenerators
-	-	-	-	-	Heat generation
-	-	-	-	-	Petroleum refineries
-	-	-	-	-	Coke manufacture
-	-	-	-	-	Blast furnaces
-	-	-	-	-	Patent fuel manufacture
-	-	-	-	-	Other
-	-	-	-	-	**Energy industry use**
-	-	-	-	-	Electricity generation
-	-	-	-	-	Oil and gas extraction
-	-	-	-	-	Petroleum refineries
-	-	-	-	-	Coal extraction
-	-	-	-	-	Coke manufacture
-	-	-	-	-	Blast furnaces
-	-	-	-	-	Patent fuel manufacture
-	-	-	-	-	Pumped storage
-	-	-	-	-	Other
-	-	-	-	-	**Losses**
151r	**25**	**-**	**-**	**715r**	**Final consumption**
56r	**-**	**-**	**-**	**265r**	**Industry**
56r	-	-	-	265r	Unclassified
-	-	-	-	-	Iron and steel
-	-	-	-	-	Non-ferrous metals
-	-	-	-	-	Mineral products
-	-	-	-	-	Chemicals
-	-	-	-	-	Mechanical engineering, etc
-	-	-	-	-	Electrical engineering, etc
-	-	-	-	-	Vehicles
-	-	-	-	-	Food, beverages, etc
-	-	-	-	-	Textiles, leather, etc
-	-	-	-	-	Paper, printing, etc
-	-	-	-	-	Other industries
-	-	-	-	-	Construction
-	-	-	-	-	**Transport**
-	-	-	-	-	Air
-	-	-	-	-	Rail
-	-	-	-	-	Road
-	-	-	-	-	National navigation
-	-	-	-	-	Pipelines
95r	**25**	**-**	**-**	**449**	**Other**
23	25	-	-	252	Domestic
51	-	-	-	104	Public administration
10	-	-	-	10	Commercial
2	-	-	-	74	Agriculture
9	-	-	-	9	Miscellaneous
-	-	-	-	-	**Non energy use**

7.3 Commodity balances 2003

Renewables and waste

	Wood waste	Wood	Poultry litter, meat and bone, biomass, straw, farm waste and SRC(3)	Sewage gas	Landfill gas
Supply					
Production	196r	204	460r	165	1,088
Other sources	-	-	-	-	-
Imports	-	-	110	-	-
Exports	-	-	-	-	-
Marine bunkers	-	-	-	-	-
Stock change (1)	-	-	-	-	-
Transfers	-	-	-	-	-
Total supply	196r	204	570r	165	1,088
Statistical difference (2)	-	-	-	-	-
Total demand	196r	204	570r	165	1,088
Transformation	-	-	499r	113	1,075
Electricity generation	-	-	499r	113	1,075
Major power producers	-	-	292r	-	-
Autogenerators	-	-	207r	113	1,075
Heat generation	-	-	-	-	-
Petroleum refineries	-	-	-	-	-
Coke manufacture	-	-	-	-	-
Blast furnaces	-	-	-	-	-
Patent fuel manufacture	-	-	-	-	-
Other	-	-	-	-	-
Energy industry use	-	-	-	-	-
Electricity generation	-	-	-	-	-
Oil and gas extraction	-	-	-	-	-
Petroleum refineries	-	-	-	-	-
Coal extraction	-	-	-	-	-
Coke manufacture	-	-	-	-	-
Blast furnaces	-	-	-	-	-
Patent fuel manufacture	-	-	-	-	-
Pumped storage	-	-	-	-	-
Other	-	-	-	-	-
Losses	-	-	-	-	-
Final consumption	196r	204	72	53	14
Industry	196r	-	-	-	14
Unclassified	196r	-	-	-	14
Iron and steel	-	-	-	-	-
Non-ferrous metals	-	-	-	-	-
Mineral products	-	-	-	-	-
Chemicals	-	-	-	-	-
Mechanical engineering, etc	-	-	-	-	-
Electrical engineering, etc	-	-	-	-	-
Vehicles	-	-	-	-	-
Food, beverages, etc	-	-	-	-	-
Textiles, leather, etc	-	-	-	-	-
Paper, printing, etc	-	-	-	-	-
Other industries	-	-	-	-	-
Construction	-	-	-	-	-
Transport	-	-	-	-	-
Air	-	-	-	-	-
Rail	-	-	-	-	-
Road	-	-	-	-	-
National navigation	-	-	-	-	-
Pipelines	-	-	-	-	-
Other	-	204	72	53	-
Domestic	-	204	-	-	-
Public administration	-	-	-	53	-
Commercial	-	-	-	-	-
Agriculture	-	-	72	-	-
Miscellaneous	-	-	-	-	-
Non energy use	-	-	-	-	-

(1) Stock fall (+), stock rise (-).
(2) Total supply minus total demand.
(3) SRC is short rotation coppice and other energy crops.
(4) Municipal solid waste, general industrial waste and hospital waste.
(5) The amount of shoreline wave included is less than 0.1 ktoe.

7.3 Commodity balances 2003 (continued)
Renewables and waste

Thousand tonnes of oil equivalent

Waste(4) and tyres	Geothermal and active solar heat	Hydro	Wind and wave (5)	Total renewables	
					Supply
874r	21	278	111	3,396	Production
-	-	-	-	-	Other sources
-	-	-	-	110	Imports
-	-	-	-	-	Exports
-	-	-	-	-	Marine bunkers
-	-	-	-	-	Stock change (1)
-	-	-	-	-	Transfers
874r	21	278	111	3,506r	**Total supply**
-	-	-	-	-	**Statistical difference (2)**
874r	21	278	111	3,506r	**Total demand**
723r	-	278	111	2,796	**Transformation**
723r	-	278	111	2,796	Electricity generation
89	-	221	-	602	Major power producers
634r	-	57	111	2,194r	Autogenerators
-	-	-	-	-	Heat generation
-	-	-	-	-	Petroleum refineries
-	-	-	-	-	Coke manufacture
-	-	-	-	-	Blast furnaces
-	-	-	-	-	Patent fuel manufacture
-	-	-	-	-	Other
-	-	-	-	-	**Energy industry use**
-	-	-	-	-	Electricity generation
-	-	-	-	-	Oil and gas extraction
-	-	-	-	-	Petroleum refineries
-	-	-	-	-	Coal extraction
-	-	-	-	-	Coke manufacture
-	-	-	-	-	Blast furnaces
-	-	-	-	-	Patent fuel manufacture
-	-	-	-	-	Pumped storage
-	-	-	-	-	Other
-	-	-	-	-	**Losses**
151r	21	-	-	710r	**Final consumption**
58r	-	-	-	267r	**Industry**
58r	-	-	-	267r	Unclassified
-	-	-	-	-	Iron and steel
-	-	-	-	-	Non-ferrous metals
-	-	-	-	-	Mineral products
-	-	-	-	-	Chemicals
-	-	-	-	-	Mechanical engineering, etc
-	-	-	-	-	Electrical engineering, etc
-	-	-	-	-	Vehicles
-	-	-	-	-	Food, beverages, etc
-	-	-	-	-	Textiles, leather, etc
-	-	-	-	-	Paper, printing, etc
-	-	-	-	-	Other industries
-	-	-	-	-	Construction
-	-	-	-	-	**Transport**
-	-	-	-	-	Air
-	-	-	-	-	Rail
-	-	-	-	-	Road
-	-	-	-	-	National navigation
-	-	-	-	-	Pipelines
93	21	-	-	443	**Other**
23	21	-	-	247r	Domestic
51	-	-	-	104	Public administration
10	-	-	-	10	Commercial
-	-	-	-	72	Agriculture
9	-	-	-	9	Miscellaneous
-	-	-	-	-	**Non energy use**

7.4 Capacity of, and electricity generated from, renewable sources

	2001	2002	2003	2004	2005
Installed Capacity (MWe) *(1)*					
Wind:					
Onshore	423.4	530.6	678.4	809.4	1,351.2
Offshore	3.8	3.8	63.8	123.8	213.8
Shoreline wave	0.5	0.5	0.5	0.5	0.5
Solar photovoltaics	2.7	4.1	6.0	8.2	10.9
Hydro:					
Small scale	188.7	194.2	118.6r	135.9r	157.9
Large scale *(2)*	1,440.0	1,396.0	1,366.6r	1,367.9r	1,355.2
Biofuels and wastes:					
Landfill gas	464.7	472.9	619.1	722.2	817.8
Sewage sludge digestion	85.0	96.0	100.6	119.0	127.9
Municipal solid waste combustion	260.0	278.9	298.8	307.4	321.4
Other *(3)*	157.0	176.5	183.9	176.3r	186.1
Total biofuels and wastes	966.8	1,024.3	1,202.4	1,324.8r	1,453.2
Total	**3,025.9**	**3,153.6**	**3,436.2r**	**3,770.5r**	**4,542.8**
Co-firing *(4)*	-	..	92.4	146.2	308.8
Generation (GWh)					
Wind:					
Onshore *(5)*	960	1,251	1,276	1,736	2,505
Offshore *(6)*	5	5	10	199	403
Solar photovoltaics	2	3	3	4	8
Hydro:					
Small scale *(5)*	210	204	143r	283r	467
Large scale *(2)*	3,845	4,584	3,085r	4,647r	4,494
Biofuels:					
Landfill gas	2,507	2,679	3,276	4,004	4,290
Sewage sludge digestion	363	368	343	379	400
Municipal solid waste combustion *(7)*	880	907	965	971	964
Co-firing with fossil fuels	-	286	602	1,022	2,533
Other *(8)*	776	840	937	927	855
Total biofuels	4,526	5,080	6,122	7,302	9,042
Total generation	**9,549**	**11,127**	**10,638**	**14,171**	**16,919**
Non-biodegradable wastes *(9)*	528	545	579	583	578
Load factors (per cent) *(10)*					
Onshore wind	26.4	29.9	24.1	26.6	26.5
Offshore wind (from 2004 only)	..	..	..	24.2	27.2
Hydro	28.7	34.0	24.0r	37.7r	37.5
Biofuels and wastes (excluding co-firing)	61.1r	61.2r	62.5r	62.0r	58.2
Total (including wastes)	38.6	42.1r	36.8r	43.5r	41.1
Load factors on an unchanged configuration basis (per cent) *(11)*					
Onshore wind	25.6	28.3	26.1	29.2	28.2

(1) Capacity on a DNC basis is shown in Long Term Trends Table 7.1.1 available on the DTI web site - see paragraph 7.78.
(2) Excluding pumped storage stations. Capacities are as at the end of December.
(3) Includes the use of farm waste digestion, waste tyres, poultry litter, meat and bone, straw combustion, and short rotation coppice.
(4) This is the proportion of fossil fuelled capacity used for co-firing of renewables based on the proportion of generation accounted for by the renewable source.
(5) Actual generation figures are given where available, but otherwise are estimated using a typical load factor or the design load factor, where known.
(6) Latest years include electricity from shoreline wave but this amounts to less than 0.05 GWh.
(7) Biodegradable part only.
(8) Includes the use of farm waste digestion, poultry litter combustion, meat and bone combustion, straw and energy crops.
(9) Non-biodegradable part of municipal solid waste plus waste tyres, hosptal waste and general industrial waste.
(10) Load factors are calculated based on installed capacity at the beginning and the end of the year - see paragraph 7.79.
(11) For a definition see paragraphs 7.80 and 7.81.

7.5 Electricity generated from renewable sources - Renewables Obligation basis and Renewables Directive basis

					GWh
	2001	2002	2003	2004	2005
Generation : Renewables Obligation basis					
Wind:					
Onshore (1)	960	1,251	1,276	1,736	2,505
Offshore (2)	5	5	10	199	403
Solar photovoltaics	2	3	3	4	8
Hydro:					
Small scale (1)	210	204	115	282	467
Refurbished large scale hydro	61	120	616	1,434	1,710
Biofuels:					
Landfill gas	2,507	2,679	3,276	4,004	4,290
Sewage sludge digestion	363	368	343	379	400
Co-firing with fossil fuels	-	286	602	1,022	2,533
Other (3)	776	840	937	927	855
Total biofuels	3,646	4,173	5,158	6,331	8,078
Total renewables generation on an obligation basis (4)	**4,884**	**5,755**	**7,177**	**9,986**	**13,171**
Generation : Renewables Directive basis					
Wind:					
Onshore (1)	960	1,251	1,276	1,736	2,505
Offshore (2)	5	5	10	199	403
Solar photovoltaics	2	3	3	4	8
Hydro:					
Small scale (1)	210	204	115	282	467
Large scale (5)	3,845	4,584	3,113	4,648	4,494
Biofuels:					
Landfill gas	2,507	2,679	3,276	4,004	4,290
Sewage sludge digestion	363	368	343	379	400
Municipal solid waste combustion (7)	880	907	965	971	964
Co-firing with fossil fuels	-	286	602	1,022	2,533
Other (3)	776	840	937	927	855
Total biofuels	4,526	5,080	6,122	7,302	9,042
Total renewables generation on a directive basis (4)	**9,549r**	**11,127r**	**10,638r**	**14,171r**	**16,919**
Imports of electricity certified as CCL exempt (6)	1,740	1,668	2,865r	3,522	2,243

(1) Actual generation figures are given where available, but otherwise are estimated using a typical load factor or the design load factor, where known.

(2) Latest years include electricity from shoreline wave but this amounts to less than 0.05 GWh.

(3) Includes the use of farm waste digestion, poultry litter combustion, meat and bone combustion, straw and short rotation coppice.

(4) See paragraphs 7.7 and 7.8 for definitions. Note that the Renewables Directive definition has been amended - see footnote (6).

(5) Excluding pumped storage stations.

(6) Mainly hydro electricity exported to England from France. In the 2005 Digest these figures were included within the Renewables Directive basis but have now been removed following clarification by the European Commission.

(7) Biodegradable part only.

7.6 Renewable orders and operational capacity

Technology band	Contracted projects		Live projects operational at 31 December 2005 (1)	
	Number	Capacity MW	Number	Capacity MW
England and Wales				
NFFO - 1 (1990) Hydro	26	11.85	13	4.83
Landfill gas	25	35.50	13	25.09
Municipal and industrial waste	4	40.63	4	40.63
Other	4	45.48	3	45.38
Sewage gas	7	6.45	4	4.08
Wind	9	12.21	5	8.14
Total *(2)*	**75**	**152.11**	**42**	**128.16**
NFFO - 2 (late 1991) Hydro	12	10.86	9	10.43
Landfill gas	28	48.45	21	34.64
Municipal and industrial waste	10	271.48	2	31.50
Other	4	30.15	1	12.50
Sewage gas	19	26.86	17	18.56
Wind	49	84.43	22	51.97
Total *(2)*	**122**	**472.23**	**72**	**159.60**
NFFO - 3 (1995) Energy crops and agricultural and forestry waste - gasification	3	19.06	-	-
Energy crops and agricultural and forestry waste - other	6	103.81	2	69.50
Hydro	15	14.48	8	11.74
Landfill gas	42	82.07	41	80.55
Municipal and industrial waste	20	241.87	9	114.62
Wind - large	31	145.92	12	50.50
Wind - small	24	19.71	15	13.52
Total	**141**	**626.90**	**87**	**340.43**
NFFO - 4 (1997) Hydro	31	13.22	9	2.49
Landfill gas	70	173.68	62	161.46
Municipal and industrial waste - CHP	10	115.29	4	33.48
Municipal and industrial waste - fluidised bed combustion	6	125.93	-	-
Wind - large	48	330.36	6	38.67
Wind - small	17	10.33	6	4.03
Anaerobic digestion of agricultural waste	6	6.58	1	1.43
Energy crops and forestry waste gasification	7	67.34	-	-
Total	**195**	**842.72**	**88**	**241.57**
NFFO - 5 (1998) Hydro	22	8.87	-	-
Landfill gas	141	313.73	80	170.41
Municipal and industrial waste	22	415.75	-	-
Municipal and industrial waste - CHP	7	69.97	-	-
Wind - large	33	340.16	-	-
Wind - small	36	28.67	9	7.45
Total	**261**	**1,177.15**	**89**	**177.86**
NFFO Total	**794**	**3,271.11**	**378**	**1,047.61**

(1) Sites that have closed and sites that are not currently using renewables as fuel have been excluded.

(2) See footnote 2, on next page.

7.6 Renewable orders and operational capacity (continued)

Technology band	Contracted projects		Live projects operational at 31 December 2005 (1)	
	Number	Capacity MW	Number	Capacity MW
Scotland				
SRO - 1 (1994) Biomass	1	9.80	1	9.80
Hydro	15	17.25	10	10.75
Waste to Energy	2	3.78	2	3.78
Wind	12	45.60	7	25.13
Total	**30**	**76.43**	**20**	**49.46**
SRO - 2 (1997) Biomass	1	2.00	-	-
Hydro	9	12.36	2	1.46
Waste to Energy	9	56.05	6	17.65
Wind	7	43.63	5	31.29
Total	**26**	**114.04**	**13**	**50.40**
SRO - 3 (1999) Biomass	1	12.90	-	-
Hydro	5	3.90	-	-
Waste to Energy	16	49.11	10	22.36
Wave	3	2.00	1	0.20
Wind - large	11	63.43	1	8.29
Wind - small	17	14.06	5	4.28
Total	**53**	**145.40**	**17**	**35.13**
SRO Total	**109**	**335.87**	**50**	**134.99**
Northern Ireland				
NI NFFO - 1 (1994) Hydro	9	2.37	9	2.37
Sewage gas	5	0.56	-	-
Wind	6	12.66	6	12.66
Total	**20**	**15.60**	**15**	**15.03**
NI NFFO - 2 (1996) Biogas	1	0.25	-	-
Biomass	2	0.30	2	0.30
Hydro	2	0.25	1	0.08
Landfill gas	2	6.25	-	-
Municipal and industrial waste	1	6.65	-	-
Wind	2	2.57	2	2.57
Total	**10**	**16.27**	**5**	**2.95**
NI NFFO Total	**30**	**31.87**	**20**	**17.98**
All NFFO and equivalents (2)	**933**	**3,638.85**	**448**	**1,200.59**

(1) Sites that have closed and sites that are not currently using renewables as fuel have been excluded.

(2) The NFPA NFFO database has reported that at the end of December 2005 473 sites totalling 1,226.19 MW had gone live under NFFO, but this includes all NFFO-1 and NFFO-2 sites for England and Wales, some of which have closed or are not currently using renewables as fuels. The following table compares the totals for live projects, above, with the overall NFFO total:

	Number	MW
All live NFFO and equivalents	448	1,200.59
NFFO-1 no longer classed as live and operational	17	12.85
NFFO-2 no longer classed as live and operational	8	12.76
All NFFO and equivalents	473	1,226.19

7.7 Renewable sources used to generate electricity and heat[1][2]

				Thousand tonnes of oil equivalent	
	2001	2002	2003	2004	2005
Used to generate electricity (3)					
Wind:					
Onshore	82.5	107.6	109.7	149.3	215.4
Offshore	0.4	0.4	0.8	17.1	34.6
Solar photovoltaics	0.2	0.2	0.3	0.3	0.7
Hydro:					
Small scale	18.1	17.5	12.3r	24.3r	40.2
Large scale (4)	330.7	394.2	265.3r	399.5r	386.4
Biofuels:					
Landfill gas	822.2	878.5	1,074.5	1,313.1	1,407.2
Sewage sludge digestion	119.0	120.6	112.5	124.1	131.1
Municipal solid waste combustion (5)	387.1	420.2	445.8	429.5	426.3
Co-firing with fossil fuels	-	94.0	197.3	335.1	830.7
Other (6)	282.2	273.6	304.3r	301.1r	288.5
Total biofuels	1,610.5	1,786.8	2,134.5r	2,502.9r	3,083.7
Total	**2,042.4**	**2,306.7**	**2,522.8r**	**3,093.5r**	**3,761.0**
Non-biodegradable wastes (7)	266.2	286.1	273.8r	263.9	262.0
Used to generate heat					
Active solar heating	13.2	16.1	19.8	24.6	29.4
Biofuels :					
Landfill gas	13.6	13.6	13.6	13.6	13.6
Sewage sludge digestion	49.4	53.4	52.5	52.5	48.0
Wood combustion - domestic	204.2	204.2	204.2	204.2	204.2
Wood combustion - industrial	195.6r	195.6r	195.6r	195.6r	80.9
Straw combustion, farm waste digestion and short rotation coppice	72.2	72.2	72.2	73.9	73.9
Municipal solid waste combustion (5)	26.2r	33.7r	33.7r	33.7r	33.7
Total biofuels	561.1r	572.8r	571.9r	573.6r	454.3
Geothermal aquifers	0.8	0.8	0.8	0.8	0.8
Total	**575.2r**	**589.7r**	**592.5r**	**598.9r**	**484.5**
Non-biodegradable wastes (7)	80.7r	92.2r	117.1r	115.7r	115.7
Total use of renewable sources and wastes					
Solar heating and photovoltaics	13.4	16.3	20.0	24.9	30.1
Onshore and offshore wind (9)	83.0	108.0	110.5	166.4	250.1
Hydro	348.7	411.7	277.5	423.9	426.6
Biofuels	2,171.6r	2,359.6r	2,706.3r	3,076.4r	3,538.0
Geothermal aquifers	0.8	0.8	0.8	0.8	0.8
Total	**2,617.6r**	**2,896.4r**	**3,115.2r**	**3,692.4r**	**4,245.5**
Non-biodegradable wastes (7)	347.0r	378.3r	390.9r	379.6r	377.7
All renewables and wastes (8)	**2,964.6r**	**3,274.7r**	**3,506.1r**	**4,072.0r**	**4,623.2**

(1) Includes some waste of fossil fuel origin.
(2) See paragraphs 7.40 to 7.81 for technical notes and definitions of the categories used in this table.
(3) For wind, solar PV and hydro, the figures represent the energy content of the electricity supplied but for biofuels the figures represent the energy content of the fuel used.
(4) Excluding pumped storage stations.
(5) Biodegradable part only.
(6) Includes electricity from farm waste digestion, poultry litter combustion, meat and bone combustion, straw and energy crops.
(7) Non-biodegradable part of municipal solid waste plus waste tyres, hospital waste, and general industrial waste.
(8) The figures in this row correspond to the total demand and total supply figures in Tables 7.1, 7.2 and 7.3.
(9) Latest years include energy from shoreline wave but this is less than 0.05 ktoe.

Digest of United Kingdom Energy Statistics 2006

Annexes

Annex A: Energy and commodity balances, conversion factors and calorific values

Annex B: Glossary and Acronyms

Annex C: Further sources

Annex D: Major events in the Energy Industry, 2004-2006

Department of Trade and Industry

Annex A
Energy and commodity balances, conversion factors and calorific values

Balance principles

A.1   This Annex outlines the principles behind the balance presentation of energy statistics. It covers these in general terms. Fuel specific details are given in the appropriate chapters of this publication.

A.2   Balances are divided into two types, each of which performs a different function.

a) *commodity balance* – a balance for each energy commodity that uses the units usually associated with that commodity. By using a single column of figures, it shows the flow of the commodity from its sources of supply through to its final use. Commodity balances are presented in the individual fuel chapters of this publication.

b) *energy balance* - presents the commodity balances in a common unit and places them alongside one another in a manner that shows the dependence of the supply of one commodity on another. This is useful as some commodities are manufactured from others. The layout of the energy balance also differs slightly from the commodity balance. The energy balance format is used in Chapter 1.

A.3   Energy commodities can be either primary or secondary. Primary energy commodities are drawn (extracted or captured) from natural reserves or flows, whereas secondary commodities are produced from primary energy commodities.   Crude oil and coal are examples of primary commodities, whilst petrol and coke are secondary commodities manufactured from them.   For balance purposes, electricity may be considered to be both primary electricity (for example, hydro, wind) or secondary (produced from steam turbines using steam from the combustion of fuels).

A.4   Both commodity and energy balances show the flow of the commodity from its production, extraction or import through to its final use.

A.5   A simplified model of the commodity flow underlying the balance structure is given in Chart A.1.   It illustrates how primary commodities may be used directly and/or be transformed into secondary commodities.   The secondary fuels then enter final consumption or may also be transformed into another energy commodity (for example, electricity produced from fuel oil). To keep the diagram simple these "second generation" flows have not been shown.

A.6   The arrows at the top of the chart represent flows to and from the "pools" of primary and secondary commodities, from imports and exports and, in the case of the primary pool, extraction from reserves (eg the production of coal, gas and crude oil).

Commodity balances (Tables 2.1 to 2.6, 3.1 to 3.6, 4.1, 5.1, and 7.1 to 7.3)
A.7   A commodity balance comprises a supply section and a demand section. The supply section gives available sources of supply (ie exports are subtracted). The demand section is divided into a transformation section, a section showing uses in the energy industries (other than for transformation) and a section covering uses by final consumers for energy or non-energy purposes.   Final consumption for energy purposes is divided into use by sector of economic activity.   The section breakdowns are described below.

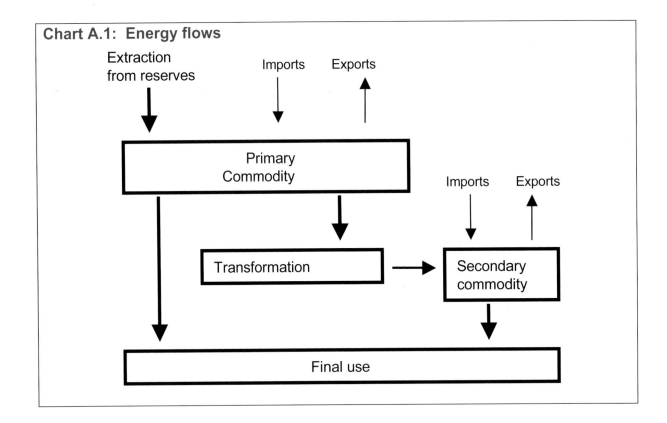

Chart A.1: Energy flows

Supply

Production
A.8   Production, within the commodity balance, covers indigenous production (extraction or capture of primary commodities) and generation or manufacture of secondary commodities. Production is always gross, that is, it includes the quantities used during the extraction or manufacturing process.

Other sources
A.9   Production from other sources covers sources of supply that do not represent "new" supply. These may be recycled products, recovered fuels (slurry or waste coal), or electricity from pumped storage plants. The production of these quantities will have been reported in an earlier accounting period or have already been reported in the current period of account. Exceptionally, the *Other sources* row in the commodity balances for ethane, propane and butane is used to receive transfers of these hydrocarbons from gas stabilisation plants at North Sea terminals. In this manner, the supplies of primary ethane, propane and butane from the North Sea are combined with the production of these gases in refineries, so that the disposals may be presented together in the balances.

Imports and exports
A.10   The figures for imports and exports relate to energy commodities moving into or out of the United Kingdom as part of transactions involving United Kingdom companies. Exported commodities are produced in the United Kingdom and imported commodities are for use within the United Kingdom (although some may be re-exported before or after transformation).   The figures thus exclude commodities either exported from or imported into HM Revenue and Customs bonded areas or warehouses. These areas, although part of the United Kingdom, are regarded as being outside of the normal United Kingdom's customs boundary, and so goods entering into or leaving them are not counted as part of the statistics on trade used in the balances.

A.11   Similarly, commodities that only pass through the United Kingdom on their way to a final destination in another country are also excluded. However, for gas these transit flows are included because it is difficult to identify this quantity separately, without detailed knowledge of the contract information covering the trade. This means that for gas, there is some over statement of the level of imports and exports, but the net flows are correct.

A.12   The convention in these balances is that exports are shown with a negative sign.

Marine bunkers
A.13   These are deliveries of fuels (usually fuel oil or gas oil) to ships of any flag (including the United Kingdom) for consumption during the voyage to other countries. Marine bunkers are treated rather like exports and shown with a negative sign.

Stock changes
A.14   Additions to (- sign) and withdrawals from stocks (+ sign) held by producers and transformation industries correspond to withdrawals from and additions to supply, respectively.

Transfers
A.15   There are several reasons why quantities may be transferred from one commodity balance to another:
- a commodity may no longer meet the original specification and be reclassified;
- the name of the commodity may change through a change in use;
- to show quantities returned to supply from consumers. These may be by-products of the use of commodities as raw materials rather than fuels.

A.16   A quantity transferred from a balance is shown with a negative sign to represent a withdrawal from supply and with a positive sign in the receiving commodity balance representing an addition to its supply.

Total supply
A.17   The total supply available for national use is obtained by summing the flows above this entry in the balance.

Total demand
A.18   The various figures for the disposals and/or consumption of the commodities are summed to provide a measure of the demand for them. The main categories or sectors of demand are described in paragraphs A.32 to A.42.

Statistical difference
A.19   Any excess of supply over demand is shown as a statistical difference. A negative figure indicates that demand exceeds supply. Statistical differences arise when figures are gathered from a variety of independent sources and reflect differences in timing, in definition of coverage of the activity, or in commodity definition. Differences also arise for methodological reasons in the measurement of the flow of the commodity eg if there are differences between the volumes recorded by the gas producing companies and the gas transporting companies. A non-zero statistical difference is normal and, provided that it is not too large, is preferable to a statistical difference of zero as this suggests that a data provider has adjusted a figure to balance the account.

Transformation
A.20   The transformation sector of the balance covers those processes and activities that transform the original primary (and sometimes secondary) commodity into a form which is better suited for specific uses than the original form. Most of the transformation activities correspond to particular energy industries whose main business is to manufacture the product associated with them. Certain activities involving transformation take place to make products that are only partly used for energy needs (coke oven coke) or are by-products of other manufacturing processes (coke oven and blast furnace gases). However, as these products and by-products are then used, at least in part, for their energy content they are included in the balance system.

A.21 The figures given under the activity headings of this sector represent the quantities used for transformation. The production of the secondary commodities will be shown in the *Production* row of the corresponding commodity balances.

Electricity generation
A.22   The quantities of fuels burned for the generation of electricity are shown in their commodity balances under this heading. The activity is divided into two parts, covering the major power

199

producers (for whom the main business is the generation of electricity for sale) and autogenerators (whose main business is not electricity generation but who produce electricity for their own needs and may also sell surplus quantities). The amounts of fuels shown in the balance represent the quantities consumed for the gross generation of electricity. Where a generator uses combined heat and power plant, the figures include only the part of the fuel use corresponding to the electricity generated.

A.23   In relation to autogenerators' data, the figures for quantities of fuel used for electricity generation appear under the appropriate fuel headings in the *Transformation* sector heading for *Autogenerators,* whilst the electricity generated appears in the *Electricity* column under *Production*. A breakdown of the information according to the branch of industry in which the generation occurs is not shown in the balance but is given in Chapter 1, Table 1.9. The figures for energy commodities consumed by the industry branches shown under final consumption include all use of electricity, but exclude the fuels combusted by the industry branches to generate the electricity.

Heat generation
A.24   The quantities of fuel burned to generate heat that is sold under the provision of a contract to a third party are shown in their commodity balances under this heading. It includes heat that is generated and sold by combined heat and power plants and by community heating schemes (also called district heating).

Petroleum refineries
A.25   Crude oil, natural gas liquids and other oils needed by refineries for the manufacture of finished petroleum products are shown under this heading.

Coke manufacture and blast furnaces
A.26   Quantities of coal for coke ovens and all fuels used within blast furnaces are shown under this heading. The consumption of fuels for heating coke ovens and the blast air for blast furnaces are shown under *Energy industry use*.

Patent fuel manufacture
A.27   The coals and other solid fuels used for the manufacture of solid patent fuels are reported under this heading.

Other
A.28   Any minor transformation activities not specified elsewhere are captured under this heading.

Energy industry use
A.29   Consumption by both extraction and transformation industries to support the transformation process (but not for transformation itself) are included here according to the energy industry concerned. Typical examples are the consumption of electricity in power plants (eg for lighting, compressors and cooling systems) and the use of extracted gases on oil and gas platforms for compressors, pumps and other uses. The headings in this sector are identical to those used in the transformation sector with the exception of *Pumped storage*. In this case, the electricity used to pump the water to the reservoir is reported.

Losses
A.30   This heading covers the intrinsic losses that occur during the transmission and distribution of electricity and gas (including manufactured gases). Other metering and accounting differences for gas and electricity are within the statistical difference, as are undeclared losses in other commodities.

Final consumption
A.31   *Final consumption* covers both final energy consumption (by different consuming sectors) and the use of energy commodities for non-energy purposes, that is *Non energy use*. Final consumption occurs when the commodities used are not for transformation into secondary commodities. The energy concerned disappears from the account after use. Any fuel used for electricity generation by final consumers is identified and reported separately within the transformation sector. When an enterprise generates electricity, the figure for final consumption of the industrial sector to which the enterprise belongs includes its use of the electricity it generates itself (as well as supplies of electricity it purchases from others) but does not include the fuel used to generate that electricity.

A.32   The classification of consumers according to their main business follows, as far as practicable, the *Standard Industrial Classification (SIC2003)*. The qualifications to, and constraints on, the classification are described in the technical notes to Chapter 1, paragraphs 1.24 to 1.57. Table 1E in Chapter 1 shows the breakdown of final consumers used, and how this corresponds to the SIC2003.

Industry
A.33   Two sectors of industry (iron and steel and chemicals) require special mention because the activities they undertake fall across the transformation, final consumption and non-energy classifications used for the balances. Also, the data permitting an accurate allocation of fuel use within each of these major divisions are not readily available.

Iron and steel
A.34   The iron and steel industry is a heavy energy user for transformation and final consumption activities. Figures shown under final consumption for this industry branch reflect the amounts that remain after quantities used for transformation and energy sector own use have been subtracted from the industry's total energy requirements. Use of fuels for transformation by the industry may be identified within the transformation sector of the commodity balances.

A.35   The amounts of coal used for coke manufacture by the iron and steel industry are in the transformation sector of the coal balance. Included in this figure is the amount of coal used for coke manufacture by the companies outside of the iron and steel industry, ie solid fuel manufacturers. The corresponding production of coke and coke oven gas may be found in the commodity balances for these products. The use of coke in blast furnaces is shown in the commodity balance for coke, and the gases produced from blast furnaces and the associated basic oxygen steel furnaces are shown in the production row of the commodity balance for blast furnace gas.

A.36   Fuels used for electricity generation by the industry are included in the figures for electricity generation by autogenerators and are not distinguishable as being used by the iron and steel sector in the balances. Electricity generation and fuel used for this by broad industry group are given in Table 1.9.

A.37   Fuels used to support coke manufacture and blast furnace gas production are included in the quantities shown under *Energy industry use.* These gases and other fuels do not enter coke ovens or blast furnaces, but are used to heat the ovens and the blast air supplied to furnaces.

Chemicals
A.38   The petro-chemical industry uses hydrocarbon fuels (mostly oil products and gases) as feedstock for the manufacture of its products. Distinguishing the energy use of delivered fuels from their non-energy use is complicated by the absence of detailed information. The procedures adopted to estimate the use are described in paragraphs A.41 and A.42 under *Non energy use.*

Transport
A.39   Figures under this heading are almost entirely quantities used strictly for transport purposes. However, the figures recorded against road transport usually include some fuel that is actually consumed in some "off-road" activities. Similarly, figures for railway fuels include some amounts of burning oil not used directly for transport purposes. Transport sector use of electricity includes all electricity used in industries classified to SIC2003 Groups 60 to 63. Fuels supplied to cargo and passenger ships undertaking international voyages are reported as *Marine bunkers* (see paragraph A.13). Supplies to fishing vessels are included under "agriculture".

Other sectors
A.40   The classification of all consumers groups under this heading, except *domestic*, follows *SIC2003* and is described in Table 1E in Chapter 1. The consistency of the classification across different commodities cannot be guaranteed because the figures reported are dependent on what the data suppliers can provide.

Non energy use
A.41   The non energy use of fuels may be divided into two types. They may be used directly for their physical properties eg lubricants or bitumen used for road surfaces, or by the petro-chemical

industry as raw materials for the manufacture of goods such as plastics. In their use by the petro-chemical industry, relatively little combustion of the fuels takes place and the carbon and/or hydrogen they contain are largely transferred into the finished product. However, in some cases heat from the manufacturing process or from combustion of by-products may be used. Data for this energy use are rarely available. Depending on the feedstock, non energy consumption is either estimated or taken to be the deliveries to the chemicals sector.

A.42 Both types of non energy use are shown under the *Non energy use* heading at the foot of the balances.

The energy balance (Tables 1.1 to 1.3)

Principles
A.43 The energy balance conveniently presents:

- an overall view of the United Kingdom's energy supplies;
- the relative importance of each energy commodity;
- dependence on imports;
- the contribution of our own fossil and renewable resources;
- the interdependence of commodities on one another.

A.44 The energy balance is constructed directly from the commodity balances by expressing the data in a common unit, placing them beside one another and adding appropriate totals. Heat sold is also included as a fuel. However, some rearrangement of the commodity balance format is required to show transformation of primary into secondary commodities in an easily understood manner.

A.45 Energy units are widely used as the common unit, and the current practice for the United Kingdom and the international organisations which prepare balances is to use the tonne of oil equivalent or a larger multiple of this unit, commonly thousands. One tonne of oil equivalent is defined as 10^7 kilocalories (41.868 gigajoules). The tonne of oil equivalent is another unit of energy like the gigajoule, kilocalorie or kilowatt hour, rather than a physical quantity. It has been chosen as it is easier to visualise than the other units. Due to the natural variations in heating value of primary fuels such as crude oil, it is rare that one tonne of oil has an energy content equivalent to one tonne of oil equivalent, however it is generally within a few per cent of the heating value of a tonne of oil equivalent. The energy figures are calculated from the natural units of the commodity balances by multiplying by factors representing the calorific (heating) value of the fuel. The gross calorific values of fuels are used for this purpose. When the natural unit of the commodity is already an energy unit (electricity in kilowatt hours, for example) the factors are just constants, converting one energy unit to another.

A.46 Most of the underlying definitions and ideas of commodity balances can be taken directly over into the energy balance. However, production of secondary commodities and, in particular, electricity are treated differently and need some explanation. The components of the energy balance are described below, drawing out the differences of treatment compared with the commodity balances.

Primary supply
A.47 Within the energy balance, the production row covers only extraction of primary fuels and the generation of primary energy (hydro, nuclear, wind). Note the change of row heading from *Production* in the commodity balances to *Indigenous production* in the energy balance. Production of secondary fuels and secondary electricity are shown in the transformation sector and not in the indigenous production row at the top of the balance.

A.48 For fossil fuels, indigenous production represents the marketable quantity extracted from the reserves. Indigenous production of *Primary electricity* comprises hydro-electricity, wind and nuclear energy. The energy value for hydro-electricity is taken to be the energy content of the electricity produced from the hydro power plant and not the energy available in the water driving the turbines. A similar approach is adopted for electricity from wind generators. The electricity is regarded as the primary energy form because there are currently no other uses of the energy resource "upstream" of the generation. The energy value attached to nuclear electricity is discussed in paragraph A.52.

A.49   The other elements of the supply part of the balance are identical to those in the commodity balances. In particular, the sign convention is identical, so that figures for exports and international marine bunkers carry negative signs. A stock build carries a negative sign to denote it as a withdrawal from supply whilst a stock draw carries a positive sign to show it as an addition to supply.

A.50   The *Primary supply* is the sum of the figures above it in the table, taking account of the signs, and expresses the national requirement for primary energy commodities from all sources and foreign supplies of secondary commodities. It is an indicator of the use of indigenous resources and external energy supplies. Both the amount and mixture of fuels in final consumption of energy commodities in the United Kingdom will differ from the primary supply. The "mix" of commodities in final consumption will be much more dependent on the manufacture of secondary commodities, in particular electricity.

Transformation

A.51   Within an energy balance the presentation of the inputs to and outputs from transformation activities requires special mention, as it is carried out using a compact format. The transformation sector also plays a key role in moving primary electricity from its own column in the balance into the electricity column, so that it can be combined with electricity from fossil fuelled power stations and the total disposals shown.

A.52   Indigenous production of primary electricity comprises nuclear electricity, hydro electricity and electricity from wind generation. Nuclear electricity is obtained by passing steam from nuclear reactors through conventional steam turbine sets. The heat in the steam is considered to be the primary energy available and its value is calculated from the electricity generated using the average thermal efficiency of nuclear stations, currently 38.2 in the United Kingdom. The electrical energy from hydro and wind is transferred from the *Primary electricity* column to the *Electricity* column using the *transfers* row because electricity is the form of primary energy and no transformation takes place. However, because the form of the nuclear energy is the steam from the nuclear reactors, the energy it contains is shown entering electricity generation and the corresponding electricity produced is included with all electricity generation in the figure, in the same row, under the *Electricity* column.

A.53   Quantities of fuels entering transformation activities (fuels into electricity generation and heat generation, crude oil into petroleum product manufacture (refineries), or coal into coke ovens) are shown with a negative sign to represent the input and the resulting production is shown as a positive number.

A.54   For electricity generated by Major power producers, the inputs are shown in the *Major power producers* row of the *coal, manufactured fuel, primary oils, petroleum products, gas, renewables* and *primary electricity* columns. The total energy input to electricity generation is the sum of the values in these first seven columns. The *Electricity* column shows total electricity generated from these inputs and the transformation loss is the sum of these two figures, given in the *Total* column.

A.55   Within the transformation sector, the negative figures in the *Total* column represent the losses in the various transformation activities. This is a convenient consequence of the sign convention chosen for the inputs and outputs from transformation. Any positive figures represent a transformation gain and, as such, are an indication of incorrect data.

A.56   In the energy balance, the columns containing the input commodities for electricity generation, heat generation and oil refining are separate from the columns for the outputs. However, for the transformation activities involving solid fuels this is only partly the case. Coal used for the manufacture of coke is shown in the coke manufacture row of the transformation section in the coal column, but the related coke and coke oven gas production are shown combined in the *Manufactured fuels* column. Similarly, the input of coke to blast furnaces and the resulting production of blast furnace gas are not identifiable and have been combined in the *Manufactured fuels* column in the *Blast furnace* row. As a result, only the net loss from blast furnace transformation activity appears in the column.

A.57   The share of each commodity or commodity group in primary supply can be calculated from the table. This table also shows the demand for primary as well as foreign supplies. Shares of primary supplies may be taken from the *Primary supply* row of the balance. Shares of fuels in final consumption may be calculated from the final consumption row.

Energy industry use and final consumption

A.58   The figures for final consumption and energy industry use follow, in general, the principles and definitions described under commodity balances in paragraphs A.29 to A.42.

Standard conversion factors

1 tonne of oil equivalent (toe)	$= 10^7$ kilocalories		

1 tonne of oil equivalent (toe) $= 10^7$ kilocalories
     $= 396.83$ therms
     $= 41.868$ GJ
     $= 11,630$ kWh
100,000 British thermal units (Btu) $= 1$ therm

This Digest follows UK statistical practice and uses the term "billion" to refer to one thousand million or 10^9.

The following prefixes are used for multiples of joules, watts and watt hours:

kilo (k)	= 1,000	or 10^3
mega (M)	= 1,000,000	or 10^6
giga (G)	= 1,000,000,000	or 10^9
tera (T)	= 1,000,000,000,000	or 10^{12}
peta (P)	= 1,000,000,000,000,000	or 10^{15}

WEIGHT

1 kilogramme (kg)	= 2.2046 pounds (lb)
1 pound (lb)	= 0.4536 kg
1 tonne (t)	= 1,000kg
	= 0.9842 long ton
	= 1.102 short ton (sh tn)
1 Statute or long ton	= 2,240 lb
	= 1.016 t
	= 1.102 sh tn

VOLUME

1 cubic metre (cu m)	= 35.31 cu ft
1 cubic foot (cu ft)	= 0.02832 cu m
1 litre	= 0.22 Imperial gallons (UK gal)
1 UK gallon	= 8 UK pints
	= 1.201 US gallons (US gal)
	= 4.54609 litres
1 barrel	= 159.0 litres
	= 34.97 UK gal
	= 42 US gal

LENGTH

1 mile	= 1.6093 kilometres
1 kilometre (km)	= 0.62137 miles

TEMPERATURE

1 scale degree Celsius (C) = 1.8 scale degrees Fahrenheit (F)

For conversion of temperatures: $^{\circ}C = 5/9 (^{\circ}F -32)$; $^{\circ}F = 9/5 \,^{\circ}C +32$

Average conversion factors for petroleum

	Imperial gallons per tonne	Litres per tonne		Imperial gallons per tonne	Litres per tonne
Crude oil:			Gas/diesel oil:		
Indigenous	264	1,199	Gas oil	262	1,193
Imported	260	1,181	Marine diesel oil	255	1,157
Average of refining throughput	262	1,192			
			Fuel oil:		
Ethane	601	2,730	All grades	226	1,027
Propane	433	1,969	Light fuel oil:		
Butane	381	1,730	1% or less sulphur	227	1,033
Naphtha (l.d.f.)	317	1,442			
			Medium fuel oil:		
Aviation gasoline	308	1,401	1% or less sulphur	232	1,053
Motor spirit:			Heavy fuel oil:		
All grades	298	1,354	1% or less sulphur	224	1,020
Unleaded Super	299	1,358			
Premium	299	1,357			
Ultra low sulphur petrol	298	1,354			
Lead replacement petrol	299	1,361	Lubricating oils:		
			White	249	1,133
Middle distillate feedstock	247	1,122	Greases	236	1,072
Kerosene:			Other	248	1,127
Aviation turbine fuel	275	1,251	Bitumen	218	990
Burning oil	275	1,250	Petroleum coke	185	843
			Petroleum waxes	259	1,177
DERV fuel:			Industrial spirit	274	1,247
0.005% or less sulphur	265	1,203	White spirit	276	1,253

Note: The above conversion factors, which for refined products have been compiled by the UK Petroleum Industry Association, apply to the year 2005, and are only approximate for other years.

A.1 Estimated average calorific values of fuels 2005

Coal

	GJ per tonne net	GJ per tonne gross
All consumers (weighted average) *(1)*	25.6	26.9
Power stations *(1)*	24.9	26.2
Coke ovens *(1)*	29.0	30.5
Low temperature carbonisation plants and manufactured fuel plants	29.0	30.5
Collieries	28.3	29.8
Agriculture	26.6	28.0
Iron and steel	28.9	30.4
Other industries (weighted average)	24.1	25.4
Non-ferrous metals	23.3	24.5
Food, beverages and tobacco	28.3	29.8
Chemicals	25.3	26.6
Textiles, clothing, leather etc.	28.0	29.5
Pulp, paper, printing etc.	27.5	28.9
Mineral products	26.5	27.9
Engineering (mechanical and electrical engineering and vehicles)	29.9	31.5
Other industries	24.2	25.5

Domestic

	GJ per tonne net	GJ per tonne gross
House coal	29.2	30.7
Anthracite and dry steam coal	32.1	33.8
Other consumers	27.9	29.4
Imported coal (weighted average)	25.9	27.3
Exports (weighted average)	31.1	32.7

	GJ per tonne net	GJ per tonne gross
Coke (including low temperature carbonisation cokes)	29.6	29.6
Coke breeze	24.8	24.8
Other manufactured solid fuel	30.9	32.5

Renewable sources

	GJ per tonne net	GJ per tonne gross
Domestic wood *(2)*	5.0	10.0
Industrial wood *(3)*	10.0	11.9
Straw	12.8	15.0
Poultry litter	7.4	8.8
Meat and bone	15.6	18.6
General industrial waste	15.2	16.0
Hospital waste	13.3	14.0
Municipal solid waste *(4)*	6.7	9.5
Refuse derived waste *(4)*	13.0	18.5
Short rotation coppice *(5)*	9.0	10.6
Tyres	..	32.0

Petroleum

	GJ per tonne net	GJ per tonne gross
Crude oil (weighted average)	43.4	45.7
Petroleum products (weighted average)	43.6	45.9
Ethane	48.1	50.7
Butane and propane (LPG)	47.1	49.5
Light distillate feedstock for gasworks	45.2	47.6
Aviation spirit and wide cut gasoline	45.0	47.4
Aviation turbine fuel	43.9	46.2
Motor spirit	44.7	47.0
Burning oil	43.9	46.2
Gas/diesel oil (DERV)	43.4	45.7
Fuel oil	41.3	43.5
Power station oil	41.3	43.5
Non-fuel products (notional value)	40.8	42.9

	MJ per cubic metre net	MJ per cubic metre gross
Natural gas *(6)*	35.6	39.6
Coke oven gas	16.2	18.0
Blast furnace gas	3.0	3.0
Landfill gas *(7)*	19-23	21-25
Sewage gas *(7)*	19-23	21-25

(1) Applicable to UK consumption - based on calorific value for home produced coal plus imports and, for "All consumers" net of exports.

(2) Based on a 50 per cent moisture content.

(3) Average figure covering a range of possible feedstock.

(4) Average figure based on survey returns.

(5) On an "as received" basis. On a "dry" basis 18.6 GJ per tonne.

(6) The gross calorific value of natural gas can also be expressed as 10.992 kWh per cubic metre. This value represents the average calorific value seen for gas when extracted. At this point it contains not just methane, but also some other hydrocarbon gases (ethane, butane, propane). These gases are removed before the gas enters the National Transmission System for sale to final consumers. As such, this calorific value will differ from that readers will see quoted on their gas bills.

(7) Calorific value varies depending on the methane content of the gas

Note: The above estimated average calorific values apply only to the year 2005. For calorific values of fuels in earlier years see Tables A.2 and A.3 and previous issues of this Digest. See the notes in Chapter 1, paragraph 1.52 regarding net calorific values. The calorific values for coal other than imported coal are based on estimates provided by the main coal producers, but with some exceptions as noted on Table A.2. The calorific values for petroleum products have been calculated using the method described in Chapter 1, paragraph 1.27. The calorific values for coke oven gas and blast furnace gas are provided by the Iron and Steel Statistics Bureau (ISSB).

Data reported in this Digest in 'thousand tonnes of oil equivalent' have been prepared on the basis of 1 tonne of oil equivalent having an energy content of 41.868 gigajoules (GJ), (1 GJ = 9.478 therms) - see notes in Chapter 1, paragraphs 1.24 to 1.26.

A.2 Estimated average gross calorific values of fuels 1980, 1990 and 2000 to 2005

GJ per tonne (gross)

	1980	1990	2000	2002	2003	2004	2005
Coal							
All consumers (1)(2)	25.6	25.5	26.2	26.2	26.1	26.0	25.6
All consumers - home produced plus imports minus exports (1)	..	..	27.0	26.9	26.7	26.8r	26.9
Power stations (2)	23.8	24.8	25.6	25.6	25.5	25.4	25.0
Power stations - home produced plus imports (1)	..	..	26.0	26.1	26.0	26.2	26.2
Coke ovens (2)	30.5	30.2	31.2	31.3	31.4	31.6	31.5
Coke ovens - home produced plus imports (1)	..	..	30.4	30.5	30.5	30.5	30.5
Low temperature carbonisation plants and manufactured fuel plants	19.1	29.2	30.3	30.5	30.5	30.5	30.5
Collieries	27.0	28.6	29.6	29.7	30.1	29.9	29.8
Agriculture	30.1	28.9	29.2	28.5	28.0	28.0	28.0
Iron and steel industry (3)	29.1	28.9	30.7	30.4	30.4	30.4	30.4
Other industries (1)	27.1	27.8	26.7	26.5	26.6r	25.6r	25.4
Non-ferrous metals	..	23.1	25.1	25.0	25.3	24.8	24.5
Food, beverages and tobacco	28.6	28.1	29.5	30.0	30.5	29.4	29.8
Chemicals	25.8	27.3	28.7	27.4	27.8	26.6	26.6
Textiles, clothing, leather and footwear	27.5	27.7	30.4	29.9	29.9	29.5	29.5
Pulp, paper, printing, etc.	26.5	27.9	28.7	28.9	28.8	28.7	28.9
Mineral products (4)	..	28.2	27.0	27.0	27.9	27.9	27.9
Engineering (5)	27.7	28.3	29.3	30.7	30.6	30.6	31.5
Other industry (6)	28.4	28.5	30.2	28.4	28.3	25.7	25.5
Unclassified	..	27.1	..	..	..	..	..
Domestic							
House coal	30.1	30.2	30.9	31.1	31.0	30.9	30.7
Anthracite and dry steam coal	33.3	33.6	33.6	33.9	33.8	33.8	33.8
Other consumers	27.5	27.5	29.2	30.1	29.6	29.8	29.5
Imported coal (1)	..	28.3	28.0	27.6	27.6	27.3	27.3
of which Steam coal	..	..	26.6	26.5	26.7	26.7	26.7
Coking coal	..	..	30.4	30.4	30.4	30.4	30.4
Anthracite	..	..	31.2	30.4	30.1	30.6	31.7
Exports (1)	..	29.0	32.0	31.7	31.6	32.3	32.7
of which Steam coal	..	..	31.0	30.0	29.9	29.9	32.9
Anthracite	..	..	32.6	32.6	32.3	32.5	32.6
Coke (7)	28.1	28.1	29.8	29.8	29.8	29.8	29.6
Coke breeze	24.4	24.8	24.8	24.8	24.8	24.8	24.8
Other manufactured solid fuels (1)	27.6	27.6	30.8	30.9	31.1	31.8	32.5
Petroleum							
Crude oil (1)	45.2	45.6	45.7	45.7	45.7	45.7	45.7
Liquified petroleum gas	49.6	49.4	49.4	49.4	49.4	49.4	49.5
Ethane	52.3	50.6	50.7	50.7	50.7	50.7	50.7
LDF for gasworks/Naphtha	47.8	47.9	47.7	47.6	47.2	47.5	47.6
Aviation spirit and wide-cut gasoline (AVGAS and AVTAG)	47.2	47.3	47.3	47.3	47.3	47.5	47.4
Aviation turbine fuel (AVTUR)	46.4	46.2	46.2	46.2	46.2	46.2	46.2
Motor spirit	47.0	47.0	47.0	47.1	47.1	47.1	47.0
Burning oil	46.5	46.2	46.2	46.2	46.2	46.2	46.2
Vaporising oil	45.9	45.9	..	..	..	..	..
Gas/diesel oil (including DERV)	45.5	45.4	45.6	45.6	45.6	45.6	45.7
Fuel oil	42.8	43.2	43.1	43.4	43.6	43.5	43.5
Power station oil	42.8	43.2	43.1	43.4	43.6	43.5	43.5
Non-fuel products (notional value)	42.2	43.2	43.8	42.7	43.2	43.4	42.9
Petroleum coke	..	39.5	35.8	35.8	35.8	35.8	35.8
Orimulsion (8)	..	29.7	..	..	..	..	..

(1) Weighted averages.
(2) Home produced coal only.
(3) From 2001 onwards almost entirely sourced from imports.
(4) Based on information provided by the British Cement Industry Association; almost all coal used by this sector in the latest 4 years was imported.
(5) Mechanical engineering and metal products, electrical and instrument engineering and vehicle manufacture.
(6) Includes construction.
(7) Since 1995 the source of these figures has been the ISSB.
(8) Orimulsion use ceased in 1997.

A.3 Estimated average net calorific values of fuels 1980, 1990 and 2000 to 2005

GJ per tonne (net)

	1980	1990	2001	2002	2003	2004	2005
Coal							
All consumers (1)(2)	24.3	24.2	24.8	24.9	24.8	24.7	24.3
All consumers - home produced plus imports minus exports (1)	..	..	25.6	25.6	25.4	25.5r	25.6
Power stations (2)	22.6	23.6	24.1	24.3	24.2	24.1	23.8
Power stations - home produced plus imports (1)	..	..	24.8	24.8	24.7	24.9	24.9
Coke ovens (2)	29.0	28.7	29.9	29.7	29.8	30.0	29.9
Coke ovens - home produced plus imports (1)	..	..	29.0	29.0	29.0	29.0	29.0
Low temperature carbonisation plants and manufactured fuel plants	18.1	27.7	28.8	29.0	29.0	29.0	29.0
Collieries	25.7	27.2	28.3	28.2	28.6	28.4	28.3
Agriculture	28.6	27.5	27.6	27.1	26.6	26.6	26.6
Iron and steel industry (3)	27.6	27.5	27.9	28.9	28.9	28.9	28.9
Other industries (1)	25.7	26.4	25.3	25.2	25.3	24.3	24.1
Non-ferrous metals	..	21.9	23.7	23.8	24.0	23.6	23.3
Food, beverages and tobacco	27.2	26.7	27.8	28.5	29.0	27.9	28.3
Chemicals	24.5	25.9	25.7	26.0	26.4	25.3	25.3
Textiles, clothing, leather and footwear	26.1	26.3	28.4	28.4	28.4	28.0	28.0
Pulp, paper, printing, etc.	25.2	26.5	27.4	27.5	27.4	27.3	27.5
Mineral products (4)	..	26.8	25.7	25.7	26.5	26.5	26.5
Engineering (5)	26.3	26.9	27.8	29.2	29.1	29.1	29.9
Other industry (6)	27.0	27.1	29.0	27.0	26.9	24.4	24.2
Unclassified	..	25.7	..	..	..	..	..
Domestic							
House coal	28.6	28.7	29.4	29.5	29.5	29.4	29.2
Anthracite and dry steam coal	31.6	31.9	32.2	32.2	32.1	32.1	32.1
Other consumers	26.1	26.1	27.7	28.6	28.1	28.3	28.0
Imported coal (1)	..	26.9	26.2	26.2	26.2	25.9	25.9
of which Steam coal	..	..	25.4	25.2	25.4	25.4	25.4
Coking coal	..	..	28.9	28.9	28.9	28.9	28.9
Anthracite	..	..	29.5	28.9	28.6	29.1	30.1
Exports (1)	..	27.6	30.5	30.1	30.0	30.7	31.1
of which Steam coal	..	..	29.2	28.5	28.4	28.4	31.3
Anthracite	..	..	31.1	31.0	30.7	30.9	31.0
Coke (7)	28.1	28.1	29.8	29.8	29.8	29.8	29.6
Coke breeze	24.4	24.8	24.8	24.8	24.8	24.8	24.8
Other manufactured solid fuels (1)	26.2	26.2	29.1	29.4	29.5	30.2	30.9
Petroleum							
Crude oil (1)	42.9	43.3	43.4	43.4	43.4	43.4	43.4
Liquified petroleum gas	47.1	46.9	46.9	46.9	46.9	46.9	47.1
Ethane	49.7	48.1	48.2	48.2	48.2	48.2	48.1
LDF for gasworks/Naphtha	45.4	45.5	45.2	45.2	44.8	45.1	45.2
Aviation spirit and wide-cut gasoline (AVGAS and AVTAG)	44.8	44.9	44.9	44.9	44.9	45.1	45.0
Aviation turbine fuel (AVTUR)	44.1	43.9	43.9	43.9	43.9	43.9	43.9
Motor spirit	44.7	44.7	44.7	44.7	44.7	44.7	44.7
Burning oil	44.2	43.9	43.9	43.9	43.9	43.9	43.9
Vaporising oil	43.6	43.6	..	..	..	..	..
Gas/diesel oil (including DERV)	43.2	43.1	43.3	43.3	43.3	43.3	43.4
Fuel oil	40.7	41.0	41.3	41.2	41.4	41.3	41.3
Power station oil	40.7	41.0	41.3	41.2	41.4	41.3	41.3
Non-fuel products (notional value)	40.1	41.0	40.7	40.6	41.0	41.2	40.8
Petroleum coke	..	37.5	34.0	34.0	34.0	34.0	34.0
Orimulsion (8)	..	28.2	..	..	..	..	..

For footnotes see table A.2
The net calorific values of natural gas and coke oven gas are the gross calorific values x 0.9.

Annex B
Glossary and Acronyms

Advanced gas-cooled reactor (AGR)   A type of nuclear reactor cooled by carbon dioxide gas.

AES   Association of Electricity Supplies

Anthracite   Within this publication, anthracite is coal classified as such by UK coal producers and importers of coal. Typically it has a high heat content making it particularly suitable for certain industrial processes and for use as a domestic fuel.

Anthropogenic   Produced by human activities.

Associated Gas   Natural gas found in association with crude oil in a reservoir, either dissolved in the oil or as a cap above the oil.

Autogeneration   Generation of electricity by companies whose main business is not electricity generation, the electricity being produced mainly for that company's own use.

Aviation spirit   A light hydrocarbon oil product used to power piston-engined aircraft power units.

Aviation turbine fuel   The main aviation fuel used for powering aviation gas-turbine power units (jet aircraft engine).

BE   British Energy

Benzole   A colourless liquid, flammable, aromatic hydrocarbon by-product of the iron and steel making process. It is used as a solvent in the manufacture of styrenes and phenols but is also used as a motor fuel.

BETTA   British Electricity Trading and Transmission Arrangements (BETTA) refers to changes to electricity generation, distribution and supply licences. On 1 April 2005, the England and Wales trading arrangements were extended to Scotland by the British Electricity Trading and Transmission Arrangements creating a single GB market for trading of wholesale electricity, with common arrangements for access to and use of GB transmission system. From 1 April 2005, NGC has become the System Operator for the whole of GB. BETTA replaced NETA (see page 213) on 4 April 2005.

Biogas   Energy produced from the anaerobic digestion of sewage and industrial waste.

Bitumen   The residue left after the production of lubricating oil distillates and vacuum gas oil for upgrading plant feedstock. Used mainly for road making and construction purposes.

Blast furnace gas   Mainly produced and consumed within the iron and steel industry. Obtained as a by-product of iron making in a blast furnace, it is recovered on leaving the furnace and used partly within the plant and partly in other steel industry processes or in power plants equipped to burn it. A similar gas is obtained when steel is made in basic oxygen steel converters; this gas is recovered and used in the same way.

Breeze

Breeze can generally be described as coke screened below 19 mm (¾ inch) with no fines removed but the screen size may vary in different areas and to meet the requirements of particular markets.

BG

British Gas

BOS

Basic Oxygen Steel furnace gas

BNFL

British Nuclear Fuels plc.

BRE

Building Research Establishment

Burning oil

A refined petroleum product, with a volatility in between that of motor spirit and gas diesel oil primarily used for heating and lighting.

Butane

Hydrocarbon (C_4H_{10}), gaseous at normal temperature but generally stored and transported as a liquid. Used as a component in Motor Spirit to improve combustion, and for cooking and heating (see LPG).

Calorific values (CVs)

The energy content of a fuel can be measured as the heat released on complete combustion. The SI (Système International - see note below) derived unit of energy and heat is the Joule. This is the energy per unit volume of the fuel and is often measured in GJ per tonne. The energy content can be expressed as an upper (or gross) value and a lower (or net) value. The difference between the two values is due to the release of energy from the condensation of water in the products of combustion. Gross calorific values are used throughout this publication.

CCL

Climate Change Levy

CO_2

Carbon dioxide. Carbon dioxide contributes about 60 per cent of the potential global warming effect of man-made emissions of greenhouse gases. Although this gas is naturally emitted by living organisms, these emissions are offset by the uptake of carbon dioxide by plants during photosynthesis; they therefore tend to have no net effect on atmospheric concentrations. The burning of fossil fuels, however, releases carbon dioxide fixed by plants many millions of years ago, and thus increases its concentration in the atmosphere.

Co-firing

The burning of biomass products in fossil fuel power stations

Coke oven coke

The solid product obtained from carbonisation of coal, principally coking coal, at high temperature, it is low in moisture and volatile matter. Used mainly in iron and steel industry.

Coke oven gas

Gas produced as a by-product of solid fuel carbonisation and gasification at coke ovens, but not from low temperature carbonisation plants. Synthetic coke oven gas is mainly natural gas which is mixed with smaller amounts of blast furnace and basic oxygen steel furnace gas to produce a gas with almost the same quantities as coke oven gas.

Coking coal

Within this publication, coking coal is coal sold by producers for use in coke ovens and similar carbonising processes. The definition is not therefore determined by the calorific value or caking qualities of each batch of coal sold, although calorific values tend to be higher than for steam coal. Not all coals form cokes. For a coal to coke it must exhibit softening and agglomeration properties, ie the end product must be a coherent solid.

Colliery methane	Methane released from coal seams in deep mines which is piped to the surface and consumed at the colliery or transmitted by pipeline to consumers.
Combined cycle gas Turbine (CCGT)	Combined cycle gas turbine power stations combine gas turbines and steam turbines which are connected to one or more electrical generators in the same plant. The gas turbine (usually fuelled by natural gas or oil) produces mechanical power (to drive the generator) and heat in the form of hot exhaust gases. These gases are fed to a boiler, where steam is raised at pressure to drive a conventional steam turbine, which is also connected, to an electrical generator.
Combined Heat and Power (CHP)	CHP is the simultaneous generation of usable heat and power (usually electricity) in a single process. The term CHP is synonymous with cogeneration and total energy, which are terms often used in the United States or other Member States of the European Community. The basic elements of a CHP plant comprise one or more prime movers driving electrical generators, where the steam or hot water generated in the process is utilised via suitable heat recovery equipment for use either in industrial processes, or in community heating and space heating. For further information see Chapter 6 paragraph 6.32.
CHPQA	Combined Heat and Power Quality Assurance Scheme
Conventional thermal power stations	These are stations which generate electricity by burning fossil fuels to produce heat to convert water into steam, which then powers steam turbines.
Cracking/conversion	A refining process using combinations of temperature, pressure and in some cases a catalyst to produce petroleum products by changing the composition of a fraction of petroleum, either by splitting existing longer carbon chain or combining shorter carbon chain components of crude oil or other refinery feedstock's. Cracking allows refiners to selectively increase the yield of specific fractions from any given input petroleum mix depending on their requirements in terms of output products.
Crude oil	A mineral oil consisting of a mixture of hydrocarbons of natural origins, yellow to black in colour, of variable density and viscosity.
DEFRA	Department for Environment, Food and Rural Affairs
DERV	Diesel engined road vehicle fuel used in internal combustion engines that are compression-ignited (see gas diesel oil).
DFT	Department for Transport
Distillation	A process of separation of the various components of crude oil and refinery feedstocks using the different temperatures of evaporation and condensation of the different components of the mix received at the refineries.
DNC	Declared net capacity and capability are used to measure the maximum power available from generating stations at a point in time. See Chapter 5 paragraphs 5.54 and 5.55 and Chapter 7 paragraph 7.75 for a fuller definition.
DNO	Distribution Network Operator
Downstream	Used in oil and gas processes to cover the part of the industry after the production of the oil and gas. For example, it covers refining, supply and trading, marketing and exporting.

DUKES	Digest of United Kingdom Energy Statistics, the Digest provides essential information for everyone, from economists to environmentalists and from energy suppliers to energy users.
ECA	Enhanced Capital Allowances
EHCS	English House Condition Survey
Embedded Generation	Embedded generation is electricity generation by plant which has been connected to the distribution networks of the public electricity distributors rather than directly to the National Grid Company's transmission systems. Typically they are either smaller stations located on industrial sites, or combined heat and power plant, or renewable energy plant such as wind farms, or refuse burner generators. The category also includes some domestic generators such as those with electric solar panels. For a description of the current structure of the electricity industry in the UK see Chapter 5 paragraphs 5.3 to 5.8.
Energy use	Energy use of fuel mainly comprises use for lighting, heating or cooling, motive power and power for appliances. See also non-energy use.
ESA	European System of National and Regional Accounts. An integrated system of economic accounts which is the European version of the System of National Accounts (SNA).
EESs	The Energy Efficiency Commitment (formerly known as Energy Efficiency Standards of Performance) is an obligation placed on all energy suppliers to offer help and advice to their customers to improve the energy efficiency of their homes.
Ethane	A light hydrocarbon gas (C_2H_6) in natural gas and refinery gas streams (see LPG).
EU-ETS	European Union Emissions Trading Scheme. This began on 1st January 2005 and involves the trading of emissions allowances as means of reducing emissions by a fixed amount.
EUROSTAT	Statistical Office of the European Communities (SOEC).
Exports	For some parts of the energy industry, statistics on trade in energy related products can be derived from two separate sources. Firstly, figures can be reported by companies as part of systems for collecting data on specific parts of the energy industry (eg as part of the system for recording the production and disposals of oil from the UK continental shelf). Secondly, figures are also available from the general systems that exist for monitoring trade in all types of products operated by HM Revenue and Customs.
FES	Future Energy Solutions, part of the company AEA Technology Environment (AEAT)
Feedstock	In the refining industry, a product or a combination of products derived from crude oil, destined for further processing other than blending. It is distinguished from use as a chemical feedstock etc. See non-energy use.
Final energy consumption	Energy consumption by final user – ie which is not being used for transformation into other forms of energy.

Fossil fuels	Coal, natural gas and fuels derived from crude oil (for example petrol and diesel) are called fossil fuels because they have been formed over long periods of time from ancient organic matter.
Fuel oils	The heavy oils from the refining process; used as fuel in furnaces and boilers of power stations, industry, in domestic and industrial heating, ships, locomotives, metallurgic operations, and industrial power plants etc.
Fuel oil - Light	Fuel oil made up of heavier straight-run or cracked distillates and used in commercial or industrial burner installations not equipped with pre-heating facilities.
Fuel oil - Medium	Other fuel oils, sometimes referred to as bunker fuels, which generally require pre-heating before being burned, but in certain climatic conditions do not require pre-heating.
Fuel oil - Heavy	Other heavier grade fuel oils which in all situations require some form of pre-heating before being burned.
Fuel poverty	The common definition of a fuel poor household is one needing to spend in excess of 10 per cent of household income to achieve a satisfactory heating regime (21°C in the living room and 18°C in the other occupied rooms).
Gas Diesel Oil	The medium oil from the refinery process; used as a fuel in diesel engines (ie internal combustion engines that are compression-ignited), burned in central heating systems and used as a feedstock for the chemical industry.
GDP	Gross Domestic Product.
GDP deflator	An index of the ratio of GDP at current prices to GDP at constant prices. It provides a measure of general price inflation within the whole economy.
Gigajoule (GJ)	A unit of energy equal to 10^9 joules (see note on joules below).
Gigawatt (GW)	A unit of electrical power, equal to 10^9 watts.
Heat sold	Heat (or steam) that is produced and sold under the provision of a contract. Heat sold is derived from heat generated by Combined Heat and Power (CHP) plants and from community heating schemes without CHP plants.
HMRC	HM Revenue and Customs.
Imports	See the first paragraph of the entry for exports above. Before the 1997 edition of the Digest, the term "arrivals" was used to distinguish figures derived from the former source from those import figures derived from the systems operated by HM Revenue and Customs. To make it clearer for users, a single term is now being used for both these sources of figures (the term imports) as this more clearly states what the figures relate to, which is goods entering the UK.
International Energy Agency (IEA)	The IEA is an autonomous body located in Paris which was established in November 1974 within the framework of the Organisation for Economic Co-operation and Development (OECD) to implement an international energy programme.

Indigenous production	For oil this includes production from the UK Continental Shelf both onshore and offshore.
Industrial spirit	Refined petroleum fractions with boiling ranges up to 200ºC dependent on the use to which they are put – eg seed extraction, rubber solvents, perfume etc.
ISSB	Iron and Steel Statistics Bureau
ITF	Industry Technology Facilitator
Joules	A joule is a generic unit of energy in the conventional SI system (see note on SI below). It is equal to the energy dissipated by an electrical current of 1 ampere driven by 1 volt for 1 second; it is also equal to twice the energy of motion in a mass of 1 kilogram moving at 1 metre per second.
Kilowatt (kW)	1,000 watts
Landfill gas	The methane-rich biogas formed from the decomposition of organic material in landfill.
LDF	Light distillate feedstock
LDZ	Local distribution zone
Liquefied petroleum Gas (LPG)	Gas usually propane or butane, derived from oil and put under pressure so that it is in liquid form. Often used to power portable cooking stoves or heaters and to fuel some types of vehicle, eg some specially adapted road vehicles, forklift trucks.
Lead Replacement Petrol (LRP)	An alternative to Leaded Petrol containing a different additive to lead (in the UK usually potassium based) to perform the lubrication functions of lead additives in reducing engine wear.
Lubricating oils	Refined heavy distillates obtained from the vacuum distillation of petroleum residues. Includes liquid and solid hydrocarbons sold by the lubricating oil trade, either alone or blended with fixed oils, metallic soaps and other organic and/or inorganic bodies.
Magnox	A type of gas-cooled nuclear fission reactor developed in the UK, so called because of the magnesium alloy used to clad the uranium fuel.
Major power producers	Companies whose prime purpose is the generation of electricity (paragraph 5.50 of Chapter 5 gives a full list of major power producers).
Megawatt (MW)	1,000 kilowatts. MWe is used to emphasise when electricity is being measured. MWt is used when heat ("thermal") is being measured.
Micro CHP	Micro CHP is a new technology that is expected to make a significant contribution to domestic energy efficiency in the future.
MMC	Monopolies and Mergers Commission
Motor spirit	Blended light petroleum product used as a fuel in spark-ignition internal combustion engines (other than aircraft engines).
NAEI	National Atmospheric Emmissions Inventory

National Allocation Plan (NAP)	Under the EU Emissions Trading Scheme (EU-ETS) Directive each EU country must have a National Allocation Plan which lays down the overall contribution of the EU-ETS participants (the "cap") for the country and the allowances that each sector and each individual installation covered under the Directive is allocate, effectively stating how much that sector can emit over the trading period of the scheme
Naphtha	(Light distillate feedstock) – Petroleum distillate boiling predominantly below 200ºC.
Natural gas	Natural gas is a mixture of naturally occurring gases found either in isolation, or associated with crude oil, in underground reservoirs. The main component is methane; ethane, propane, butane, hydrogen sulphide and carbon dioxide may also be present, but these are mostly removed at or near the well head in gas processing plants.
Natural gas - compressed	Natural gas that has been compressed to reduce the volume it occupies to make it easier to transport other than in pipelines. Whilst other petroleum gases can be compressed such that they move into liquid form, the volatility of natural gas is such that liquefaction cannot be achieved without very high pressures and low temperatures being used. As such, the compressed form is usually used as a "half-way house".
Natural gas liquids (NGLs)	A mixture of liquids derived from natural gas and crude oil during the production process, including propane, butane, ethane and gasoline components (pentanes plus).
NDA	Nuclear Decommissioning Authority
NETA	New Electricity Trading Arrangements - In England and Wales these arrangements replaced "the pool" from 27 March 2001. The arrangements are based on bi-lateral trading between generators, suppliers, traders and customers and are designed to be more efficient, and provide more market choice.
NETCEN	National EnvironmentTechnology Centre
NIE	Northern Ireland Electricity
NI NFFO	Northern Ireland Non Fossil Fuel Obligation
Non-energy use	Includes fuel used for chemical feedstock, solvents, lubricants, and road making material.
NFFO	Non Fossil Fuel Obligation. The 1989 Electricity Act empowers the Secretary of State to make orders requiring the Regional Electricity Companies in England and Wales to secure specified amounts of electricity from renewable sources.
NFPA	Non Fossil Purchasing Agency
NO$_x$	Nitrogen oxides. A number of nitrogen compounds including nitrogen dioxide are formed in combustion processes when nitrogen in the air or the fuel combines with oxygen. These compounds can add to the natural acidity of rainfall.
NSCP	National Statistics Code of Practice
NUTS	Nonmenclature of Units for Territorial Statistics

OFGEM	The regulatory office for gas and electricity markets
OFT	Office of Fair Trading
Orimulsion	An emulsion of bitumen in water that can be used as a fuel in some power stations.
ONS	Office for National Statistics
OTS	Overseas Trade Statistics of the United Kingdom
OXERA	Oxford Economic Research Association Ltd
Patent fuel	A composition fuel manufactured from coal fines by shaping with the addition of a binding agent (typically pitch). The term manufactured solid fuel is also used.
Petrochemical feedstock	All petroleum products intended for use in the manufacture of petroleum chemicals. This includes middle distillate feedstock of which there are several grades depending on viscosity. The boiling point ranges between 200°C and 400°C.
Petroleum cokes	Carbonaceous material derived from hydrocarbon oils, uses for which include metallurgical electrode manufacture and in the manufacture of cement.
PILOT	Phase 2 (PILOT) is the successor body to the Oil & Gas Industry Task Force (OGTIF) and was established on 1 January 2000, to secure the long-term future of the oil and gas industry in the UK. A forum that brings together Government and industry to address the challenges facing the oil and gas industry. One outcome of PILOT's work is the published Code of Practice on Supply Chain Relationships.
Photovoltaics	The direct conversion of solar radiation into electricity by the interaction of light with the electrons in a semiconductor device or cell.
Plant capacity	The maximum power available from a power station at a point in time (see also Chapter 5 paragraph 5.54).
Plant loads, demands and efficiency	Measures of how intensively and efficiently power stations are being used. These terms are defined in Chapter 5 paragraphs 5.56 and 5.57
PPRS	Petroleum production reporting system. Licensees operating in the UK Continental Shelf are required to make monthly returns on their production of hydrocarbons (oil and gas) to the DTI. This information is recorded in the PPRS, which is used to report flows, stocks and uses of hydrocarbon from the well-head through to final disposal from a pipeline or terminal (see paragraphs F.29 to F.31 of Annex F on DTI's energy statistics web site).
Process oils	Partially processed feedstocks which require further processing before being classified as a finished product suitable for sale. They can also be used as a reaction medium in the production process.
Primary fuels	Fuels obtained directly from natural sources, eg coal, oil and natural gas.
Primary electricity	Electricity obtained other than from fossil fuel sources, eg nuclear, hydro and other non-thermal renewables. Imports of electricity are also included.

Propane	Hydrocarbon containing three carbon atoms (C_3H_8), gaseous at normal temperature, but generally stored and transported under pressure as a liquid.
PWR	Pressurised water reactor. A nuclear fission reactor cooled by ordinary water kept from boiling by containment under high pressure.
Reforming	Processes by which the molecular structure of different fractions of petroleum can be modified. It usually involves some form of catalyst, most often platinum, and allows the conversion of lower grades of petroleum product into higher grades, improving their octane rating. It is a generic term for processes such as cracking, cyclization, dehydrogenation and isomerisation. These processes generally led to the production of hydrogen as a by-product, which can be used in the refineries in some desulphurization procedures.
Refinery fuel	Petroleum products produced by the refining process that are used as fuel at refineries.
Renewable energy sources	Renewable energy includes solar power, wind, wave and tide, and hydroelectricity. Solid renewable energy sources consist of wood, straw, short rotation coppice, other biomass and the biodegradable fraction of wastes. Gaseous renewables consist of landfill gas and sewage gas. Non-biodegradable wastes are not counted as a renewables source but appear in the Renewable sources of energy chapter of this Digest for completeness.
Reserves	With oil and gas these relate to the quantities identified as being present in underground cavities. The actual amounts that can be recovered depend on the level of technology available and existing economic situations. These continually change; hence the level of the UK's reserves can change quite independently of whether or not new reserves have been identified.
RESTATS	The Renewable Energy Statistics System
RO	Renewables Obligation
ROC	Renewables Obligation Certificates
SEPN	Sustainable Energy Policy Network represents the body of people responsible for delivering the white paper directly or indirectly through having links to business and other organidsations nationally and regionally.
SI (Système International)	Refers to the agreed conventions for the measurement of physical quantities.
SIC	Standard Industrial Classification in the UK. Last revised in 2003 and known as SIC(2003), replaced previous classifications SIC(92), SIC(80) and SIC(68). SIC(92) was compatible with European Union classification NACE Rev1 (Nomenclature générale des activités économiques dans les Communautés européennes as revised in October 1990) and similarly SIC(2003) is consistent with NACE Rev1.1 which came into effect in January 2003. Classification systems need to be periodically revised because over time new products, processes and industries emerge.
Secondary fuels	Fuels derived from natural primary sources of energy. For example electricity generated from burning coal, gas or oil is a secondary fuel, as are coke and coke oven gas.

Steam coal	Within this publication, steam coal is coal classified as such by UK coal producers and by importers of coal. It tends to be coal having lower calorific values; the type of coal that is typically used for steam raising.
SO_2	Sulphur Dioxide. Sulphur dioxide is a gas produced by the combustion of sulphur-containing fuels such as coal and oil.
SOEC	Statistical Office of the European Communities
SRO	Scottish Renewable Orders
Synthetic coke oven gas	Mainly a natural gas, which is mixed with smaller amounts of blast furnace, and BOS (basic oxygen steel furnace) gas to produce a gas with almost the same quantities as coke oven gas.
Temperature correction	The temperature corrected series of total inland fuel consumption indicates what annual consumption might have been if the average temperature during the year had been the same as the average for the years 1961 to 1990.
Terawatt (TW)	1,000 gigawatts
TWh	Terawatt Hour
Thermal Sources of Electricity	These include coal, oil, natural gas, nuclear, landfill gas, sewage gas, municipal solid waste, farm waste, tyres, poultry litter, short rotation coppice, straw, coke oven gas, blast furnace gas, and waste products from chemical processes.
Tonne of oil equivalent (toe)	A common unit of measurement which enables different fuels to be compared and aggregated. (See Chapter 1 paragraphs 1.24 to 1.25 for further information and Annex A page 203 for conversion factors).
Tars	Viscous materials usually derived from the destructive distillation of coal which are by-products of the coke and iron making processes.
Therm	A common unit of measurement similar to a tonne of oil equivalent which enables different fuels to be compared and aggregated. (see Annex A).
Thermal efficiency	The thermal efficiency of a power station is the efficiency with which heat energy contained in fuel is converted into electrical energy. It is calculated for fossil fuel burning stations by expressing electricity generated as a percentage of the total energy content of the fuel consumed (based on average gross calorific values). For nuclear stations it is calculated using the quantity of heat released as a result of fission of the nuclear fuel inside the reactor.
UKCS	United Kingdom Continental Shelf
UKOOA	United Kingdom Ofshore Operators Association
UKPIA	UK Petroleum Industry Association. The trade association for the UK petroleum industry.
Ultra low sulphur Diesel (ULSD)	A grade of diesel fuel which has a much lower sulphur content (less than 0.005 per cent or 50 parts per million) and of a slightly higher volatility than ordinary diesel fuels. As a result it produces fewer emissions when burned. As such it enjoys a lower rate of excise duty in the UK than ordinary diesel (by 3 pence per litre) to promote its use. Virtually 100 per cent of sales of DERV fuel in the UK are ULSD.

Ultra low sulphur Petrol (ULSP)	A grade of motor spirit with a similar level of sulphur to ULSD (less than 0.005 per cent or 50 parts per million). In the March 2000 Budget it was announced that a lower rate of excise duty than ordinary petrol for this fuel would be introduced during 2000, which was increased to 3 pence per litre in the March 2001 Budget. It has quickly replaced ordinary premium grade unleaded petrol in the UK market place.
Upstream	A term to cover the activities related to the exploration, production and delivery to a terminal or other facility of oil or gas for export or onward shipment within the UK.
USBS	United States Bureau of Standards refers to legislation that sets minimum safety standards in the coal market and mining industry.
VAT	Value added tax
Watt (W)	The conventional unit to measure a rate of flow of energy. One watt amounts to 1 joule per second.
White spirit	A highly refined distillate with a boiling range of about 150ºC to 200ºC used as a paint solvent and for dry cleaning purposes etc.

Annex C
Further sources of United Kingdom energy publications

Some of the publications listed below give shorter term statistics, some provide further information about energy production and consumption in the United Kingdom and in other countries, and others provide more detail on a country or fuel industry basis. The list also covers recent publications on energy issues and policy, including statistical information, produced or commissioned by the DTI. The list is not exhaustive and the titles of publications and publishers may alter. Unless otherwise stated, all titles are available from

DTI Publications Orderline
Web: http://www.dti.gov.uk/publications
Phone: 0845 015 0010
Address: ADMAIL, 528, London, SW1W 0YT
Email: publications@dti.gsi.gov.uk

and can also be found on the DTI Web site at www.dti.gov.uk/energy/.

Department of Trade and Industry publications on energy

Energy Statistics
Monthly, quarterly and annual statistics on production and consumption of overall energy and individual fuels in the United Kingdom together with energy prices is available in MS Excel format on the Internet at http://www.dti.gov.uk/energy/statistics/source/index.html.

Energy Trends
A quarterly publication covering all major aspects of energy. It provides a comprehensive picture of energy production and use and contains analysis of data and articles covering energy issues. Available on subscription, with Quarterly Energy Prices. Annual subscriptions run from June to March and are available at £40 to UK subscribers from Amey Plc, 7th Floor, Clarence House, Clarence Place, Newport, Wales NP19 7AA, Tel. 01633 224712. A subscription form is available at:
http://www.dti.gov.uk/energy/statistics/publications/trends/index.html
An electronic version of the latest four editions can be found at the same address. Single copies are available from the DTI Publications Orderline priced at £6.

Quarterly Energy Prices
A quarterly publication from June 2001, replaced energy prices information formerly available in the monthly publication Energy Trends and the annual Digest of UK Energy Statistics. Contains tables, charts and commentary covering energy prices to domestic and industrial consumers for all the major fuels as well as presenting comparisons of fuel prices in the European Union and G7 countries. It is available on the web site at: http://www.dti.gov.uk/energy/statistics/publications/prices/index.html
Available on subscription, with Energy Trends, (details given above). Single copies are available from the DTI Publications Orderline priced at £8.

Energy Sector Indicators 2006
Energy Sector Indicators for 2006 were published in June 2006 as a supplement to the Third Annual Report on the Energy White Paper (see below). The content is designed to show the extent to which secure, diverse and sustainable supplies of energy to UK Businesses and consumers at competitive prices are ensured. This year, only the four key indicators used in the Report, and 28 supporting indicators have been published in print, but the full range of background indicators have been updated and are available on the internet. The printed section of Energy Sector Indicators 2006 is available at the same address: http://www.dti.gov.uk/energy/statistics/publications/indicators/page29741.html
and in hard copy (free of charge) from DTI Publications Orderline.

UK Energy in Brief 2006

This booklet summarises the latest statistics on energy production, consumption and prices in the United Kingdom. The figures are taken from "Digest of UK Energy Statistics". Available free from ESU-SID2, Department of Trade and Industry, Bay 209, 1 Victoria Street, London, SW1H 0ET, tel. 020-7215 2697/2698 and from the DTI Publications Orderline. It is also available on the web site at: http://www.dti.gov.uk/energy/statistics/publications/in-brief/page17222.html

Our Energy Challenge: Securing Clean, Affordable Energy for the Long Term

This booklet summarises the key issues that are being discussed in the Energy Review, completed in June 2006. It explores the options and challenges in the years ahead. It was published as part of a consultation period during which DTI sought views on the measures that are needed by 2020 and beyond to tackle climate change, and ensure secure and affordable energy supplies in the UK. Our Energy Challenge is available on the DTI web site at: http://www.dti.gov.uk/energy/review/index.html

Development of the Oil and Gas Resources of the United Kingdom

Publication of Development of UK Oil and Gas Resources, commonly known as the "Brown Book", ended with the 2001 edition. That edition, as well as more up-to-date information on the UK offshore industry, is available via DTI's Oil and Gas web site: www.og.dti.gov.uk .

Industrial Energy Markets: Energy markets in UK manufacturing industry 1973 to 1993 - Energy Paper 64

Using tables of data drawn from the 1989 Purchases Inquiry conducted by the Office for National Statistics, the report, which updates one produced in 1989, sets out the implications for the trends in industrial energy consumption over the period from 1973 to 1993. Available from The Stationery Office, tel 0870 600 5522 and can be ordered through Government Bookshops. Not available on the Internet.

Energy Consumption in the UK

Energy Consumption in the United Kingdom brings together statistics from a variety of sources to produce a comprehensive review of energy consumption in the UK since the 1970s. This booklet describes the key trends in energy consumption in the UK since 1970 with a particular focus on trends since 1990. The information is presented in five sections covering firstly overall energy consumption, then energy consumption in the transport, domestic, industrial and service sectors. It includes an analysis of the factors driving the changes in energy consumption, the impact of increasing activity, increased efficiency, and structural change in the economy, while detailed tables can be found on the Internet at: http://www.dti.gov.uk/energy/statistics/publications/energy-consumption/page17658.html

UK Energy and CO2 emissions projection: updated projections to 2020

This paper provides key information on updated energy and emission projections. The projections represent key underpinning analysis for the government's review of the Climate Change Programme. The projections will also feed into decision making on allocations for the second phase of the EU ETS. The 69 page document illustrates the historic and projected trends in final energy demand and carbon intensity and the impact of the current Climate Change Programme measures. The report includes assessments of outputs from the UK's energy supply industries and of fuel mix within the electricity generating sector. The report is to be found at:
http://www.dti.gov.uk/files/file26363.pdf

Social Effects of Energy Liberalisation: The UK Experience

This paper reviews the impact of liberalisation of the energy markets, and the effects on the fuel industries, the consumer and the environment. Available free from ESU-SID2, Department of Trade and Industry, Bay 209, 1 Victoria Street, London, SW1H 0ET, tel. 020 7215 2697/2698.

Energy Liberalisation Indicators in Europe: A preliminary report of a study carried out by OXERA for the Governments of the UK and the Netherlands.

This paper presents preliminary results from a study carried out by OXERA on behalf of the Governments of the UK and the Netherlands. The study develops a set of indicators, within a hierarchical structure, for monitoring the development of competition in gas and electricity markets across Europe. The study mainly concentrates on the electricity market and presents some preliminary results for a subset of European countries including the UK and Netherlands. Available free from ESU-SID2, Department of Trade and Industry, Bay 209, 1 Victoria Street, London, SW1H 0ET, tel. 020 7215 2697/2698.

Energy Liberalisation Indicators in Europe: A consultation paper based on a study carried out by OXERA for the Governments of the UK and the Netherlands.

This consultation paper sets out the methodology used and presents results for a subset of European countries including the UK and the Netherlands. Available free from ESU-SID2, Department of Trade and Industry, Bay 209, 1 Victoria Street, London SW1H 0ET, tel. 020 7215 2697/2698.

Social, Environmental and Security of Supply Policies in a Competitive Energy Market: A Review of Delivery Mechanisms in the United Kingdom, Summary Paper

This paper outlines the UK experience so far in using competitive energy markets to deliver social, environmental and security of supply policies. It highlights the benefits that have emerged from this approach and sets out the instruments the Government has used to enhance policy delivery. Available free from ESU-SID2, Department of Trade and Industry, Bay 209, 1 Victoria Street, London, SW1H 0ET, tel. 020 7215 2697/2698.

The UK Fuel Poverty Strategy: November 2001

Produced by the Department of Trade and Industry and the Department for Environment, Food and Rural Affairs (Defra). The strategy sets out the Government's objectives, policies and targets for alleviating fuel poverty in the UK over the next 10 years. Available free from Department of Trade and Industry Publications Orderline and on the web site at: http://www.dti.gov.uk/files/file16495.pdf

The UK Fuel Poverty Strategy: 4th Annual Report 2006

Produced by Defra and the Department of Trade and Industry in association with the Devolved Administrations. This report sets out the progress that has been made on tackling fuel poverty and is available on the DTI web site at http://www.dti.gov.uk/files/file29688.pdf or free from DTI Publications Orderline.
It is accompanied by detailed annexes also published on the DTI web site at:
http://www.dti.gov.uk/energy/fuel-poverty/strategy/index.html

Energy – Its impact on the environment and society

In 2005 DTI published this booklet outlining the environmental and social impacts of energy production and use and covering similar ground to the previous version published in 2002. An updated web-based version will be available on the DTI energy web site from August 2006 at http://www.dti.gov.uk/energy/environment/energy-impact/page20248.html . It sets out the key social and environmental consequences of the production and use of energy and shows through figures and charts, where we have come from, where we are now, what the policy challenges are, and what the current responses are. The 2005 booklet is available free from ESU-SID2, Department of Trade and Industry, Bay 209, 1 Victoria Street, London SW1H 0ET, tel. 020-7215 2697/2698 and from the DTI Publications Orderline.

Energy White Paper, 3rd Annual Report

The Government's Energy White Paper, "Our energy future - creating a low carbon economy", was published by the Secretary of State for Trade and Industry on 24 February 2003. The report addresses the challenges facing energy, by setting out a long-term strategic vision for energy policy. It is the product of extensive consultative and analytical work and has over 6,500 contributions. The White Paper is available on the DTI web site at
http://www.dti.gov.uk/energy/policy-strategy/energy-white-paper/page21223.html and in hard copy from The Stationery Office or through Government Bookshops.
The 3rd Annual Report was due to be published in July 2006 and will be available at:
http://www.dti.gov.uk/energy/policy-strategy/energy-white-paper/page21223.html

Other publications including energy information

General
Basic Statistics of the Community (annual); *Statistical Office of the European Communities - Statistical Office of the European Communities - Eurostat*
Digest of Welsh Statistics (annual); *Welsh Assemly Government*
Eurostatistics - Data for Short Term Analysis; *Statistical Office of the European Communities - Eurostat*
Monthly Digest of Statistics; *Office for National Statistics*
Northern Ireland Annual Abstract of Statistics (annual); *Department of Finance and Personnel,* (available from the Policy & Planning Unit, Department of Finance & Personnel, Stormont, Belfast BT4 3SW)
Overseas Trade Statistics of the United Kingdom; *H.M. Revenue and Customs*
- Business Monitor MM20 (monthly) (extra-EU trade only)
- Business Monitor MM20A (monthly) (intra and extraEU
- trade data, relatively limited level of production detail)
- Business Monitor MQ20 (quarterly) (intra-EU trade only)
- Business Monitor MA20 (annual) (intra- and extra-EU trade);

Purchases Inquiry 1989, 1994-1998; *Office for National Statistics*
Rapid Reports - energy and industry (ad hoc); *Statistical Office of the European Communities - Eurostat*
Regional Trends (annual); *Office for National Statistics*
High Level Summary of Statistics: Key Trends for Scotland; *Scottish Executive*
United Kingdom Minerals Yearbook (annual); *British Geological Survey* (available from the British Geological Survey, Keyworth, Nottingham, NG12 5GG)
Yearbook of Regional Statistics (annual); *Statistical Office of the European Communities - Eurostat*

Energy
Annual Bulletin of General Energy Statistics for Europe; *United Nations Economic Commission for Europe*
BP Statistical Review of World Energy (annual); (available from The Editor, BP Statistical Review, The British Petroleum Company plc, Corporate Communications Services, Britannic House, 1 Finsbury Circus, London EC2M 7BA)
Energy - Monthly Statistics; *Statistical Office of the European Communities - Eurostat*
Energy Balances of OECD Countries (annual); *OECD International Energy Agency*
Energy Statistics and Balances of OECD Countries (annual); *OECD International Energy Agency*
Energy Statistics and Balances of Non-OECD Countries (annual); *OECD International Energy Agency*

Energy - Yearly Statistics; *Statistical Office of the European Communities - Eurostat*
UN Energy Statistics Yearbook (annual); *United Nations Statistical Office*

Coal
Annual Bulletin of Coal Statistics for Europe; *United Nations Economic Commission for Europe*
Annual Reports and Accounts of The Coal Authority and the private coal companies; (*apply to the Headquarters of the company concerned)*
Coal Information (annual); *OECD International Energy Agency*

Oil and gas
Annual Bulletin of Gas Statistics for Europe; *United Nations Economic Commission for Europe*
BP Review of World Gas (annual); (*available from British Petroleum Company plc, Corporate Communications Services, Britannic House, 1 Finsbury Circus, London EC2M 7BA)*
Annual Reports and Accounts of National Grid, Centrica and other independent gas supply companies; (contact *the Headquarters of the company concerned directly)*
Oil and Gas Information (annual); *OECD International Energy Agency*
Quarterly Oil Statistics and Energy Balances; *OECD International Energy Agency*
UK Petroleum Industry Statistics Consumption and Refinery Production (annual and quarterly); *Institute of Petroleum (available from IP, 61 New Cavendish Street, London W1M 8AR)*

Electricity

Annual Bulletin of Electric Energy Statistics for Europe; *United Nations Economic Commission for Europe*

Annual Reports and Accounts of the Electricity Supply Companies, Distributed Companies and Generators; (*apply to the Headquarters of the company concerned*)

Annual Report of the Office of Electricity Regulation; OFGEM

Electricity Supply in OECD Countries; *OECD International Energy Agency*

National Grid - Seven Year Statement - (annual) *National Grid - For further details telephone 01203 423065*

Operation of Nuclear Power Stations (annual); *Statistical Office of the European Communities*

Electricity Information (annual); *OECD International Energy Agency*

Prices

Energy Prices (annual); *Statistical Office of the European Communities* (summarises price information published in the European Commissions Weekly Oil Price, and half-yearly Statistics in Focus on Gas Prices and Electricity Prices)

Energy Prices and Taxes (quarterly); *OECD International Energy Agency*

Electricity prices (annual); *Statistical Office of the European Communities - Eurostat*

Gas prices (annual); *Statistical Office of the European Communities - Eurostat*

Environment

Digest of Environmental Statistics (Annual); *Department for Environment, Food and Rural Affairs (Defra).*

Indicators of Sustainable Development for the United Kingdom; *Department for Environment, Food and Rural Affairs (Defra)*

Quality of life counts, Indicators for a strategy for sustainable development for the United Kingdom: a baseline assessment; *Department for Environment, Food and Rural Affairs (Defra)*

Environment Statistics (annual); *Statistical Office of the European Communities - Eurostat*

UK Environment (adhoc/one-off release); *Department for Environment, Food and Rural Affairs (Defra)*

Renewables

New and Renewable Energy, Prospects for the 21st Century. A series of consultation papers reports on the outcome of the review conducted by the Government and the possible ways forward in implementing the Government's new drive for renewables. Available on the DTI web site and via the DTI Publications Orderline, publications@dti.gsi.gov.uk

Useful energy related web sites

The DTI web site can be found at www.dti.gov.uk, the energy information and statistics web site is at www.dti.gov.uk/energy/statistics/index.html

Other Government web sites

Central Office of Information	www.coi.gov.uk
HM Revenue and Customs	www.hmrc.gov.uk
Department for Environment, Food and Rural Affairs	www.defra.gov.uk
HM Government Online	www.direct.gov.uk/
Department for Transport	www.dft.gov.uk
National Statistics	www.statistics.gov.uk
Northern Ireland Departments	www.northernireland.gov.uk
Department for Communities and Local Government.	www.communities.gov.uk
Ofgem (The Office of Gas and Electricity Markets)	www.ofgem.gov.uk
Scottish Executive	www.scotland.gov.uk
The Scottish Parliament	www.scottish.parliament.uk
National Assembly for Wales	www.wales.gov.uk
UK Parliament	www.parliament.uk

Other useful energy related web sites

Air Quality Archive	www.airquality.co.uk
Association of Electricity Producers	www.aepuk.com
BP	www.bp.com/home.do
British Wind Energy Association	www.bwea.com
Building Research Establishment	www.bre.co.uk
Coal Authority	www.coal.gov.uk/
Energywatch	www.energywatch.org.uk/
Energy Institute	www.energyinst.org.uk
Energy Networks Association	www.energynetworks.org
Environmental Industries Sector Unit	www.eisu.org.uk
Europa (European Union Online)	http://europa.eu
Eurostat	http://epp.eurostat.cec.eu.int/
Future Energy Solutions	www.future-energy-solutions.com
Interconnector (UK) Ltd	www.interconnector.com
International Energy Agency	www.iea.org
Iron and Steel Statistics Bureau	www.issb.co.uk
National Grid	www.nationalgrid.com
NETCEN (National Environmental Technology Centre)	www.netcen.co.uk
The Stationery Office	www.tso.co.uk/
UKOOA (UK Offshore Operators Association)	www.ukooa.co.uk
UK Petroleum Industry Association	www.ukpia.com
United Nations Statistics Division	http://unstats.un.org/unsd/default.htm
US Department of Energy	www.energy.gov
US Energy Information Administration	www.eia.doe.gov

Annex D
Major events in the Energy Industry

2006

Sustainable Energy Policy

On 16th February 2006 the Government issued a consultation paper on carbon dioxide emissions projections for industrial sectors covered by the EU Emissions Trading Scheme. These projections are being used as an input to the development of the UK National Allocation Plan for Phase II of the scheme, informing the allocation of carbon dioxide allowances to installations in the 2008-12 period. The consultation closes on April 13th.

The Third Annual Report to the Energy White Paper was published in May 2006, reviewing progress made over the last 12 months towards the targets and strategy for energy policy until 2050. Published as a supplement to the Third Annual Report, Energy Sector Indicators 2006 was also published in May 2006.

Energy Review

The 12 week consultation period for the energy review ended on the 12 April 2006 with over 2000 responses from individuals, businesses, academics and NGOs. A summary of the responses will be published within three months of the end of the consultation period.

Climate Change

An ambitious programme to tackle climate change domestically and to secure agreement on action to reduce global greenhouse gas emissions was published by the Government on 28 March 2006. The Programme is expected to reduce the UK's emissions of greenhouse gases to 23-25 per cent below base year levels and reduce the UK's carbon dioxide emissions to 15-18 per cent below 1990 levels by 2010.

Fuel Poverty

The Government published its UK Fuel Poverty Strategy Fourth Annual Report in June 2006, reporting on the progress made since the last year's report, and setting out the fuel poverty figures for 2004. Also published were a series of annexes, setting out the detailed profile of the fuel poor, as well as outlining the many activities in which energy companies are involved to tackle fuel poverty and associated problems. In the report, we also responded to the recommendations made by The Fuel Poverty Advisory Group in its Third Annual Report, which was published in March 2006. The new Home Heat Helpline operated by the Energy Retail Association has been up and running since October 2005.

Emissions Trading

On 21st March 2006 the Government published 15 (independently produced) reports reviewing and revising methodologies for calculating the New Entrants' benchmarks for sectors covered by Phase II of the EU – Emission Trading Scheme. The benchmarks will form the basis for the calculation of New Entrant allocations of carbon dioxide allowances to installations in the 2008-2012 period and will therefore form an important part of the development of the UK National Allocation Plan for Phase II of the EU – Emissions Trading Scheme

The draft Phase II National Allocation Plan was published for consultation, alongside the Climate Change Programme Review, on 28 March. The number of CO2 allowances for Phase II will be set within a range representing a reduction of 3 to 8 MtC a year against projected business as usual emissions. The final decision on this should be made in June. The NAP also incorporate proposals on scope (some new sectors added in); allocation methodology; sector classification and new entrant policy.

Coal
UK Coal's Rossington colliery closed on 31 March 2006.

Oil and Gas
The UK is expected to be a net importer of oil and oil products in 2006, returning to being a net exporter in 2007 as a result of the very large Buzzard field that is due to commence production in the fourth quarter of 2006.

Electricity
Centrica announced in June 2006 that it would construct an 885 MW CCGT power station at Langage, Plymouth which is expected to be operational by 2008.

Renewables
The Renewables Obligation Order 2006 has been laid before Parliament. It will come into force on 1 April 2006.

A recent Carbon Trust report has concluded that wave and tidal could in time provide up to a fifth of UK's energy needs.

2005

Energy Review
On 29 November 2005 The Prime Minister and Secretary of State for Trade and Industry Alan Johnson announced that asked Energy Minister Malcolm Wicks to lead a review of UK energy policy. The main scope of the review will include aspects of both energy supply and demand and will focus on policy measures to help us deliver our objectives beyond 2010. The Review will aim to ensure the UK is on track to meet the goals of the 2003 Energy White Paper in the medium and long term.

Sustainable Energy Policy
The Energy White Paper published in February 2003 set out the strategy for energy policy until 2050. A second annual report reviewing progress over the last 12 months and the way ahead is to be published in July 2005. Energy Sector Indicators for 2005 was also to be published in July 2005 as a supplement to the Second Annual Report on the Energy White Paper.

Fuel Poverty
The Fuel Poverty Advisory Group published its Third Annual Report. Whilst welcoming progress made, as well as the enhancements to the Warm Front. Energy Ministers held a follow up event with the energy supply companies with a proposal to set up a new helpline; a central point of contact for fuel poverty referrals, developed by the energy companies.

Emissions Trading
The EU Emissions trading scheme (ETS) commenced on 1 January. It is one of the policies being introduced across Europe to tackle emissions of carbon dioxide and other greenhouse gases and combat the serious threat of climate change. The first phase runs from 2005-2007 and the second phase will run from 2008-2012 to coincide with the first Kyoto Commitment Period. Further 5-year periods are expected subsequently.

The scheme works on a "Cap and Trade" basis. EU Member State governments are required to set an emission cap for all installations covered by the scheme. Each installation is then be allocated allowances for the particular commitment period in question. The number of allowances allocated to each installation for any given period, (the number of tradable allowances each installation will receive), will be set down in a document called the National Allocation Plan.

On 14 February the UK published revised provisional list of installation level allocations under the EU Emissions Trading Scheme, but on 12 April the European Commission formally rejected the British Government's request to increase the number of allowances for use in the first phase by 20 million tonnes, but the UK has lodged an appeal. Distribution of the 736 million tonnes of CO_2 allowances by Defra to eligible installations in the UK began in 2005.

Coal

Ellington colliery ceased production in January 2005.

The Live Fast Track Offer Scheme for respiratory disease claimants, which will see around 80,000 miners offered optional risk payments where initial medical tests show very low levels of lung disease, went live on 28 February.

The cut-off date for the majority of live Vibration White Finger Services claimants passed on 31 March 2005. However, there are some agreed exceptions to this date – live claimants have until 6 months from the General Damages medical to claim and beneficiaries have up to 31 January 2006 to make claims on behalf of claimants who died before 31 March 2005.

Oil and gas

February 2005 - BP's Clair field inaugurated. Clair was the largest undeveloped UKCS resource. BP and partners invested around £650 million in the project, which is expected to recover reserves of up to 300 million barrels of oil, with potential for a further 400 million barrels.

21 March 2005 - The UK and Netherlands Governments signed an interconnector treaty to allow the construction and operation of the BBL gas pipeline between Balgzand in the Netherlands to Bacton in the UK. This will provide a second direct link between the UK's gas transmission system and that of continental Europe. It is due to be operational from December 2006.

4 April 2005 – The UK and Norwegian Governments signed a new oil and gas co-operation treaty designed to remove the need for a separate treaty each time there is a new project involving cross-boundary development. In particular it will underpin the construction of the Norwegian Langeled gas pipeline (supplying up to 20 per cent of UK gas demand from Winter 2006/07) and will also cover the development of new trans-boundary fields and the use of host infrastructures for developments across the median line.

July 2005 – Imports of liquefied natural gas (LNG) commenced at the Isle of Grain import/storage facility.

6 September 2005 - A record 152 oil and gas production licences were offered to 99 companies under the 23rd Oil and Gas Licensing Round, the highest number since licensing began in 1964. The results, a vote of confidence in the future of oil and gas exploration in the UK, herald the entry of 24 new firms to the North Sea. The licences, covering 264 blocks, are broken down as follows: 70 Traditional licence offers, 38 more than in 2004, 6 Frontier licence offers, 1 less than in 2004, 76 Promote licence offers, 18 more than 2004.

November 2005 - Malcolm Wicks announced that 24 of the 54 "Promote" Licences issued in the 21st Round (2003) would continue. Recognising £90 million exploration investment, Mr. Wicks said "These results prove the innovative drive of the firms involved and the success of the promote licence concept, without which this acreage would not have been touched. With clear work commitments it's a great vote of confidence in the future of the North Sea."

8 November – The UK import capacity of the Bacton – Zeebrugge Interconnector was increased from 8.5bcm/y to 16.5bcm/y. A second phase enhancement, due to be completed by December 2006, is progressing to schedule and will bring the UK import capacity of the system to 23.5 bcm/y.

11 December 2005 – An explosion, said to be the largest incident of its kind in peacetime Europe, destroyed a large section of the Buncefield Oil Depot in Hemel Hempstead. In total 20 petrol tanks were involved in the fire, each said to contain three million gallons of fuel.

21 December 2005 - First gas began flowing from BP's Rhum field, the UK's largest undeveloped gas discovery. BP said, with the combination of a high-pressure, high-temperature gas reservoir developed using a long-distance subsea tieback, that Rhum was a world first. With development costs of £350 million, Rhum is expected to recover reserves of around 800 billion cubic feet of gas, with daily production likely to peak at around 300 million cubic feet. The gas, to come ashore at St Fergus, is expected to meet 2% of UK demand in 2006.

2006 – The UK continued to be a net exporter of oil and oil products in volume terms, but because of the differential in prices of oil and the various oil products, the UK was a net importer in value terms for the first time since the early 1980's.

Electricity
On 1 April 2005, the British Electricity Trading and Transmission Arrangements (BETTA) took effect. BETTA has introduced a single wholesale electricity market across Britain by extending the England and Wales market arrangements to Scotland. This will push prices down for Scottish consumers, and will open up the market and increase competition. The legislation underpinning BETTA was delivered in the Energy Act 2004. Under BETTA, National Grid, who previously operated the transmission network in England and Wales, is now the System Operator for the whole GB network.

Coolkeeragh's new gas-fired power station replaced the Londonderry coal fired power station in March 2005.

In May 2005, E.On UK announced that it had purchased the 392 MW Enfield Energy CCGT power station.

Nuclear
British Energy announced on 14 January that it had successfully completed the restructuring plan it announced in November 2002.

The Nuclear Decommissioning Authority was established on 1 April, following the transfer of assets and other property rights from BNFL and the signature of initial site Management and Operation contracts between NDA and BNFL/UKAEA.

Renewables
Malcolm Wicks announced at the British Wind Energy Annual Conference in Cardiff, that he was giving development consent to a 78 megawatts windfarm at Little Cheyne Court in Walland Marsh, Kent. The decision follows a public inquiry.

On 8 March 2005, the Energy Minister announced that the Government intended to exercise the power in section 185 of the Energy Act to adjust the level of transmission charges paid by renewable generators on the Scottish islands, and possibly the North of mainland Scotland, subject to consultation. A consultation will be launched in the summer of 2005.

The DTI has developed and will implement this year a "Wave and Tidal Stream Energy Demonstration Scheme" worth up to £42 million that will support the first larger-scale wave and tidal farms. This is funded under the £50 million 'Marine Renewables

Deployment Fund' announced by the Secretary of State for Trade and Industry in August 2004.

The final conclusions and recommendations of the Eskdalemuir Working Group have been accepted by the Ministry of Defence in full. Defence Estates are removing all associated holding objections in place against the 1.6 GW of wind developments in the vicinity of the seismic array at Eskdalemuir.

2004

Sustainable Energy Policy
DTI published the first annual report on implementation of the Energy White Paper on 26 April as part of a series of documents, all of which contribute to creating a low-carbon economy. These included the Government's Energy Efficiency Implementation Plan (Defra), the Combined Heat and Power strategy (Defra), a consultation paper about biofuels (DFT), and a range of statistical indicators to monitor progress towards the goals of the White Paper (DTI).

Energy Act
The Energy Act 2004 received Royal Assent on 22 July 2004. It will promote "cleaner, greener power" and competitive and reliable energy supplies for now and generations to come. It implements a range of commitments made in the Energy White Paper.

For the first time, one public body (the new Nuclear Decommissioning Authority), which published its draft Annual Plan for public consultation on 10 December 2004 will have complete responsibility for the decommissioning and clean-up of the UK's civil nuclear sites, and for the safe and effective management of our nuclear waste.

The Act also creates a single wholesale electricity market for Britain, the British Electricity Trading and Transmission Arrangements ("BETTA"). Provisions within the Act covering electricity and gas interconnectors implement a number of requirements in the EU's 2003 Gas and Electricity Directives and its Electricity Regulation.

Fuel Poverty
The Fuel Poverty Action Plan, which is a Government publication, was issued on 30 November 2004 and sets out how the Government intends to meet its first fuel poverty target for England – that of eradicating fuel poverty in vulnerable households.

Emissions Trading
On 27 October 2004, an announcement was made of the UK's intention to amend the National Allocation Plan for Phase 1 of the EU Emissions Trading Scheme (2005-07) to a higher number of allowances. This reflects finalisation of emission projections showing higher forecast emissions. The new proposed allocation represented a greater reduction against projections than previously indicated.

On 11 November 2004, the final Updated Energy Projections (UEP) informing the National Allocation Plan (NAP) for EU Emissions Trading Scheme (EUETS) were published on the DTI web site. This paper presented the results of further revisions to the carbon emission projections that have taken place since May 2004.

Renewables
On 2 August 2004, the Secretary of State announced the new £50m Marine Research Development Fund. This is another step towards promoting renewable energy and complements support already given for other emerging technologies including wind, solar and biomass.

On 4 November 2004, the final terms of reference for the 2005/06 review of the Renewables Obligation (RO) were published. In a separate exercise, a statutory consultation excise for proposed amendments to secure the Renewables Obligation was published on 8 September 2004.

Climate Change

On 8 December 2004 the consultation on the review of the UK Climate Change Programme was launched. The consultation highlights areas where the Government has identified opportunities further to reduce carbon emissions.

Coal

Hatfield colliery closed in January 2004. As part of the closure of the Selby complex Wistow mine closed in May 2004, Stillingfleet in September 2004 and Riccall in December 2004.

Period 2 of the Coal Investment Aid scheme closed on 1 June 2004. 13 applications were received requesting £94.7 million of aid.

The Department reached the key milestone of £1 billion in British Coal Vibration White Finger compensation being paid in week commencing 19 July 2004.

Oil and gas

US oil firm Apache announced plans to spend around £137 million in 2004 on various projects in the Forties field in the North Sea. This included drilling more than 20 wells to gain a "substantial" increase in production.

The 22nd Offshore and 12th Onshore Oil and Gas Licensing Rounds were announced on 4 March 2004. The 22nd Round made available the largest number of offshore blocks since the 2nd Round in 1965. As well as continuing to include options for "promote" licences and traditional licences, the Round offered a further new form of licence, the "frontier" licence, for blocks in the Atlantic Margin, West of the Shetland Islands.

On 6 July 2004, DTI approved the 300th North Sea field development, Total's Glenelg field, with expected peak production of 30,000 barrels of oil equivalent a day.

On 28 July 2004, DTI approved the Saturn gas field development. Operator, ConocoPhillips, expected first gas in Q4 2005 at an initial rate of 74 million cubic feet a day, with a maximum daily rate of 169 million cubic feet in the following year. Produced gas will be transported via the Lincolnshire Offshore Gas Gathering System to the Theddlethorpe Terminal.

On 3 August 2004, production started from the Lundin-operated Broom field. Oil reserves were estimated to be 36 million barrels for the first phase, with further development opportunities in area currently being evaluated. Broom will also assist substantially in extending the Heather field life.

On 8 October 2004, the UK and Norwegian Governments agreed arrangements to allow the development of two new North Sea fields - Boa and Playfair.

The official launch of the 'Goldeneye' development took place on 11 November 2004. The £300m project, supported by co-venturers Shell, ExxonMobil, Paladin Resources and Centrica Energy, will provide around 3 per cent of the UK's gas.

Electricity

On 1 September 2004, the British Electricity and Trading Arrangements (BETTA) went "Active". This involved the Secretary of State using her powers in the Energy Act 2004 to change licence conditions so that trailing and testing of the new arrangements could begin, in preparation for BETTA going "Live" on 1 April 2005.

The findings of the investigation by DTI's Engineering Inspectorate into the major power failures in London on 28 August 2003 and in Birmingham on 5 September 2003 were communicated to the respective electricity companies in January 2004. Inspectors worked closely with the companies to ensure their recommendations were taken forward.

2004 (continued) Scottish Power purchased Damhead Creek power station in June 2004 and became the sole owner of the Shoreham Power station in September 2004. Centrica purchased Killingholme power station in June 2004. In July 2004 Scottish and Southern Energy acquired the Ferrybridge C and Fiddlers Ferry power stations formerly owned by American Electric Power. Carron Energy re-opened the Fifoots Point power station in August 2004 and changed the name of the power station back to Uskmouth.

Nuclear

The Secretary of State announced on 5 January 2004 that British Energy (BE) had completed the sale of its interest in its US joint venture, Amergen, in December 2003. All amounts outstanding under the Government's loan facility to BE have been paid off, but facility remained available to BE up to a maximum of £200 million.

At the end of February 2004 BNFL's Chapelcross nuclear power station closed.

For major events in earlier years see the DTI web site version of this annex at:
http://www.dti.gov.uk/energy/statistics/publications/dukes/page29812.html

NOTES

234